Three po...
unforgettab...
irresistible a...
be incredibl...

GW00367154

Millionaires

**Fantastic novels from favourite, fabulous
bestselling author**

Lynne
GRAHAM

Lynne Graham Collection

February 2012

March 2012

April 2012

May 2012

Lynne
GRAHAM

Millionaires

MILLS & BOON

All the characters in this book have no existence outside the imagination of the author, and have no relation whatsoever to anyone bearing the same name or names. They are not even distantly inspired by any individual known or unknown to the author, and all the incidents are pure invention.

All Rights Reserved including the right of reproduction in whole or in part in any form. This edition is published by arrangement with Harlequin Enterprises II B.V./S.à.r.l. The text of this publication or any part thereof may not be reproduced or transmitted in any form or by any means, electronic or mechanical, including photocopying, recording, storage in an information retrieval system, or otherwise, without the written permission of the publisher.

This book is sold subject to the condition that it shall not, by way of trade or otherwise, be lent, resold, hired out or otherwise circulated without the prior consent of the publisher in any form of binding or cover other than that in which it is published and without a similar condition including this condition being imposed on the subsequent purchaser.

® and ™ are trademarks owned and used by the trademark owner and/or its licensee. Trademarks marked with ® are registered with the United Kingdom Patent Office and/or the Office for Harmonisation in the Internal Market and in other countries.

Mills & Boon, an imprint of Harlequin (UK) Limited, Eton House, 18-24 Paradise Road, Richmond, Surrey TW9 1SR

MILLIONAIRES © Harlequin Enterprises II B.V./S.à.r.l. 2012

Rafaello's Mistress © Lynne Graham 2001
Damiano's Return © Lynne Graham 2000
Contract Baby © Lynne Graham 1998

ISBN: 978 0 263 89723 4

052-0312

Harlequin (UK) policy is to use papers that are natural, renewable and recyclable products and made from wood grown in sustainable forests. The logging and manufacturing processes conform to the legal environmental regulations of the country of origin.

Printed and bound in Spain
by Blackprint CPI, Barcelona

RAFAELLO'S MISTRESS

Lynne Graham

Lynne Graham was born in Northern Ireland and has been a keen Mills & Boon® reader since her teens. She is very happily married, with an understanding husband who has learned to cook since she started to write! Her five children keep her on her toes. She has a very large dog, which knocks everything over, a very small terrier, which barks a lot, and two cats. When time allows, Lynne is a keen gardener.

Look out for Lynne Graham's latest exciting new trilogy, available from March to May in Mills & Boon® Modern™.

CHAPTER ONE

When Glory walked into the London headquarters of Grazzini Industries, every male head in the vicinity swivelled to watch her.

Her face was unforgettable: wide slanted cheekbones, bright eyes the colour of bluebells and a wide, full pink mouth. Even with her honey-blonde hair caught back, and clad in khaki combats and a casual top, she attracted attention. All the men stared: they couldn't help themselves. That stunning face and lush figure endowed her with an extraordinary degree of sex appeal.

Impervious to the attention that she was receiving, Glory was engaged in frantically talking up her flagging courage. Rafaello would listen to her, *of course* he would listen. So what if it had been five years since they had last met? So what if they had parted on bad terms? He had hurt her so much that even now she could not bring herself to recall how she had felt back then but she knew she had not hurt him. Powerful, influential businessmen were not known for their sensitivity. Maybe she had dented his ego a little but then he had never suffered from any lack in that department. She wouldn't be at all surprised to discover that Rafaello barely recalled their painfully brief fling.

Yet she remembered every day, every hour, every minute. She remembered how naïve and trusting and stupid she had been. She remembered that last night she had hoped to spend with him and the resulting humiliation followed by the agony of loss and rejection. The oldest story in the book, she told herself, fighting to suppress those debilitating memories. She had wanted love but he had only wanted a temporary distraction. He might so easily have become her first lover but they had broken up before she trusted him enough to say yes.

Left alone in the steel-walled lift as it climbed higher and higher, Glory rested her hot, damp brow against the cooling metal surface. Pull yourself together, girl. Chin up, hold your head high. Never mind that her nerves were eating her alive. Or that her wardrobe did not run to a smart suit. Or that she felt horribly intimidated by Rafaello's giant steel and glass office building. None of that mattered, she told herself. She was here to help her family: her dad, her kid brother, Sam.

Stepping out on to the top floor into an atmosphere of exclusive comfort and elegance, Glory approached the smart reception desk.

'I have an appointment with Mr Grazzini...' Her voice emerged all small and crushed by the sheer weight of her nervous tension.

The attractive brunette looked her up and down with a faint frownline etched between her perfect pencilled brows. 'Your name, Miss...?'

'Little. Glory Little,' Glory supplied hurriedly.

'Please take a seat...' The cool ice-blue leather seating area was indicated.

Glory reached for a glossy women's magazine. She flicked through fashion pages adorned by women wearing single garments that cost more than she earned in six months. Interest wandering, she glanced around herself, hugely impressed by her surroundings but anything but comfortable with them. Though it was certainly no surprise to her that Rafaello was doing extravagantly well in business. He had started out rich and would no doubt go on getting richer. Didn't it run in his genes? He had once told her that the Grazzini clan had started coining it as merchants during the Middle Ages.

No wonder they hadn't ended up together, she reflected, striving to see the humour of her own pitiful ignorance at the age of eighteen. Youthful bravado had persuaded her that things like different backgrounds and what some people called 'breeding' didn't matter in a world approaching the second millennium. To think otherwise was incredibly old-fashioned, she had told a less naïve friend, who had implied that Rafaello could only be after 'one thing'. When her father had tried to warn her off too, she had just laughed and pointed out that Rafaello didn't give two hoots about silly stuff, like her having left school at sixteen!

'Miss Little...?'

Snatched from her teeming thoughts, Glory glanced up to see a young man in a smart suit studying her. Clutching her bag, she got up. 'Yes?'

'Mr Grazzini will see you now.'

Glory managed a rather strained version of her usual sunny smile and looked down at her watch. 'Right on the dot of ten o'clock. Rafaello hasn't changed a bit. He was always dead keen on punctuality.'

In receipt of that chatty response, the young man looked taken aback. Glory flushed, hot embarrassed colour drenching her peaches and cream complexion right to the roots of her hair. She had said more than was required and city people didn't gush like that and offer up unnecessary facts at the drop of a hat. But nerves had always run away with Glory's tongue and, given the chance, she tended to rush to fill every awkward silence. Not this time, however. She knew why he had looked momentarily astonished and knowing did nothing for her self-esteem. The guy just could not imagine someone as ordinary as her *ever* having been on first-name terms with his rich and sophisticated employer.

'I'm Mr Grazzini's executive assistant,' he informed her. 'The name's Jon...Jon Lyons.'

'My name's Glory,' she said in turn, grateful her companion wasn't being as stand-offish as she had expected and scolding herself for her own prejudice.

'Very unusual…' Jon Lyons, who was traversing the wide corridor that lay before them at the crawling speed of a snail, paused to throw her a warm and appreciative smile. 'But very apt.'

Glory resisted the temptation to tell him that she owed her name to the fact that her father had celebrated his only daughter's birth rather too thoroughly and had then registered her name wrongly on her birth certificate. Instead of getting to be the lofty-sounding Gloriana as her fond mother had planned, she had ended up just being called Glory. Being only five feet one inch tall and blessed with a surname like Little, she was well-accustomed to being teased. And if Jon Lyons was trying to flirt with her, she didn't want to know.

At the age of twenty-three, she had met far too many men whose sole interest in her related to her embarrassingly lush curves. Dates that turned into wrestling sessions followed by aggrieved and aggressive 'Why nots?' had figured all too often in her experience. She cringed from that male attitude, found it demeaning and threatening. It was as if her body wasn't her own and she was expected to share it whether she wanted to or not. Being bone-deep stubborn and determined to hang on in there waiting for love and commitment, she had always been punitively mean in the sharing stakes.

Her companion kept on trying to chat her up but she played dumb. The closer they got to the imposing door and the foot of the corridor, the more enervated she became and her steps grew shorter and slower. Rafaello would be on the other side of that door waiting for her. But he had agreed to see her, hadn't he? Wasn't that hopeful? At least, his secretary had come back to her with an appointment fairly quickly and she wasn't fool enough to think that she could have got that far without Rafaello's agreement. Rafaello was rich and important and much in demand. She was really lucky that he was giving her the chance to speak up in her family's defence, she reminded herself.

So what was she actually going to say to Rafaello? Please, please think again? Please don't sack my father? Please don't blame him for my kid brother's antics?

Sam had done a stupid, stupid thing. Helping himself to the keys entrusted to their parent during the housekeeper's overnight absence, Sam had thrown an impromptu party in the Grazzini family's fabulous English home, Montague Park. The party had got out of hand. Panicking at the damage being done, Sam had run to their father for help. Then their father had made *his* mistake. Instead of admitting his son's guilt, her father had foolishly and unsuccessfully attempted to cover Sam's tracks and deny his involvement. Paling as she contemplated the challenge of trying to excuse such dishonest behaviour, Glory walked in through the door spread wide for her. Once over the threshold, she froze.

Her companion, who had remained in the corridor, had to nudge her a few inches deeper into the room to get the door closed behind her. Dry-mouthed, Glory scanned the vast office, her attention jumping from the contemporary glass and wrought-iron furniture to the wall of tinted glass windows and the sheer luxury of so much unoccupied and wholly unnecessary space. Where was Rafaello? Appreciating that he had yet to join her, she breathed in deeply and slowly exhaled again, fighting to get a firmer grip on herself.

But her own mind was working against her like a secret enemy. As she stood there doing the careful breathing exercises that a magazine article had said were a great aid to achieving a calm state of mind, she started getting something rather akin to flashbacks. Her first true sighting of Rafaello Grazzini eight years earlier...

Glory's father, Archie Little, was the head gardener at Montague Park. Just as his father had been and his father before him, for her ancestors had worked on the Montague estate for a couple of centuries. About seventy-odd years back, Rafaello's grandfather had married the last of the Montague line and had resisted all pleas to assume his wife's maiden name. The fair and rather chinless Montagues had been replaced by the infinitely more exotic and good-looking Grazzinis with their dark flashing eyes and aggressive jawlines.

Before her father became head gardener the Littles had lived in the village several miles from Montague Park, but when he was promoted he had been provided with a comfortable cottage on the estate. Her parents had been delighted but Glory had been distraught because all her friends had lived in the village. Being stuck in the midst of several thousand acres of beautiful unspoilt countryside had seemed to her a fate worse than death.

One afternoon soon after that move, out walking and still wallowing in self-pity, Glory had enjoyed one of those rare life-changing experiences: she had seen Rafaello Grazzini on a scrambler motorbike, racing a friend with a breathtaking lack of caution for his own safety. No youthful male had ever appeared to greater advantage to an impressionable fifteen-year-old girl than he did that day. She had watched him wheeling the powerful bike to a halt and wrenching off his helmet. His black hair had blown back from his vibrant dark features, strong and bold against the washed-out colours of a too dry English summer. Glory had discovered right there and then that living in the rural depths had one major consolation: Rafaello Grazzini, six years older, and unlikely to notice she occupied the same earth but very worthy of becoming the target of her first besotted crush.

Only somewhere along the line something had gone wrong, Glory conceded dully. She had *not* outgrown the crush. Even when he had maddened and mortified her beyond belief in an unfortunate first encounter the following year, she had stayed dangerously loyal and keen. And when, two years later, all her dreams came true and she actually went *out* with Rafaello it had taken precious little encouragement for her to move from the base of that juvenile infatuation into being passionately in love.

Without warning, a door on the far side of the office opened. Sprung from her unwelcome mental trawl back through past events, Glory jumped as though someone had fired a gun behind her and spun round.

'I'm afraid I was waylaid by one of the directors,' Rafaello murmured, cool as a long drink of icy water on a hot day.

Glory was trembling and she couldn't help herself. It had been five years since she had seen him. Five long years that had taken her from girl to woman but, in the blink of an eye, all that painfully acquired maturity was wrenched from her by the simple act of Rafaello walking into the same room. She gazed at him in shock, for nothing could have prepared her for the strength of her own reaction. At eighteen, her cure had been steadily and repeatedly telling herself that she had romanticised and embellished her image of him beyond belief. And there he stood, every inch of him a blatant rejection of such wishful thinking...

Six feet two inches tall, much taller than she had allowed him to be in her memory, and with the wide shoulders, broad chest, narrow hips and long muscular legs of a natural athlete. Not even that formal fine grey pinstripe suit so superbly tailored to his powerful frame could shield her from the acknowledgement that whatever he had been doing in recent years he had not been allowing himself to run to seed.

Having only reached as high in her appraisal as the pristine white collar encircling the elegant knot on his dark red silk tie, Glory tipped her head back and ran headlong into the stunning effect of brilliant dark eyes fringed by inky individual lashes that stood out against his smooth olive skin. Mouth dry and heart suddenly racing so fast that it felt as if it was lodged in her throat, Glory just stared back, dragged at terrifying speed up onto the heights of helpless excitement.

'Take a seat,' Rafaello urged with complete calm.

Her big blue eyes widened slightly. All around her the atmosphere was churning with so much fiery tension that she felt dizzy. Yet he was not turning a single strand of that luxuriant black hair so well-styled to his arrogant dark head. He felt nothing…he felt *nothing*, Glory realised, and she felt gutted. Even as he went through the polite motions of lifting a chair with one lean brown hand and planting it helpfully beside her, she was incapable of suppressing the sudden violent rise of tempestuous emotion attacking her.

Memory and bitter pain seemed to coalesce inside her. She saw the worst moment of her life afresh. Five years ago. Rafaello kissing that snobby redhead whose father was a merchant banker, standing Glory up in the restaurant that had been *their* place. His well-bred friends had been very amused by her tearful flight but equally relieved that Rafaello had dumped the gardener's daughter with her local-yokel accent and lack of further education.

Stepping behind her, Rafaello curved light hands to her stiff arms and guided her down into the chair. Like a child who had just seen a very nasty accident, she sat there staring straight ahead of her while she crushed out that tormenting recollection of her humiliation and sought to resurrect her defences.

'When people ask to see me, they usually talk a mile a minute because my time is valuable,' Rafaello spelt out in the same collected dark drawl.

'Maybe I don't know what to say…I mean, it's kind of traumatic…I mean, *awkward*,' Glory stressed in an uneven rush, 'seeing you again…'

Rafaello strolled with fluid grace back into her line of vision. He lounged back against the edge of his fancy desk and dealt her a smooth smile that somehow turned her churning tummy cold as ice. 'I don't feel at all awkward, Glory.'

Glory focused on his tie with deadly concentration. 'Well, I'm sure you're not wondering what I'm doing here, so I'll just get on with it...'

'Hopefully,' Rafaello encouraged.

Just when she was about to break into her prepared speech, her mind went blank again on the helpless acknowledgement that she just loved his voice: that husky Italian accent that purred along every syllable and transformed the plainest word into something special. Something special that danced down her spine like a caress. *Caress?*

Cheeks crimsoning, Glory broke back into harried speech. 'First I want to say how very sorry I am for what my brother did. Sam was very much in the wrong. I mean, he was brought up to respect other people's property just as I was but he's very young—'

'I am aware of that,' Rafaello said rather drily. 'Do you think you could bring yourself to look me in the face? It's rather distracting to have someone addressing my tie.'

A nervous giggle bubbled up in Glory's throat and escaped in a rather choky sound. She lifted her chin, tilted back her honey-blonde head.

'Better, *cara*,' Rafaello pronounced, gazing at her with hooded dark eyes that gave her the shivers all over again.

'It's not really better for me,' Glory muttered helplessly. 'I'm so nervous that I keep on forgetting what I'm saying.'

'Nervous? Of me?' Rafaello purred like a prowling predator. 'Surely not?'

All of a sudden, she felt controlled. Like a little toy train being wound up and set on a circular track he had already laid out. She stared at him. Lethal, dark and dangerous but so undeniably gorgeous that the average woman forgot the danger. He was so still, almost as if he was letting her gaze her fill, and suddenly she was past caring and greedy where

minutes earlier she had been cautious. That lean bronzed
face had haunted her dreams but had always blurred in
daylight. The hard, high cheekbones, the strong nose, the
beautiful, sensual mouth. She was looking for the cruelty
that she had found in him too late to protect herself. But
all she could recognise was his aura of tempered steel
toughness, his incredibly intimidating self-command and
the amount of authority he could put out even when in a
relaxed pose.

'Let's chat for a while,' Rafaello suggested, stretching
out a lean hand to stab a button on some piece of office
equipment and ordering coffee for two. 'I doubt that we
have any herbal tea on the premises.'

'Coffee will be fine.' *Chat?* Chat about what? What did
they have to chat about?

'Where are you living now?' Rafaello enquired casually.

'Near where I work—'

'With?'

'Nobody. It's a bedsit—'

'In?'

'A house…?' Glory asked, transfixed by the questions
flying like bullets at her and unable to keep up.

Rafaello sighed. 'I meant…where is the bedsit situated?'

'Birmingham,' she told him.

'I always thought of you as a country girl.'

'There aren't many jobs going in the country these days,'
Glory pointed out tightly, thinking that his idea of chatting
more closely resembled an interrogation. But then why
shouldn't he be curious? Being curious was only human,
wasn't it?

'So where do you work?'

The knock on the door and the rattle of approaching
china came as a welcome interruption. Obviously coffee
was always on offer at the speed of light: a tray sitting
already prepared and some fancy machine ready to dispense
the hot, viciously strong brew he favoured. Her mind was

going all over the place again. He never had taken to her
herbal tea, Glory recalled dimly.

'You were saying...?' As a china cup and saucer were
slid onto the small table that had appeared by her elbow
by someone she did not even have the time to look at,
Rafaello returned to his rather forbidding concept of casual
chat.

'Was I?' Glory reached for the coffee. 'Oh, yes, where
I work. A factory—'

'What kind of factory?'

'Well...it's nothing very interesting...'

Brilliant dark eyes settled on her. 'You might be surprised at what interests me.'

Glory jerked a slight shoulder in submission and her coffee slopped out of the cup into the saucer. 'The factory
makes polystyrene for packaging and all sorts of other
things...'

Rafaello continued to observe her as though her every
word was fascinating. 'And what do you do there?'

'I pack it...the polystyrene. Sometimes I do other
jobs—'

Rafaello was studying her with intense concentration.
'And for how long have you been thrilling to the excitement of the factory floor?'

'Look, it's not exciting but I work alongside a nice bunch
of people and the pay's not bad.' Her beautiful eyes reflecting reproach at that tone of sarcasm, Glory coloured. 'I've
been there two years.'

'Forgive me for asking, *cara*,' Rafaello drawled softly,
'but what happened to your burning ambition to become a
model?'

Glory paled and stiffened. 'It wasn't exactly a burning
ambition. As you know, I had that offer and it...well, it
just didn't pan out—'

'Why not?'

The pink tip of her tongue snaked out to moisten the taut

line of her lower lip. She was extremely uncomfortable
with his line of questioning and dismayed by the extent of
his interest. His dark gaze dropped to her soft, full mouth
and lingered with visible force. Sudden tension seemed to
make the atmosphere sizzle. She felt her lips tingle as if he
were touching them and her breathing seemed to choke off
at source. Her bra felt too tight for her full breasts and her
nipples pinched tight into straining buds of sensitivity. In
dismay, she began sipping at the coffee she didn't want
with a hand that shook. Please no, she was praying, please,
no, don't let me be feeling like this again...

'Why not?' Rafaello persisted without remorse. 'Why
didn't the modelling offer work out?'

He was going to dig and dig until he hit paydirt, Glory
registered in mortification, and so she decided to just be
honest. 'It wasn't the kind of modelling I wouldn've done.
It was what they call "glamour" stuff...you know...like
where you take your clothes off for the camera, rather than
put clothes on?'

Rafaello surveyed her steadily, not a muscle moving on
his darkly handsome face.

'So they asked you to get your kit off...and you said no?
Didn't they offer you enough money?'

Glory looked at him in considerable embarrassment.
'The money had nothing to do with it. I just wasn't prepared to *do* that sort of stuff—'

Rafaello dealt her a look of derision. 'I didn't come down
in the last shower of rain, *cara*. Are you or are you not the
woman my father bought off with five thousand pounds?'

At that unexpected question, Glory turned whiter than
his shirt and stared back at him in horror. As her fingers
involuntarily loosened their grip on the saucer it fell clean
out of her hand. The cup tipped and she gasped as coffee
went flying over the perfect pale carpet.

'*Si*...yes,' Rafaello confirmed as the spilt liquid flowed
over the expensive fibres in a spreading stain and she just

stared fixedly at it, paralysed where she sat. 'Naturally my father told me what it cost to persuade you that I was not, after all, the love of your life. And it was a fitting footnote to our relationship. A lousy five grand when you could have had ten, twenty, thirty times that for the asking. But I guess five grand seemed like a small fortune to you then.'

Glory was still watching the seeping pool of coffee. She was appalled that he had found out about that payment. She felt sick. She was in an agony of shame. Rafaello knew, Rafaello *knew* about the money. 'He said it would be a secret, he said you would never know...' she mumbled strickenly.

'*Dio mio*...do you believe everything you're told?' Rafaello murmured with a cruel enjoyment that she could feel like a knife plunging between her ribs. 'I was amused—'

'Amused?' Folding her arms over her churning tummy, Glory gazed up at him in shaken disbelief.

'My father acting like some clumsy Victorian squire trying to pay off a maidservant he saw as a threat to family unity. So unnecessary,' Rafaello mused. 'I never entertained a single serious thought about our relationship. But I *wasn't* amused when you took the money like the greedy little gold-digger he said you were. That was cheap and inexcusable.'

Glory sat there as if she were turned to stone. She said nothing. She had nothing to say, for, as the money had not been returned, she could not defend herself. It would scarcely help her father's case if she was now to confide that Archie Little had refused to allow her to destroy that cheque. Indeed, he had taken her to the bank that same day and the money had been transferred into his account. Beggars couldn't be choosers, he had said when she argued with him. If she was being forced to leave home to please Benito Grazzini, her father had believed that he was due some compensation. Deprived of her help in the household, not to mention the extra money her job brought in, how was he to manage?

A greedy little gold-digger? So that was how Rafaello had learned to think of her over the past five years. True bitterness scythed through Glory. She thought of the games rich people played and the damage they could wreak. Their money could give them the power to bully smaller people and make them do what they didn't want to do. She had left home because her father's job and his very survival had been at stake and for no other reason. It seemed bitterly ironic that she was now facing Rafaello again for much the same reason.

She squared her shoulders and veiled her eyes. 'Now that you've told me what you think of me, can we discuss why I asked for this appointment?'

'Go ahead...' Rafaello said drily.

'You've given my father a month's notice—'

'Don't tell me you're surprised.' Rafaello elevated a sleek dark brow. 'If it hadn't been for your father's incompetence, your punk of a brother would never have gained access to my home—'

'Sam nicked the keys when Dad was asleep,' Glory protested, rising to her feet in a sudden defensive movement. 'Since Dad could hardly have guessed what Sam was planning to do, you can't blame him for what happened!'

'But I can certainly blame your father for telling the police a pack of lies and trying to protect your brother and his nasty destructive friends,' Rafaello cut in with ruthless bite. 'Have you any idea how much damage has been caused to the Park?'

'Sam told me everything.' However, Glory's combative stance had instantly evaporated when she was faced with that daunting question. 'Rugs stained and furniture scratched and windows broken, but at least the damage was restricted to two rooms. As soon as Sam realised that his mates were too drunk for him to control, he ran for help.

Dad should have called the police himself and he should have told the truth when the housekeeper called the police in the next morning—'

'But he *didn't*,' Rafaello slotted in with lethal timing.

'He was scared of the consequences. My brother's only sixteen. But Sam *did* tell the truth when the police questioned him. He's very ashamed and very sorry—'

'Of course he is. He doesn't want to be prosecuted.'

Having turned noticeably paler at that blunt statement of possible intent, Glory said in desperation, 'Didn't you ever kick up a lark that went horribly wrong at his age?'

'If you're asking, did I ever trespass on someone else's property or vandalise it?...the answer is *no*.'

'But then, I bet you had more exciting outlets at Sam's age,' Glory persisted. 'Only there's virtually nothing for teenagers to do in the area and nowhere for them to go either. None of them have any money—'

'Cut the bleeding-heart routine,' Rafaello advised with cold impatience. 'I've got no time for anyone who violates either my home or my property. The clean-up bill alone will run into thousands—'

'*Thousands?*' she stressed in astonishment.

She received a nod of confirmation.

'You're being ripped off!' Glory told him. 'Everybody knows that you're loaded. I bet you're being quoted a crazy figure for the clean-up because the firm knows you can afford it.'

Rafaello surveyed her with sardonic cool. 'Glory...it takes highly trained professionals to repair valuable antiques and restore damaged plasterwork. That kind of expertise comes at a premium charge.'

Feeling very foolish, feeling all the confused embarrassment of someone who had not a clue about the care of antiques, Glory subsided and set off doggedly on another tack. 'I feel awful that we can't offer you any financial compensation—'

'I feel awful that sentencing tearaway teenagers to thirty lashes has gone out of fashion,' Rafaello imparted very drily. 'But the return of the snuff box that was removed from the drawing-room might…just *might* persuade me not to prosecute your brother.'

Glory had gone very still. 'Something was—er—taken? But why didn't the police mention that to Sam yesterday?'

'They weren't aware of it until this morning when *I* realised that it was missing,' Rafaello explained grimly. 'The snuff box is tiny and would've been easily slipped into a pocket.'

'A snuff box?' Glory parrotted weakly, aghast at the news that an item of value might have been stolen from the Park, for that was an infinitely more serious offence.

'German, eighteenth century, made of gold and covered with precious stones. It will be virtually impossible to replace,' Rafaello outlined.

Glory parted her taut lips. 'How much is it worth?'

'About sixty grand.'

Glory tried and failed to swallow. 'Sixty thousand… *pounds*?'

'I have excellent taste—'

'And you think it's been stolen?' Glory exclaimed. 'I mean, have you searched? Are you *sure*?'

'I would not have reported it to the police otherwise. It puts rather a different complexion on your touching portrayal of bored teenagers with nowhere to go and nothing to do, and I have every intention of pressing charges on the score of that theft.'

Her lips bloodlessly compressed and her knees wobbling, Glory sank down almost clumsily into the seat she had vacated mere minutes before. 'No way would Sam have stolen anything—'

'Someone did.'

Her head felt as if it was going round and round. The situation was even worse than she had realised. There had been around twenty teenagers at that impromptu party. Any one of them could have lifted something small without attracting attention. A tiny box worth *sixty* thousand pounds? She felt physically sick. Sam having let himself into the huge house to throw a party for his drunken friends had been serious enough...but theft as well?

'Obviously you're planning to press charges against Sam and you have no intention of changing your mind about dismissing my dad.' Glory could see that she had no hope of dissuading him on either count now.

'Did you think I would be so overwhelmed by your fabulous face and body that I would write it all off for old times' sake?' Rafaello murmured softly and smoothly but she felt his contempt right down into her bones and recoiled from it.

'No...but I had to *try* to reason with you,' she stressed shakily, looking up to encounter hard dark eyes with a shocking sense of betrayal. She could neither bear nor yet accept how low she had sunk in his estimation. 'My father and my brother deserve to be in trouble for being stupid but you're talking about wrecking their lives. Dad's got no fancy gardening qualifications and he won't get another job at his age. All because of this snuff box going missing? What do you need with a stupid box costing that much anyway?'

'Beautiful things give me pleasure,' Rafaello admitted without hesitation.

'Is there anything I can say or do...?' Glory demanded feverishly.

'You're asking *me* to advise you on how to change *my* mind?' Rafaello slung her a sardonic appraisal and then he vented a husky laugh. 'What have you got to offer me in return?'

'Undying gratitude?' Glory suggested without much hope.

'Something for nothing is not my style. Perhaps you

should appeal to my baser instincts. Let me think. What do *I* want that *you* can give me?' Rafaello rested dark deep-set eyes that were shimmering with glints of awakening on her taut seated figure. 'Only one thing. Sex.'

CHAPTER TWO

SEX? What sort of a crack was that to make? Glory released a nervous laugh. Eyes very wide and blue pinned to him, she muttered unevenly, 'You don't mean that...you don't mean that like it sounds.'

'Don't I? I'm the guy you sold out for a derogatory five grand. You'll never convince me that moral standards are a subject likely to keep you awake at night,' Rafaello murmured in a hypnotically quiet undertone that rasped down her taut spine like sandpaper on silk. 'So what about it, Glory?'

'What about *what*?' Glory snapped half an octave higher, still refusing to credit that he could actually mean what he was saying and springing restively upright again. She pushed back a straying strand of honey-blonde hair from her brow in a defensive movement. 'Is this your idea of a joke?'

'A joke? Far from it. You should be flattered.' Lounging at his ease, Rafaello gazed steadily back at her. 'I'm offering to whisk you off the factory floor and install you in my bed while at the same time allowing your useless male relatives off the hook. Now if that's not generous, what is?'

'You're just saying this stuff to humiliate me because you don't like me—'

'Glory...I don't need to like or respect you to want you under me, over me and any other way I can think of having you,' Rafaello countered with level cool, his unapologetic bluntness in delineating that earthy reality shattering what few illusions she still retained.

'How can you talk to me like this?' Glory demanded half

23

under her breath, her damp hands clenching into fists by
her sides.

'Don't knock the lust factor when it can work to your
advantage. Even dressed as you are now, you're gorgeous.'
Rafaello ran brilliant dark golden eyes over the full swell
of her breasts below the sweater, let his meaningful scrutiny
of her charms slide to the pronounced curve of her hips
below her tiny waist and then lower still.

She stood there with her face burning. She felt that unashamedly male appraisal like a flame of sexual contempt
singeing her sensitive skin. But, worst of all, she was experiencing sensations she had almost forgotten she *could*
feel. That enervating little tightening *frisson* of physical
response low in her pelvis, the mortifying sensation of liquid heat between her clenching thighs.

'I don't want to hear any more!' she gasped, spinning
away from him, sucking in a stark breath, fighting to stop
her body reacting to the erotic buzz in the atmosphere, to
him.

'But the more I contemplate the possibilities, the more I
warm up to the idea, *cara*,' Rafaello confided huskily.
'Straightforward sex. An honest agreement, free of all those
restrictive relationship complexities. I keep you...and you
please me.'

'You are not going to keep me and I am *not* going to
bed with you, Rafaello Grazzini!' Glory launched at him
furiously. 'I'm not a whore!'

'You have...' with offensive detachment, Rafaello
shrugged back his shirt cuff to glance at the narrow gold
watch on his strong wrist '...three and a half hours to make
your mind up. If you're not back here by two this afternoon,
the offer is closed.'

Aghast at that level announcement, Glory stared at him
with shaken bright blue eyes, finally accepting that he was
serious. 'Do you honestly think that I would trade my
body—?'

'To the highest bidder? *Yes*,' Rafaello incised without hesitation. 'Five years ago, I was very slow to catch on to what you really wanted from me. I didn't give you any expensive gifts. Nor did it occur to me to put cold, hard cash on the table and pay the price for the intimacy I wanted—'

'Stop it!' Glory exclaimed in angry chagrined despair, whirling away from him again to conceal her pained mortification. 'It wasn't like that between us.'

'You took money to stay out of my bed. Presumably you would've accepted a better offer to get into it!'

'No, I wouldn't have done!' Inflamed by that assertion, Glory turned back to yell at him, her voice breaking with distress, 'I *loved* you!'

'Only you couldn't love me to the value of five grand?' Rafaello shot her a derisive appraisal and then his expressive mouth curled into a hard smile of chilling amusement. 'You've got some nerve telling me that.'

'I hate you...' Glory bit out with a shudder of violent resentment at the humiliation he was inflicting on her. 'I really hate you now.'

'I can live with that...I can live with that fine.' Arrogant dark head high, brilliant eyes level, Rafaello surveyed her as if she had thrown down a gauntlet and challenged him.

'You won't be *asked* to live with it!' Glory shot at him tempestuously, stalking back to the chair to snatch up her bag. Her beautiful face was furiously flushed, her blue eyes bright as sapphires with anger. 'Does it give you a cheap thrill to think that you have power over me?'

'I don't call writing off a debt of eighty grand cheap. As to the power—how do I feel about that? Pretty damned good, *cara*,' Rafaello confided.

'You don't have power over me. You have no power unless I *give* it to you!' Glory snapped back in so much rage she could hardly vocalise.

'But you'd do anything for your father and your brother.

Do you think I don't know that? Where are the spineless cowards lurking, anyway?'

'What are you talking about?'

'Archie and Sam. I notice they're conspicuous by their absence,' Rafaello extended with perceptible scorn as he strolled to the door with fluid grace and held it open for her, demonstrating an inbred courtesy that set her teeth on edge even more. 'But then, maybe it was your idea to come alone in their place—'

At that moment, Glory was past caring what he thought of her, for she only wanted to escape. 'Maybe it was—'

'Maybe you fancied your chances with me again—'

'You really think you're something, don't you?' she condemned between compressed lips.

'At the very least, cleverer than you are. Either you should have brought the male back-up or sat weeping and whingeing until revulsion wore me down—'

'I don't weep or whinge!'

'I wouldn't want you if you did.' Rafaello focused on Jon Lyons, who was standing down at the reception area at the far end of the corridor, trying not to look as if he was watching them. He skimmed his attention back to her with derisive dark eyes that sent a wave of colour flaming across her slanted cheekbones. 'Five minutes here and you've got my executive assistant panting at your heels like a pet dog. Do him a favour. Give him the big freeze on the way out!'

'Go to hell!' she hissed and stalked away, shivering with rage and shame and bitterness.

For what could she do and what could she possibly say to defend herself? Rafaello thought she was greedy and unscrupulous. Whether she liked it or not, she had to accept that five years ago she had made a serious error of judgement and now she was paying the price for it. She had allowed her father to take that cheque for five thousand pounds and *keep* it. Archie Little had been in debt and desperate for money. After Glory had endured that demeaning interview with Rafaello's father she hadn't had enough fight left in her to resist her own parent's demands and stand up for what was right. She had felt microscopic in size by the time Benito Grazzini had finished talking to her. He had left her with few illusions about the myth of social equality.

Yet she had still sensed that Rafaello's father did not like what he was doing any more than she had liked having such cruel pressure put on her. He had just wanted her out of his son's life and had evidently decided that the end must justify the means. So he had pointed out that he would be well within his rights if he dismissed her father for his less than adequate job performance at that time. She had known that, shorn of stability of both home and employment, her father would have never found the strength to get his life back on track.

In that same year, six months before Glory reached her eighteenth birthday and before she even went out with Rafaello, her stable, happy home life had begun to unravel at the seams. Without the smallest warning her mother, Talitha, had died—a heart attack—there one moment, gone the next. Her mother had been the strong one in her parents' marriage and the cement that held their family together. Her father had gone to pieces and hit the bottle hard.

Glory had found herself engaged in a constant losing battle to keep the older man sober. No matter how hard she struggled to support him, he had often been in no state to work and on many occasions he had simply wandered off during working hours to drink himself into a stupor. Most employers would have sacked him. But, surprisingly, Benito Grazzini had been sympathetic towards the grieving widower and he had kept on giving Archie Little another chance to straighten himself out. That reality had given him strong ammunition when he asked Glory to leave her home.

'Look at your family background and tell me that you

are not wrong for my son. I believe that it is best for everyone concerned that *you* should move away and make a fresh start somewhere else,' Rafaello's father had pronounced with the harshness of a man who had steeled himself to perform an unpleasant duty. 'In return I will promise to do all that is within my power to help your father overcome his problems.'

Her *background*. No further explanation had been required once that word had been spoken. Her once respected father had been behaving like a drunken layabout, and her late mother? Talitha Little had never won local acceptance, for she had been born and bred a gypsy. In Romany parlance, she had 'married out' and once she had made that choice custom had demanded that even her own family have nothing more to do with her. Yet the new life she had chosen with her *gadjo* husband, Archie Little, had been no more welcoming. Her herbal lore and superstitious ways had been foreign and threatening to her village neighbours. Talitha had much preferred the privacy of their isolated woodland cottage on the Montague estate.

As Glory re-entered the lift on the top floor of Grazzini Industries she was too worked up even to register Jon Lyons' hovering presence nearby. Her brother and her father were waiting for her in a café near the train station. She wondered what on earth she was going to tell them. That Rafaello Grazzini had made her an offer she could not accept? That she would sooner boil in oil than be any man's kept woman? But most especially *his*?

Oh, yes, most especially *his* woman! Distraught with the strength of the conflicting feelings attacking her, Glory hurried through the crowded city streets. Why was Rafaello doing this to her? Five years ago, they had only been together six weeks. Long enough for her to fall irrevocably in love but not long enough to persuade her to surrender her virginity to a male who had made not the smallest mention of love.

She could thank her mother for that ingrained caution. Talitha Little had believed that a woman's most precious possession was purity, for that was exactly how she had been raised. When Glory had first been given that message she had not even properly understood what physical intimacy was. But long before she reached the age of temptation she had absorbed the unnerving impression that her life would go horribly wrong if she broke that rule before she was safely married.

Rafaello had thought that was hilariously funny until he realised over the space of several weeks that Glory was serious. Then he had suggested it was a little weird and that, with all due respect to her late mother's convictions, Glory really should not let herself be affected by such superstitious fears.

Emerging from that recollection, Glory discovered that she was lodged stock-still in front of a shop window and smiling with a silly far-away look fixed to her face. Her smile died. As she crushed out that ruefully amusing recollection of Rafaello's efforts to persuade her into his bed, her dulled eyes stung with hot tears of regret.

She walked on, striving to concentrate and find a solution to her family's predicament. Sam was a minor in the eyes of the law and Rafaello could press charges to his heart's content, but he had no proof whatsoever that her kid brother had been involved in the theft of that snuff box. The worst that was likely to happen to Sam was…what? A police caution? Sam had never been in trouble before and how would he bear up to that challenge?

'Sam's different,' Glory's mother had once muttered in exasperation. 'He's too sensitive and emotional for a boy. He'll get the life teased out of him if he doesn't toughen up.' Happily, Sam's talent on the sports field had made him popular at school. But he had once shaken Glory with the admission that he hated sport of all kinds. She wondered how many of his friends knew that Sam spent every spare

moment sketching people and animals. Or that sometimes
Sam listened to depressing items on the news and became
deeply upset by them, that he took things too much to heart.

And what about her father? Might he fall off the wagon
and begin drinking again? He was a kind man, a good man,
but he was weak, she acknowledged painfully. In times of
trouble, he crumpled.

Her father and her brother were seated at the back of the
half-empty café nursing cups of tea. Their eyes flew to her
as she drew level with their table. She sat down beside her
brother, deeply troubled by the misery that he could not
hide.

'What did Mr Grazzini say?' her father demanded, his
lined brow furrowed beneath his greying blond hair, his
faded blue eyes red-rimmed with the effects of strain and
insufficient sleep. He looked older than his fifty-seven years
and drained.

'Dad…'

'It's bad, isn't it? If only this had happened before Benito
Grazzini retired and handed over the estate to his son,'
Archie Little muttered in a bitter tone of defeat. 'That
Rafaello's as hard as nails. I don't know what you ever saw
in him, Glory. But nothing I could say would turn you away
from him—'

'Sam,' Glory cut in hurriedly, turning to address her
brother before her father could say anything more in a similar vein. There was little resemblance between brother and
sister, because Sam was much taller with very dark hair
and dark eyes. He had taken after their mother's side of the
family, while she had inherited their father's fair colouring.
But right now, for all his size and athletic breadth, Sam
looked very much like a scared ten-year-old kid.

'What happened?' her brother prompted anxiously.

'Rafaello told me that a very valuable snuff box went
missing while you and your friends were partying—'

'Are you saying something was stolen? Well, it couldn't

have been any of us!' Sam gave his sister a shocked look
of reproach. 'Do you think we're stupid?'

'You need to pass the word round your friends that that
box must be returned, because Rafaello is not going to let
it go. It's worth a great deal of money.'

'I didn't see *any* of my mates with a box,' Sam told her
with a perplexed frown.

'Rafaello said it was tiny…small enough to be hidden in
a pocket,' Glory informed him, and she was relieved at the
need to make that explanation to her brother, for his ignorance satisfied her that he could have had nothing to do
with the theft.

Listening to that dialogue between his son and daughter,
Archie Little had turned a sickly grey shade. 'Something
being stolen finishes us. No wonder you couldn't get anywhere with Rafaello Grazzini,' he said heavily. 'He'll be
furious. Can't blame him either. Sam had enough cheek
even going into the Park, never mind the damage he and
his mates caused, and now *this*…'

'I'm sorry, Dad…' Sam mumbled chokily. 'I swear I'll
never do anything like that again—'

'You're not likely to get the chance, son.' Rising wearily
to his feet, the older man studied his troubled daughter and
sighed. 'We'll go home now and you go on back to
Birmingham. I'm sorry, Glory. I wish I hadn't dragged you
into this mess.'

'Why did you think Rafaello would listen to me?' Glory
could not help asking.

Her father sighed. 'Something your mother once said.
You know, one of those strange notions she used to take…'

'What did she say?'

'That he would always look after you. Silly,' he said
wryly. 'It didn't make sense then and it makes even less
now.'

But those words that she had never heard before sent the
oddest shiver down Glory's spine. Just before they parted

outside the café, her brother grabbed her in a sudden bone-crushing hug that let her know just how frantic with worry he was. With tears in her eyes, she watched her brother and father walk away. She hadn't even been asked what had passed between her and Rafaello. But then, would she have told the truth *had* she been asked? The minute she had mentioned that stolen snuff box, her father had given up all hope of matters being settled more amicably.

And how did she feel now? Horribly guilty, she discovered, for protecting herself when she might have helped her father and brother. But at what cost might she have helped? By putting herself in the power of a male who despised her? Two wrongs did not make a right, and Rafaello had wronged her in his big flashy office. She should have told him that too, should have told him that he had had no business treating her like that. And while she was doing that she ought to have told him the unlovely truth about his *own* father's treatment of her five years earlier! Benito Grazzini might've informed Rafaello that she had taken that cheque for five thousand pounds. But she was darned sure that Rafaello's father had not also admitted the cruel pressure he had brought to bear on a frightened eighteen-year-old girl, fearful of the consequences to her family if she dared to stand up for herself!

In a sudden decisive movement, Glory turned in her tracks and headed back in the direction of Grazzini Industries. She was going to tell Rafaello Grazzini what she thought of him! And his lousy, rich, bullying father, that fine upstanding man whom Rafaello had always regarded with such immense respect. She wasn't the *only* one with embarrassing and dishonest relatives and it was time he faced that fact!

By the time Glory arrived on the top floor of Grazzini Industries for the second time that day, she was dizzy with the number of emotions buzzing about inside her. The receptionist called Rafaello on the phone.

'You can go straight in,' Glory was told.

What was she going to say to Rafaello? Was she really about to tell Rafaello that his father had broken her heart and that it had taken the meanest and nastiest blackmail to frighten her into giving him up? Did she really *want* to tell Rafaello that? Did his ego deserve the news that she had truly loved him to distraction five years ago? Indeed, exactly *why* was she back in his office building desperate to confront him again?

Suffering a sudden loss of confidence at the way her own mind worked, Glory hovered outside Rafaello's office door. An awful suspicion was growing on her by the minute. She could not entirely ignore the amount of exhilaration that the prospect of seeing him again induced inside her...

Disorientatingly while she was still engaged in her inner battle the door opened. '*Still* having second thoughts?' Rafaello murmured with expressionless cool.

Glory studied him. Her tongue was glued to the dry roof of her mouth. Her heart was suddenly beating so fast that she could hardly get breath into her straining lungs. That lean, strong face and those dark deep-set eyes of his. Having once made that visual connection, she could not break it. It was as if a very powerful magnet had been turned on her and she was too weak to fight the strength of that pull.

She gulped. 'Don't get this wrong. I came here...I came back here *solely* to give you a piece of my mind.'

'You can do it over lunch,' Rafaello countered in his lazy accented drawl, curving a casual arm around her spine to flip her round and urge her back in the direction of the lift again.

'Lunch?' Glory exclaimed, taken aback.

'I'm hungry.' Rafaello rested shimmering dark golden eyes on her. 'I am *so* hungry.'

Glory trembled, her bemused blue eyes sinking to the level of the sensual slant of his beautiful mouth and noting the faint blue-tinged roughness of the skin on his strong jawline. She recalled that he had always had to shave twice a day. And that stray abstracted reflection somehow sent her off on the memory of how he kissed, how he had once made her feel. She had never truly appreciated the depth of her own hunger for him until she had discovered that *no* other man had the ability to send her temperature rocketing as he had.

'Intense, isn't it, *cara*?' Rafaello purred like a big jungle cat, emanating an amount of masculine satisfaction that suddenly made her want to slap him hard and snapped her free of the potent spell he cast for long enough to make her think again.

Why had she come back? Had it been a case of grabbing at any excuse just to see him again? For what good reason had she raced back to Grazzini Industries? What had happened five years ago didn't matter any more. What he thought of her no longer mattered either. And if her reappearance had now given him entirely the wrong impression, wasn't that her fault too?

'I've decided I don't want to give you a piece of my mind any more,' Glory confided in a rush as he swept her inexorably into the lift with him. 'I shouldn't *be* here, but while I am here I might as well tell you that I told Sam about that box and I'm absolutely convinced that he had *nothing* to do with its disappearance—'

As Glory paused for the breath with which to continue, Rafaello backed her into the corner of the lift and rested his lean hands on her slight, tense shoulders. 'You're talking too much.'

'But Sam's going to pass the word round his friends, so hopefully something will come from that, and I'm going back to Birmingham,' Glory continued at an even faster and more breathless trot. She was hugely aware of the lean, powerful length of him within inches of her own taut body and the wave of heat darting up through her no matter how hard she fought to hold it down.

'You're *not* going back to Birmingham...' Rafaello intoned, allowing his lean fingers to glide down her slender arms and then enclosing her smaller hands in his without warning.

'No!' Glory cried, yanking herself free of that imprisoning hold with the abruptness of a woman suddenly waking up to the threat. 'You're not listening to me, are you? I'm not accepting your offer. I want nothing to do with you—'

With a roughened groan of raw impatience, Rafaello meshed one hand into the soft coils of her honey-blonde hair to hold her still and he brought his mouth crashing down with hungry intensity on hers. For a split-second, she went rigid with shock and he took advantage. He backed her up against the cool metallic wall and splayed his hands beneath her hips to lift her up to him. And then he let his tongue drive between her parted lips with erotic force, plundering the tender interior within, and every nerve-ending in her quivering body went haywire.

She wrapped her arms round his neck and clung, kissing him back with mindless fervour. A tormented moan of response was dragged from low in her throat. She couldn't get enough of that drugging passion which she had once worked so hard to forget. The very strength and power of the hard male physique keeping her pinned back to the wall inflamed her with dangerous heat. Helpless in the grip of her own increasing excitement, she was beyond thought or objection when he splayed her thighs round him, the better to anchor her to him.

And then, without any warning whatsoever, Rafaello froze. With a ragged groan, he released her swollen mouth and gazed down at her with heavily lidded smouldering golden eyes that had a faintly dazed light. '*Per meraviglia*... We are in a lift in a public building!'

In an equally sudden movement, Rafaello settled her back down onto her own feet. In shock, Glory finally realised that the lift was still and that all the lights on the control panel were flashing but that the doors had yet to open. 'Why isn't it moving?'

'I stopped it,' Rafaello admitted curtly, stabbing a couple of buttons.

With a slight lurch the lift set off downward again, while Glory smoothed shaking hands down her rucked sweater. She could not bring herself to look at him. It was one of those moments when intense mortification and essential honesty combined to prevent her from coming up with a single face-saving excuse. Her lips burning from the heat of his, her trembling body still struggling to come down from the heights of anticipation he had contrived to fire within seconds of touching her, she felt shattered.

'We'll go back to my apartment,' Rafaello breathed thickly.

Sensing that lunch would not be Rafaello's most pressing goal, Glory reddened to the roots of her hair with shame. 'Nothing doing. I'm going home. I told you that. This was an accident—'

'An...accident?' Rafaello repeated in thunderous disbelief.

'Like when you take your eyes off the road and *crash*!' Glory stressed shakily, almost being eaten alive by the strength of her own self-loathing.

The lift doors swept back with an electronic beep of warning, exposing them to all onlookers. There was a crush of bodies waiting outside but their impatient surge forward was arrested by the sight of the male within. A sea of wildly curious faces stared in at Rafaello and Glory.

Glory lurched into frantic motion. She pushed her way through the stilled crowd and then raced across the busy ground-floor foyer for the exit doors. She ran a good half of the way back to the train station and then, winded and barely able to catch her breath, was forced to halt her mad flight and walk instead.

However, the sense of panic and severe embarrassment induced by what she had allowed to happen between herself and Rafaello was in no way lessened. How *could* she have behaved like that? One minute telling him she had only come back to give him a piece of her mind, the next winding herself round him like the weakest of choking vines. Talk about handing out conflicting signals!

CHAPTER THREE

THE following day Glory had an early shift at the factory and then finished work early, as was the norm on a Friday afternoon.

Feeling exhausted, she trudged up the stairs to her top-floor bedsit. She had her key in the door before she actually noticed the slip of paper stuck to the scarred wood. 'Urgent,' ran the message in the girl next door's handwriting. 'Phone your dad!'

Her heart in her mouth at the thought of what those four words might mean, Glory clattered back down the stairs again to use the coinbox phone in the hall.

Her father answered her call almost immediately. 'Is that you, Glory?'

'What is it? What's happened?' she prompted breathlessly.

'The police arrived first thing this morning with a search warrant.'

'A s-search warrant?' Glory stammered in horror.

'They found that stolen snuff box hidden in our fuel shed,' Archie Little told her heavily. 'Sam was arrested. The police have charged him, but he didn't do it. I *know* he didn't do it!'

As Glory absorbed what her father was telling her, shock chilled her skin to the temperature of ice. 'Sam was arrested…and charged?'

'His best mate is the one who did the stealing,' he asserted bitterly. 'When Sam came to me for help during that party Joe was with him, but he insisted on staying outside. When I left the cottage to go up and turf their mates out of the Park I saw Joe coming out of the shed—'

'Oh, Dad...' Glory mumbled sickly, her heart sinking like a stone.

'I wondered what the kid had been doing but I was too keen to get that party stopped to waste time asking him. But Joe must've panicked and hidden the box then. But who's going to believe that when it was found in *our* shed?' Archie Little demanded on the rising note of a man already taxed beyond his endurance level. 'What are we going to do, Glory? I don't know what to do or where to turn now—'

'I'll sort something out,' Glory heard herself insist with forced confidence. 'Tell Sam I'm thinking of him and that I believe in him—'

'How are you going to sort out anything? It's too late,' her father groaned, and she could hear the thickness of tears and the defeat in his response. 'The solicitor says we just have to wait until it comes to court.'

'Trust me...I'll arrange something, I *swear* I will. Don't let Sam get too upset about this,' Glory warned, because her kid brother was an emotional boy and now she was worried sick. Suppose he ran away or, even worse, became even more depressed and did something foolish? She shivered. Her father was not the rock that a scared teenager needed for support, nor the best person to persuade Sam that they could fight to prove his innocence.

Only when Glory came off the phone did she discover that she was shaking like a leaf. Momentarily she closed her eyes in anguish. She could have saved Sam from the ordeal of being arrested and charged. But now that the forces of law and order had got involved, was it even possible that the theft charge could be dropped? And even if it was possible, would Rafaello now be willing to do it?

She lifted out her purse and searched for the phone number she had used forty-eight hours earlier to contact Rafaello's London office and ask for her appointment. She got passed through to his secretary, but there the trail as such threatened to go cold. Rafaello was not available, she was told starchily.

'Has he gone abroad?' Glory pressed fearfully. 'Look, this is very urgent. I really need to know where he is.'

'Mr Grazzini is at his country house and I'm afraid I'm not able to give you either the address or the phone number. However, I will pass on your message—'

'No, please don't do that!' Glory interrupted in dismay, thinking that forewarning of her change of heart might only harden his. In another mood she might have smiled at the secretary's mistake in mentioning Rafaello's whereabouts. Naturally the woman had no idea that Glory would know exactly where that country house was situated.

An element of surprise might be the only thing she had going for her, Glory reflected in desperation as she yanked out her travel bag. She would catch the train down to Montague Park and try to see Rafaello before she went to see her family. What else could she do? Leave Sam facing theft charges? But would Rafaello even *listen* to her now?

After her senseless behaviour the afternoon before Glory knew that Rafaello would be furious with her. Her second visit to his office and her wild response to that steamy embrace, followed by her equally sudden flight, had been madness. Even with the best will in the world, she knew she could never explain why she had gone back while still maintaining that she had no intention of accepting his offer. If she couldn't explain that to herself, how could she possibly hope to explain it to him?

Zipping up her bag, she looked at herself in the mirror and almost had a heart attack! Her hair was falling down in messy strands from an unglamorous pony-tail. Her pale, anxious face was bare of make-up and her jeans and shirt were hardly of the ilk calculated to persuade a man that she was worth sacrificing a principle for. And, where principles were concerned, Rafaello could make a person feel distinctly uncomfortable. He had said the offer would be

closed if she did not take it up in the time frame he had
set. So if she was to persuade him otherwise she would
have to look good, look *seductive*…?

Not a challenge Glory had ever taken on before, when
her greatest need had always been to find one special man
who would see her as a person rather than a sexual challenge and a trophy. Already painfully aware that her full-
lipped face, blonde hair and hourglass shape encouraged
men to assume that she would be an easy lay, Glory never
wore provocative clothes. But provocative was the look required, wasn't it? Reminding herself of her kid brother's
current plight, she left her bedsit to knock on her neighbour's door.

Tania, a small, bubbly brunette, currently working nights
in a busy city bar, opened her door. 'Glory…did you get
my message?'

'Yes, thanks. Look, I was wondering, would you let me
borrow one of your clubbing outfits?' Glory asked hesitantly.

Tania surveyed her with an exaggerated dropped jaw.

'I'd be really careful with it,' Glory promised in a humble tone.

'Are you the woman who told me you wouldn't be seen
dead flashing your legs in a short skirt just to give some
sick bloke a cheap thrill?'

Glory reddened and nodded slowly.

'Are you the same woman who told me boobs were made
to be covered, not put out like cut-price fruit on a stall?'

Glory winced at that second reminder and nodded again
in guilty confirmation.

Tania gave her cringing visitor a hugely amused grin and
let Glory in. 'So tell me…who's the guy you're hanging
up your combat trousers and workman's boots for?'

Glory paled and thought. 'A challenge?'

'I *love* a challenge!' Tania threw wide the door of her

crammed wardrobe. 'Trust me, Glory. Now that you've owned up to your desperation, I'll be your best pal.'

Three-quarters of an hour later Glory studied her transformed appearance in her own room. A frilly pink top hugged her lush bosom, and she had had to squeeze into the stretchy short pink skirt with its racy split. Her stiletto-heeled shoes had only two tiny narrow satin bands studded with diamanté to hold in her feet. Above one ankle she now sported a fashionable henna transfer tattoo in an oriental design. Tattoos drive men *wild* Tania had assured her. Glory had wondered out loud whether some males might prefer greater subtlety. But Tania it had to be admitted, had far more experience, and had said that at heart men were one and all the same: they were just slaves to their hormones every time.

'You're gonna stop the traffic. Next time we go out together, you put on your combat trousers and boots again.' Tania warned her, smoothing the shining mane of honey-blonde hair which hung halfway down Glory's narrow back. 'I couldn't stick this amount of competition. I'd be so jealous, I'd never speak to you again.'

'No problem. I don't like looking like this...not that I'm not grateful,' Glory added hurriedly as she pulled on her raincoat.

'I hope he's worth the effort—'

'*He* probably thinks he is.' Glory set off for the bus that would take her to the train.

Shortly after seven that evening, Glory finally reached the imposing gates of Montague Park and contemplated the mile-long driveway that stretched before her.

Chafed by the diamanté straps, her feet were already in agony. And, in truth, she did not actually *want* to arrive at her destination. Or that ghastly moment when she would have to tell Rafaello that he had won and that she would be his for as long as he wanted it that way. While she

cringed for herself and grovelled, she would also have the
added torment of knowing that he was enjoying every minute of her major climbdown.

Twenty minutes later she reached the grand front doors
of the superb Georgian mansion and hit the bell.

The housekeeper, Maud Belper, gazed out at her in
astonished recognition. 'Glory?'

'I'd be really grateful if you wouldn't mention to my dad
that you saw me here,' Glory whispered guiltily, sidling in
past the older woman, who had known her since childhood.
'Is Mr Grazzini home?'

'Would that be Mr Benito or Mr Rafaello?' Maud enquired, deciding that two could play the mystery game of
mutual ignorance.

'Rafaello,' Glory mumbled, her colour heightening.

'Let me take your coat—'

Glory clutched her coat to her. 'No...no, thanks. I've got
a cold coming on and I'm feeling the chill.'

'Mr Grazzini's in the library.'

Glory nodded and listened to the housekeeper's steps retreat at a tellingly slow pace.

Leaving her travel bag behind, she limped over to the
library door on her poor, tortured feet and undid the belt
on her raincoat. She felt like a flasher. Suppose Rafaello
laughed? Suppose she did genuinely look as trashy and silly
as she feared that she did? This is for *Sam*, she reminded
herself, and on the spur of that she walked into the room,
paused and discarded the coat in almost the same movement. He could only interpret her announced arrival and
her vampish appearance in one way. And, if he took that
hint, hopefully she wouldn't have to grovel quite so much.

Talking on the phone over by the window, Rafaello froze
as though Glory had burst in waving a hand grenade. He
blinked. He looked again, kept on looking. Stunned dark
golden eyes started afresh at the crown of her honey-blonde
head, worked slowly down over her taut but beautiful face

and back over the full pouting thrust of her breasts as delineated in skintight pink. There he seemed to pause to take
a much needed break and he breathed in audibly before
meeting the challenge of proceeding further in a downward
direction.

Glory stood there like a martyr tied to the stake with a
face hotter than any flames could have provoked. She could
feel every ragged breath struggling past her convulsed
throat as the tension rose. Staying still and silent was the
hardest thing she had ever done. He had forced her to reduce herself to the level of a sex object desperate to sell
herself to the highest bidder, and her pride was crushed.

Rafaello had trouble dragging his attention from the
well-defined curve of her hips, but when he reached her
legs he appeared to be even more challenged to keep his
intent appraisal moving. Finally his scrutiny screamed to a
halt above the slender ankle displaying the henna transfer
tattoo.

Suddenly he flashed his smouldering eyes back up to her
severely strained features. An aristocratic black brow was
elevated. 'What *is* this? A pantomime in which you star as
the sex bomb?'

Glory had never been very confident that Rafaello would
be a slave to his hormones as Tania had forecast, for
Rafaello had a natural stubborn streak that rejoiced in never
doing exactly what was expected of him. A 'pantomime'?
She shrivelled with embarrassment at his use of that particular word. His sardonic response annihilated her where
she stood.

Stepping painfully off one foot onto the other, striving
to spread the agony of her complaining toes, Glory stooped.
In a harried movement she snatched up her coat and dived
back into its concealing folds. Once again she had made a
total fool of herself, she reflected in choked mortification.
Scorching tears lashed the backs of her eyes so hard she

had to widen them and focus on a point over his shoulder
to keep them from falling.

'No, of course I am not talking to *you*,' Rafaello breathed
with chilling cool to the excusably confused and unfortunate person he had been speaking to on the phone when
she first entered and whose invisible listening presence he
had briefly forgotten. 'I have a visitor. I'll call you back.'

While he spoke Glory watched him. A powerful feeling
of torment and tragedy was now assailing her already ragged nerves. Why had she torn off her raincoat in that utterly
stupid way? She had been terrified that she would lose her
nerve at the last moment. She had hoped to strike an impression of being cool, even rather amused and scornful,
but fully in control of events. She had failed: he thought
she looked ridiculous. But there *he* was, the very image of
enviable cool and sophistication in a superbly tailored dark
suit that was probably the ultimate in Italian style.

Rafaello cast aside the receiver. Dark, deep-set eyes
hooded, he scanned Glory as she hugged her coat as if it
was the only thing standing between her and total nudity.
'I'm waiting for an explanation.'

'What do you want me to say?' Glory asked jaggedly,
her throat closing over, her wide, over-bright eyes staring
a hole into the middle distance. She had looked enough at
him. That bold masculine face in profile, the shadow his
lush black lashes cast on one high cheekbone, the arrogant
nose, the wide, sexy mouth. Even half a view of him made
her heart race and set butterflies dancing in her tummy.

'OK...' Rafaello drawled in the silken tone of a male
taking up a challenge without hesitation. 'Yesterday you
raced back to my office and fell into my arms—'

'I did not *fall* into your arms, I was grabbed—' Glory
squeezed out between gritted teeth.

Rafaello ignored that contradiction. 'If I hadn't called
time I do believe we would've had sex in the lift—'

'Speak for yourself!' Glory launched at him in strong chagrin. 'I don't behave like that—'

'Don't you?' Rafaello vented a derisive laugh. 'When you burst in here I thought some maniac had decided to treat me to a strippergram!'

'A…what?' Glory gasped in dismay.

'Dressed like that you look like a cheap little scrubber.' Rafaello skimmed her a brooding scrutiny and his hard sensual mouth twisted. 'Not my style; a definite turn-off.'

Veiling her stricken gaze, Glory dropped her head and gulped in sustaining air like a drowning swimmer. Hurt and humiliated by that blunt assessment, she had to bite back the impulsive words rising to her lips. She could not afford to antagonise Rafaello when her brother's whole future rested in his hands. A taut silence stretched while she fought an almost overwhelming urge to tell him what he could do with his uninvited opinions. So she had got the outfit wrong. But then, what had he expected? Some classy designer number? Never had the gap between her world and his seemed as great as it did at that moment.

'Since you're lousy at getting to the point, isn't it fortunate that I can work out exactly what you're doing here?' Rafaello remarked drily.

Prompted, Glory glanced up, her lovely face tense with strain. Brilliant dark eyes slammed into hers and she trembled, her mouth running dry. 'I'm certain that Sam didn't steal that snuff box, but I know things don't look good for him and that it'll be very hard to prove that he's innocent. You did say that if you got the box back you might consider *not* pressing charges—'

'Only I was talking about it being returned voluntarily,' Rafaello contradicted with chilling cool. 'Not found during a police search.'

Glory had not really had any hope that he would not make that distinction but she had felt that she ought to try out that angle. 'All right…' she breathed unevenly. 'So if you can still get the charges dropped, well…I'll do whatever you want.'

Rafaello strolled soundlessly over to the windows before swinging back round to look at her again, his lean, strong face intent. 'I can have the theft charge withdrawn but how do I know that you'll respect your side of the agreement?'

At the news that the charge of theft *could* still be withdrawn, a little colour eased back into Glory's complexion. But she was strung so high with tension that even her knees had begun to wobble. 'Whatever you think of me, I'm not a cheat or a liar.'

Rafaello scanned her with unreadable dark eyes. 'My father certainly had no grounds for complaint after the bargain he struck with you. Unless I'm very much mistaken, it *has* been five years since you set foot on Grazzini land. You can't have seen much of your father and your brother since then.'

Was that actually a hint of censure that she was hearing? Sam and Glory talked on the phone most weeks. For the first couple of years she had lived in Gloucester with her father's sister and she had often seen her family. But when her aunt passed away, Glory had had to move further north to find employment, and inevitably the frequency of their meetings had declined. No longer could Glory feel that she was as close to her younger brother as she had once been. Acknowledging that truth, she felt hugely bitter at the damage that Benito Grazzini had cruelly inflicted on her small family circle.

'Living a couple of hundred miles away hasn't exactly been a help,' Glory said defensively. 'We don't all have limos and private jets to get around in.'

'But you will have for as long as you're with me.' Losing interest in the subject that he himself had raised, Rafaello studied her with a reflective all-male intensity that sent fresh pink flying into her cheeks. 'You can take your coat off. I assume you're staying tonight.'

Glory froze. 'Tonight?'

Rafaello dealt her a lazy mocking smile. 'Were you waiting for me to schedule in a date for next month?'

'But tonight…for goodness' sake!' Glory was seriously challenged to maintain any form of cool when she realised how soon he was expecting her to meet and deliver on the terms of their agreement. 'After this I was planning to go and see Dad and Sam and surprise them.'

'Surprise me instead,' Rafaello invited softly. 'If your family aren't expecting you, you'll find yourself facing some awkward questions. I'll have the theft charge dropped and I'll personally inform your father of that decision this evening.'

'That's great,' Glory told him gratefully. 'But—'

'You will be flying out to Corfu tomorrow,' Rafaello cut in quietly.

'Tomorrow? Corfu?' Her blue eyes had widened to their fullest extent. He was expecting her to go abroad? 'Are you crazy? I have a job, a home and a whole bunch of stuff to sort out before I can go *anywhere*—'

'I'll have someone clear your bedsit, settle any final bills and inform your landlord and your employer that you're not coming back. It's not a problem.'

'Well, it is a problem for me. I can do all those things for myself within a couple of days,' Glory argued in a flustered but insistent undertone. 'But if you're expecting me to go abroad with you I want to see my family tonight.'

'If you walk out on me one more time you can forget about walking back in again.'

The silence shimmered like the menacing quiet before a storm. Chilled by that cold threat that cut unmercifully through her every argument, Glory studied Rafaello in genuine shock.

Rafaello gazed back at her with hard dark eyes that had no shade of lighter emotional gold.

'Why are you being like this?' Glory muttered helplessly.

'I've surrendered every way I can but it's still not enough for you.'

'Don't exaggerate, *cara*.' With complete cool, Rafaello reached out to loosen her tight grip on her raincoat and fold her taut fingers into the hold of his. 'I just don't want there to be any misunderstandings between us. I'm calling the shots. What else did you expect?'

At the warmth of his hands on hers, Glory trembled. She gazed up into eyes dark as midnight but she had already lost his direct attention. Her raincoat had fallen open. His lowered gaze was welded to the exposed curves of her pouting breasts. A shocking stab of hurt travelled through her. 'You said...you *said* I looked like a cheap little scrubber in this get-up, so why are you looking at me like that?'

'Intellect aside, I'm still a red-blooded male with all the usual painfully predictable reactions.' His smouldering dark golden scrutiny skimmed back up to her self-conscious face. 'You're no longer that guileless teenager who burned me up with the lure of her supposed innocence, but that's a plus now. I want an experienced lover in my bed, a woman who can satisfy my every need.'

That admission made Glory stiffen. She dropped her head to hide the hectic flush in her cheeks. She was not ashamed of being a virgin, but nor was she prepared to take the risk of telling him the truth. Suppose he changed his mind about the arrangement he had offered her? A male, who was only interested in his own sexual pleasure would naturally prefer a woman who could match his own expertise between the sheets. And by the sounds of it, Rafaello had pretty *high* expectations. However, he was destined to meet with a major disappointment in that department. But to her way of thinking, there was a certain natural rough justice to that reality. Rafaello would get exactly what he deserved.

'I think the only reason you want me is because I turned

you down five years ago,' Glory said before she could think
better of that leading comment.

Lean fingers found her chin and turned up her eyes to
encounter the scorching gold of his own. 'You could be
right, but then I never really turned up the heat, did I?'

'Didn't you?' Her own voice sounded slightly strangled
as he let that controlling hand drift down to the base of her
spine instead.

All of a sudden even catching her breath and clearing
her dry throat was a challenge. The tension in the atmosphere was electrifying. Her heart was racing like a trapped
bird inside her ribcage and she was aware of Rafaello's
potent masculinity with every fibre of her being.

'I was playing a waiting game,' Rafaello confided huskily. 'But now I don't need to wait.'

He was going to touch her and she wanted him to touch
her. Indeed, she could hardly *wait* for him to touch her, she
registered in dismay. But even the shame that followed that
acknowledgement could not still the insidious awakening
of her own body. She was painfully conscious of the swelling heaviness of her breasts and the aching sensitivity of
their rosy peaks but most of all of the betraying surge of
moist heat at the very heart of her.

He urged her closer and her nostrils flared on the heady
familiarity of his scent. The faint aroma of aftershave un-
derscored by warm male. She trembled, wanting, needing,
suddenly strung up to such a height of hunger, she was
dizzy with it. And then he took her mouth and kissed her
with sensual probing intensity and it was as if her heart
stopped on the unbearable sweetness of that sensation before thundering on faster and wilder in beat than ever before.

'Imagine saying no to this, *cara*...' Rafaello murmured
thickly, lifting his arrogant dark head while she struggled
for breath and the independent strength to hold herself upright instead of holding on to him for support.

Glory was devastated by her own sheer longing to be back in his arms again. 'Stop teasing me...'

'Is this what you call teasing?' Shimmering golden eyes scanned her with predatory amusement. 'Slow and seductive not what you're used to, *cara mia*?'

In the grip of that passionate yearning, her quivering body no longer felt like her own. She gave way to her own frustration. She reached up and dragged his mouth back down to hers again. As her seeking fingers laced into his luxuriant black hair, he loosed a sound somewhere between a laugh and a groan. But in response he let his tongue probe deep between her lips in an explicit penetration that made her shiver with helpless anticipation against his hard, muscular frame. Closing his hands to her hips, he lifted her off her feet.

'Rafaello...?' Glory was taken aback when he settled her down on top of the antique mahogany desk.

'You're too short to be fully accessible upright,' he mocked, curling his hand into the fall of her honey-blonde mane and then letting his fingertips skim appreciatively through the glossy strands. '*Santo cielo!* Your hair feels like pure silk...'

Before she could even guess his intention, he had parted her knees and drawn her right to the edge of the desk. Then he eased his hands beneath her hips and lifted her back to him in a much more intimate connection than had been possible while she had been standing. Her legs apart and left to dangle either side of his lean, powerful length as he moved into the space he had created for himself, Glory felt suddenly out of her depth and vulnerable. As she fought to force her stretchy skirt back down over her exposed thighs, even the heat of her own shivering hunger was incapable of silencing the alarm bells of panic his behaviour was rousing.

'What are you doing?' Glory exclaimed.

Rafaello looked down at her with stunning dark golden

eyes, a frownline etched between his winged dark brows. 'What's wrong?'

'What's wrong?' Glory demanded incredulously half an octave higher. 'You're expecting me to carry on with you on top of a desk and you're asking *me* what's wrong?'

Rafaello stilled as if she had thrown a stop switch. Lush black lashes dropped down to conceal his gaze.

'Because cavorting on desks is *out*!' Glory told him fiercely, the fear that he was trying to make a fool of her trammelling through her in an enervating wave. 'I've met some real full-on creeps in my time but even they didn't try to jump me on a desk—'

'Is that a fact?' Rafaello breathed not quite levelly, apparently transfixed by her frantic efforts to drag the hem of her skirt down over her thighs. Helpfully he stepped back so that she could lock her knees together again and achieve that feat.

'Yes, that is a fact,' Glory told him chokily, tears roughening her voice as her distress climbed in direct proportion to her embarrassment. 'I want respect. I want boundaries to this "anything you want" stuff—'

'I get the feeling that, on your terms, the desk is the absolute outer limits,' Rafaello murmured in a taut undertone that shook slightly, his Italian accent thicker than she had ever heard it.

'It's a question of what's decent.'

'You're not very adventurous, are you?'

'Not in lifts or on desks,' Glory agreed shakily, sliding off the wooden surface in haste and smoothing her rucked clothing down with trembling hands.

'I wasn't actually *planning* to consummate our agreement on the library desk—'

Too self-conscious to look at him, her cheeks hotter than hellfire, Glory shrugged a slight shoulder in a jerky, defensive motion. 'How was I supposed to know what you were planning? You embarrassed me—'

'Tell me, do you know what foreplay is?'

If Glory had been feeling overheated before he said that in the charged tone of a male trying hard not to laugh at what he obviously found amusing, her temperature hit boiling point in receipt of that mocking enquiry.

'I do know you're not talking about golf, if that's what you mean!' she launched back at him angrily, bright blue eyes sparking fierily. 'But I'm not here to be the butt of your smart-mouth comments, Rafaello Grazzini—'

'And you're not here to cavort on my desk either. Sorry, couldn't resist it, *cara*,' Rafaello drawled, lean, strong face expressionless. 'I think what we need here is a list—'

'A...what?'

'Of places where sexual activity is forbidden. And, while we're on the subject, possibly you ought to consider throwing in news of any other strong aversions before I share a bed with you.'

Encountering those brilliant, beautiful dark eyes, Glory paled. 'You think this is funny, don't you?'

'No, I'm fascinated. In my entire experience of women, I have never had a conversation quite like this,' Rafaello assured her, smooth as silk. 'It looks as if your mother is going to have the last laugh on me after all. And please do not take that comment as any form of insult to her memory.'

Glory swallowed hard. Her throat thickened. She felt more like bursting into tears. Just then she did not need the reminder of her late mother. Not on the very night she was being expected to abandon those principles. She saw that nerves and shyness had made her overreact to an unfamiliar and seemingly threatening situation. He had only wanted to kiss her, maybe touch her a little. But she had thrown a three-act tragedy and made an ass of herself in the process.

'I'm glad I've given you a laugh,' she muttered, cut to the bone.

Rafaello released his breath on a slight hiss and reached

for her tightly knotted fingers to urge her back to him. She
moved only when the pressure got too much to withstand.
With a rueful groan, he murmured, 'I wasn't laughing—'

'You *were*,' she mumbled tightly, the tears threatening.

'You're wearing a real in-your-face sexy outfit. I didn't
think a woman who dressed like that would take fright quite
so easily,' Rafaello admitted above her downbent head.

'I did *not* take fright,' Glory bit out in a driven tone,
picturing a panicking Victorian spinster screaming on a
stool at the sight of a mouse.

'OK…you took offence, but it's over,' Rafaello re-
phrased in his deep, husky drawl. 'Go on upstairs. After
I've called your father, I'll join you.'

Glory froze, all her nervous tension returning. 'Where?'

'In my bedroom. Of course, you've never been upstairs.
I'll take you up—'

'No, just tell me where,' Glory interrupted tautly.

A phone began to ring. Rafaello released an imprecation
in his own language, hesitated and then strode impatiently
back over to the desk. 'It's my private line. I should answer
it in case it's something important.'

'Where?' she prompted again, grabbing up her coat and
sticking her arms into the sleeves.

'First door off the main landing. *Stay*,' Rafaello urged as
he reached for the phone and, studying her, he surprised
her by stretching out an inviting hand.

Glory hovered. A smile curved his wide, expressive
mouth, a smile full of heartbreaking charm. The smile that
had once enslaved her heart as efficiently as chains. Her
heartbeat quickening, she found herself returning to his side
and reaching out to clasp that outstretched hand.

Rafaello's grip on her fingers tightened. She glanced up,
saw the frownline indented between his brows and listened
to him talk in what sounded like Italian. His tone was questioning and a faint look of irritation narrowed his incisive
gaze. He replaced the receiver and released her hand again.

'Fate seems to have it in for us tonight,' Rafaello breathed with a wry look. 'That was my father.'

'Oh...?' Glory tautened with unease.

'He's staying in London with friends this weekend. But he's just informed me that he'll be here in ten minutes to discuss some urgent matter that he insists cannot wait until tomorrow.' Raking lean brown fingers through his thick black hair, Rafaello sighed. 'Perhaps now that the novelty has worn off, he's finding retirement a challenge. But he did sound troubled and that isn't like him.'

'I should clear off down to the cottage and see my own family,' Glory proffered in an eager rush at the prospect of escape.

'*No.*' It was one word said with quiet force but it stilled her in her tracks.

'I don't want to bump into your father, Rafaello.' She almost told him that one Grazzini at a time was quite sufficient for her.

'You'll be quite safe in my bedroom. Benito hasn't tucked me in at night since I was five years old,' Rafaello informed her with sardonic bite. 'But, for what it's worth, I don't feel any need to hide you. Join us. He's going to know about us sooner or later anyway.'

Benito Grazzini would be astonished and angry to find her under his son's roof, and Glory had not the slightest desire to meet the forceful older man again. However, Rafaello's invitation shook her. 'That doesn't mean I want to be around when he finds out—'

'Coward,' Rafaello mocked, leaning down to capture her tense lips and extract a hungry kiss.

'I'll be more comfortable upstairs,' Glory protested, her reddened mouth tingling from the effect of that sensual collision and her feet inexplicably welded to the spot.

Rafaello gave her a wolfish grin. 'So will I be...'

The reminder of the true situation between them made her flush and head in haste for the door.

CHAPTER FOUR

GLORY picked up her bag where she had left it sitting in the big, elegant hall. Pausing only to slip off the diamanté sandals which had scored deep welts across her toes, Glory headed for the grand staircase as quietly and quickly as she could.

But luck was not on Glory's side. Maud Belper appeared from behind the green baize door below the stairs that led to the kitchen quarters. 'You're staying here, then?'

Hot, guilty, embarrassed pink from throat to brow, Glory gave a reluctant nod of confirmation.

'Your father's a mild man, Glory. It takes a lot to upset him but I honestly think he would lose his head with Mr Rafaello over this.'

Glory stilled and tried to act dignified. 'I'm a grown woman, not a kid.'

'It wouldn't be about that, love.' The grey-haired older woman frowned, her rounded good-natured face troubled. 'I ought to be minding my own business and I'm no tittle-tattle. But I just feel I should warn you that you're getting into a situation you don't really understand.'

Having made that far from reassuring and deeply mysterious statement, the housekeeper went back through the green baize door without another word. Glory hastened on up the stairs in craven flight. What on earth was Maud Belper talking about? *What* situation? And why, when she was about to let herself down a bucketful with Rafaello, did there have to be a talkative witness lecturing on the sidelines?

Glory hurtled in through the first door off the main landing, thrust the door shut behind her and fumbled for the light. Then she understood why Rafaello had such a big office. It was only what he was used to, she decided, scanning the huge bedroom with inquisitive eyes. A bed the size of a football pitch sat dead-centre. Skittish as a racehorse, she averted her attention from it and studied the remainder of the elegant furniture. It was a very beautiful room. The pastel rug on the floor, the subdued wallpaper and the long curtains did not match, yet somehow the overall effect was subtle and very classy, she acknowledged. Then she caught a glimpse of herself in a tall dressing mirror, and stiffened in dismay.

Unsubtle, too bold, Glory decided as she scrutinised her own reflection with newly critical eyes. She wondered how a skirt and top that had looked so pretty and feminine on Tania could look so very different on her. Of course, Tania was a brunette and a little less curvy. It had stabbed Glory to the heart when Rafaello told her that she looked cheap but she could see now that, whether she liked it or not, he had been right.

Catching sight of the transfer design above her ankle, she wrinkled her nose and went into the imposing *en suite* with its marble-set sinks. Stripping off her tights, she ran some water and tried to wash off the fake tattoo. The transfer was more resistant than she had expected. As she frowned down at her leg it occurred to her that she should be more worried by her own behaviour than about how she looked to *him*.

Here she was, selling herself like a commodity for Sam's sake. Well, not entirely for Sam's sake, Glory adjusted guiltily. There was this dreadful enemy part of her which wanted Rafaello Grazzini any way she could get him. She was deeply ashamed of that truth but too essentially honest to deny it. He had driven her into an arrangement that was going to break her heart and smash her pride forever.

She was soft where feelings were concerned. She always had been. She got attached to people. She had never quite managed to detach herself from him. And why not? They had had six enchanted weeks together before everything went wrong, and during those weeks, he had treated her better than any man she had met before or since. She hadn't had to fight for her life or deal with him getting into an all-male sulk at having his attentions refused. There had been a kind of teasing quality to his approaches, she recalled abstractedly. Only there had been nothing teasing about the manner in which Rafaello had arranged her on that desk downstairs…

Not knowing what was likely to happen next and hugely conscious that she did not want to experience intimacy for the first time on a desk in a very well-lit room, she had panicked. *Really* panicked, she conceded ruefully. Only true panic could possibly have snatched her from the intoxicating excitement of Rafaello's mouth on hers. But it shocked her that after five years he could touch her again and make her want him like that. It scared her even more that, in her heart of hearts, she still could not credit that Rafaello would actually make her his mistress.

But why not? When Glory was sixteen, and she had first met Rafaello face-to-face, he had behaved more like a protective big brother. Still barefoot, she wandered back into the bedroom but her thoughts were miles away. Having a huge crush on Rafaello had not stopped Glory from wanting a boyfriend of her own because all her school friends had been dating by then. She had believed that nothing would ever come of her dreams about Rafaello Grazzini. After all, not only had she never even had the opportunity to speak to him, but she and Rafaello had also lived and moved in different worlds.

Unfortunately, Talitha Little had refused to allow her daughter to go out to bars or clubs or to start dating. Almost inevitably, in her last term at school Glory had rebelled and gone behind her mother's back. Her best friend had set her up with one of her older brother's mates and had invited her to stay over that night so that she could get dressed up and come home late. A whole crowd of them had gone to a local bar and Glory's date, Tim, a smooth-talking twenty-five-year-old, had introduced her to alcohol.

'Hey, look who's here,' her friend had whispered, nudging her in the ribs halfway through that evening. 'Talk about slumming!'

Rafaello had been standing by the bar with a couple of other young men, their designer casuals marking them out as more than a cut above the majority of the clientele. Glory had not been able to take her eyes from him, for she had never seen him that close before. Indeed, most of her sightings of Rafaello had been when he drove past her in his sports car while she was walking home after getting off the school bus. Although he had been known to offer other people lifts on wet days, he had never once offered her one.

Even though she had been staring a hole in him, it had been a shock when Rafaello looked directly at her for the first time. She remembered going all red in the face but not being able to drag her gaze from the magnetic spell of his lustrous dark eyes.

'I think you're in with a chance there all right,' her irrepressible friend had hissed. 'It's a shame you're stuck with Tim.'

But Tim had gone to play darts at the other end of the crowded bar and Glory, emboldened by the unfamiliar effects of alcohol on her system, sat there with her entire attention shamelessly focused on Rafaello, flirting like mad with her eyes. She saw his companions noticing her and commenting and thrilled in her naïvety to the belief that if she was being discussed the commentary could only be an appreciative one. In that over-excited state, it was really not that big a surprise when, on her passage back from the cloakroom, Rafaello intercepted her.

'Would you like to go for a drive in my Porsche?' he murmured huskily.

Thrilled to death by that invitation, it could not be said that she played hard to get. 'When?'

'Now. Just follow me outside.'

And, just like that, she did. She had a little difficulty walking in a straight line across the car park.

'Not the most loyal of girlfriends, are you?' Rafaello remarked.

'I only met him tonight,' Glory hastened to inform him. 'You recognised me, didn't you?'

'Oh, yes…you're not easily missed.'

He unlocked the Porsche and settled her inside first with the kind of well-bred good manners that thrilled her. And while she was sitting there frantically trying to think of something witty to say, he drove her *home*.

'What…why are you bringing me back here?' Glory demanded, aghast at the sight of her parental home. 'I'm supposed to be staying at my friend's house tonight. I can't go home dressed like this, not when I've been drinking either… I thought you were taking me for a drive!'

'I just did—'

'No, but *I* thought—'

'You're not capable of thinking anything right now. Your date was deliberately getting you drunk. You shouldn't be drinking under age, particularly when you're not mature enough for adult company—'

'What are you talking about?' Glory screeched at him in anguish.

'You just walked out of that bar with me and got into my car. Don't you realise how dangerous it is for a woman to behave like that? You don't have the wit of a newborn baby. The safest place for you is home—'

'My mother will *kill* me!' she launched at him in complete panic.

'I'll have a word with her.' Thrusting open the driver's door, Rafaello cut short the dialogue.

Glory burst into floods of tears. He extracted her from

his passenger seat only with difficulty. 'I just couldn't stand by watching that slimeball filling you up with booze,' he breathed impatiently. 'Surely you realise how he was planning to end the evening?'

'You let me think that *you*—'

'You're out of bounds, Glory. You're only sixteen.'

'You were looking at me like you fancied me!' she condemned tearfully.

'Easiest way to get you out of there, and it wasn't difficult…you're a very beautiful girl—'

'Do you think so?' she asked him pathetically, and he laughed and her heart had gone crazy—but then her mother opened the front door.

Although Talitha Little had a hot temper, she had not said that much that night. The next morning over breakfast, while Glory was nursing a vicious hangover and being forced to explain herself, her mother had given her an odd little smile and had remarked that she was quite sure that Glory had learned her lesson well. Glory had spent the whole of that summer mulling over every word that Rafaello had said to her, and, appalled by the effect that alcohol had had on her usual caution, she had never touched it since then.

Emerging from those memories, Glory glanced at her watch and realised that she had already been upstairs for an hour. How could the same male who had protected her from her own juvenile stupidity be the same guy she was dealing with now? Was Benito Grazzini still with Rafaello? Glory crept out of the bedroom and crossed the landing to peer down into the hall. When the library door opened she backed away. She watched Rafaello and his father, a big barrel-chested man with silver hair, move to the front door together in silence. Benito Grazzini walked out and then abruptly turned to speak and to spread his hands in what looked curiously like an emotive appeal for understanding. Glory was shocked by the expression on the older man's face. He looked ravaged, almost distraught. But Rafaello's profile was taut and grim. He made no response. After a moment Benito let his hands fall back to his sides in an attitude of weary defeat. Shoulders bowed, the older man turned and walked slowly and heavily out to the waiting limo gleaming beneath the outside lights. Rafaello thrust the door shut again.

'Rafaello?' Glory called down, for she could not silence herself. 'What's happened? What's wrong?'

He froze in surprise and then threw back his dark head and looked up to where she stood at the head of the staircase. His lean, strong face was shuttered. 'How long have you been up there?'

'Only a minute. I saw your father leave. He seemed upset—'

Rafaello lifted a broad shoulder in a faint shrug of indifference, but he was unusually pale. His expressive mouth clenched hard and his dark eyes were cold. '*Did* he?'

As he mounted the stairs to draw level with her Glory coloured with discomfiture. Obviously he had had a disagreement with the older man. But then, two such powerful personalities might well have regular differences of opinion and she could hardly blame him for snubbing her: it was none of her business. Or *was* it? Was it possible that the argument might have related to her? Before she could think better of asking such a question, she said, 'Did you tell your father that I was here? Is that what caused the trouble between you?'

'Hardly,' Rafaello drawled with detached and dismissive cool. 'But my plans have changed. I know it's getting late but I'm going to have you driven back to Birmingham. Something rather more important than my libido has cropped up and I need to deal with it now.'

Wholly unprepared for that announcement, Glory stiffened in astonishment. She turned away, her face burning with sudden mortification. One minute he wanted her, the next he didn't, and she was being dismissed like a casual employee. Yet it was so foolish of her to be feeling like that in the circumstances. She ought to be delighted and relieved, she told herself. 'I'll get my bag.'

'I'll send a car to pick you up on Monday around noon. I'll need your address—'

She hesitated but did not turn back. 'Are you still planning to let Sam know tonight that he doesn't have to worry about that theft charge any more?'

A tense and unexpected silence stretched and, with a frown, she turned her head to look at him again.

'Yes,' Rafaello breathed with a grim look etched on his lean, dark features. 'Yes, you can bet on that as a sure-fire event.'

'Fine.' Without another word, Glory went back into his bedroom, grabbed up her travel bag and locked herself in the bathroom. Tears of hurt bewilderment stung her eyes as she took off the top and skirt, which she now thoroughly loathed. Something had happened, something serious that had upset him. But he had not the faintest intention of telling her what that something was or of sharing his feelings.

She put on jeans, a T-shirt and comfortable canvas shoes. She thought that he might have followed her into the bedroom to wait for her to emerge and then talk to her again but he had not. She wrote her address on the notepad by the phone. When she went downstairs again she found him standing by the superb marble fireplace in the gracious drawing-room, staring down with brooding intensity into the low-burning fire.

'I'm ready.'

'The car's outside. Don't go all female and huffy on me, *cara*,' Rafaello urged, shooting her a bleak glance from beneath his lush dark lashes. 'Tonight is just a case of bad timing—'

'Huffy? Why would I be huffy?' Glory demanded with stinging chagrin. 'All I'm hoping is that you use this weekend to think better of the idea of taking on an unwilling mistress!'

Rafaello focused dark golden eyes on her with sizzling effect. 'Unwilling? We'll find out in Corfu, won't we…?'

Three days later a Toyota Landcruiser whisked Glory away from the island airport.

She had flown out to Corfu cocooned in the incredible luxury of Rafaello's private jet and had been surprised to find that he was not on board. However, his aircrew had treated her like royalty and, although she had told herself that she was far too sensible to be impressed by rampant materialism, she had been impressed to death. His jet had been a far cry from the cramped and uncomfortable package holiday flight to Spain which she had endured with Sam a couple of years earlier. Served with a lunch that would have passed muster in a top-flight hotel, she had been offered a selection of recent films to watch and the latest copies of a dozen glossy magazines.

The Landcruiser branched off the busy main thoroughfare and eventually onto a rough road that climbed ever upward between groves of gnarled silver-green olive trees. They passed through quaint little hill villages on roads too narrow for two vehicles to pass at one and the same time. As they headed back down towards the coast on the other side of the island a series of tortuous bends and truly terrifying gradients slowed their journey even more. In all, it was an hour and a half and early evening before the car paused before a set of tall electronic gates that purred back for their entrance and drove up an avenue shaded by tall, graceful cypresses that cast long dark shadows like arrows.

The big villa was ultra-modern in design and pitched to take advantage of the sheltered seclusion of the lush green hillside and the fabulous sea views. A magnificent house in an even more magnificent setting, Glory conceded without much surprise as she climbed out of the car. But then, only the very best would satisfy a Grazzini. In the clear light in which every colour seemed sharper and brighter than it did back in England, the view of the brilliant blue Ionian Sea washing the golden strand only a hundred yards below her would have taken her breath away had not nervous tension already done that for her.

A middle-aged man in an old-fashioned steward's white jacket ushered her into a marble-tiled foyer and showed her into a superb galleried reception room that opened out onto a wooden viewing deck.

'Signor Grazzini will be with you soon, Miss Little,' the manservant informed her. 'Tea or coffee? Perhaps an aperitif before dinner?'

'Where *is* Signor Grazzini?' Glory enquired tautly, beginning to feel offensively like a parcel forever waiting to be picked up.

The older man looked uncomfortable.

'That's OK. I'll go and find him for myself.' Glory stalked back out to the hall, put her hands on her hips and yelled full volume, '*Rafaello?*'

Within fifteen seconds one of the doors off the spacious, airy hall jerked wide and Rafaello appeared. Clad in a lightweight pale cream suit, exquisitely tailored to his big, powerful frame, he looked nothing short of spectacular. He scanned her taut figure, taking in the patterned blue cotton shirt dress she wore and the plait in which she had restrained her hair.

'You wanted me here. I'm *here*!' Glory pointed out in the rushing silence, folding her arms in an effort to conceal the reality that she was trembling. For a crazy moment she had wanted to fling herself at him, and she had been shaken by that insane prompting.

'What a novel way to get attention...' a cut-glass English voice remarked.

Glory stiffened in dismay as a willowy brunette beauty with the exotic elegance of a supermodel strolled forward

to stand by Rafaello's side. Resting one possessive hand on
his sleeve and throwing him a covert glance in the age-old
communication of one lover to another, she spelt out their
intimacy in non-verbal ways that any woman would have
understood. 'Really, I must try bellowing at the top of my
voice when I next find that my host is not immediately
available. So simple and effective.' The brunette completed
her cutting little speech with saccharine-sweet scorn.

'Glory…this is Fiona Woodrow,' Rafaello told her with
unblemished composure.

The brunette extended a languid hand. Her face having
flamed and then paled to leave her as white as paper, Glory
ignored that empty gesture. Hypocrisy was not one of her
talents.

A door opened somewhere behind her. 'Jon…' Rafaello
drawled in the calmest of tones. 'If you have the time, could
you ensure that Glory gets a long cool drink?'

Jon Lyons escorted Glory out to the viewing deck. The
sun was beginning to set over the beautiful bay below. The
horizon was shot with the fiery splendour of crimson and
gold. Hands clenched into fists of restraint by her side,
Glory could not yet bring herself to look at the young blond
man. Fiona Woodrow had made her feel small and stupid
and crude in front of an audience but she blamed Rafaello
entirely for that development.

The older man who had greeted her on her arrival appeared with a tray. A tall moisture-beaded glass and an
artistic arrangement of tiny bite-sized appetisers were set
down on the table beside which she stood.

'I would need a dip in the Arctic to cool me down,'
Glory muttered finally, throwing a look of pained apology
at Jon for her self-absorption. 'Who is Fiona?'

'Rafaello has been acquainted with Lady Fiona for a long
time,' Jon Lyons responded after an awkward pause, his
clean-cut features tense, his brown eyes veiled. 'I'm afraid
that's as much as I know.'

Lady Fiona? A titled member of the British aristocracy. Glory bit down hard on her tongue and tasted the sweet tang of blood in her dry mouth. She folded her arms even tighter; indeed, felt as though that defensive barrier was crazily the only thing keeping her upright and together. Acquainted? What a delicate choice of word! The brunette had brandished the fact that her relationship with Rafaello was of the intimate variety. There was no avoiding the obvious: Rafaello had another woman. Furthermore, he had not even had the decency to get Fiona Woodrow out of the villa before Glory arrived. It was disgusting. It lacerated her pride, tore at her heart and terrified her all at one and the same time. Her emotions were on such a high, she could barely think straight.

'Does he have a lot of women he brings here? Is this like...the harem in the hills?' she demanded unsteadily.

Momentarily, Jon looked as though he might laugh. Then he met her anguished blue eyes, with a look of sympathy, he said reluctantly, 'The boss does get around. You can't really blame him—'

'Can't I?' Just then Glory needed no encouragement to heap all the sins of humanity on Rafaello's broad shoulders.

'Women go for him big-time.'

And why not? She had always wondered and now she knew for sure. Rafaello was a womaniser, spoilt for choice, spoilt by all the endless options and fresh faces available to a male with wealth, good looks and charm. Only where she herself was concerned the charm seemed to be in pretty short supply this time around.

But then, what else had she expected? He wasn't dating her, wasn't trying to please her. Caring concern and tact were not on his agenda. Suddenly she was facing unpleasant truths shorn of the hazy romantic images which had come from her own imagination alone. Of course Rafaello had not been on the flight out from England with her, of course he had not put himself out to come and meet her at the airport! All that he wanted from her was the use of her body. Casual, uncommitted sex. He had spelt that right out upfront. How had she managed to avoid facing that reality?

'Please don't be offended when I say that you don't fit the usual mould,' Jon Lyons confided in a wry undertone. 'You'll be history with Rafaello the minute he realises you're emotionally involved.'

'I'm not emotionally involved with him.' Wanting to boil Rafaello in oil and make him suffer the tortures of the damned while she watched and gloated was not emotional involvement on Glory's terms. In any case, she was *not* staying in Corfu to be a temporary distraction in any harem in the hills! Her brother, Sam, was safe. The theft charge had been withdrawn and her father had been reinstated. The crisis was over, the pressure on her already at an end. She had been able to confirm that on Saturday.

Sam had phoned her first thing that morning. She had been very surprised to learn that Rafaello had stayed talking with her father and Sam until well after midnight. What about the urgent business that had supposedly cropped up that same evening? Evidently, Rafaello had shown no apparent desire to cut his visit short. She had been even more surprised when Sam confided that Rafaello was, 'OK…in fact, quite a cool guy and very talkative.' To be frank, she had almost toppled over in shock when her kid brother had gone on to tell her that Rafaello had stated that in retrospect he felt that he might have rather overreacted to the whole situation.

Indeed, Rafaello had gone to extraordinary lengths to smooth matters over and Glory had been planning to thank him from the bottom of her heart for lying in his teeth. For, of course, he had been lying. She remembered how he had talked about having his home and his property 'violated' and had quite understood his feelings. But Rafaello's generous attitude of forgiveness had released her brother from his brooding depression and anxiety. She had not expected

Rafaello to recognise and understand just how vulnerable Sam could be.

That same evening Sam had phoned his friend, Joe, and, once reassured that confessing to stealing the snuff box would not result in his being charged in Sam's place, Joe had come over to own up and apologise to Rafaello face-to-face. Joe had taken the box on impulse, thinking it would make a nice present for his mother's birthday, but within half an hour of succumbing to temptation the teenager had panicked. He had hidden the tiny item in the Littles' fuel shed sooner than retain possession of it and had hoped that something so very small would not even be missed at the Park.

Emerging from the recollection of that enlightening phone call from her brother, Glory lifted the tall glass and let her parched mouth rejoice in the refreshing fruit drink. Sam might be all right now but it really was time that *she* grew up and let go of her old memories of Rafaello Grazzini. Fanciful girlish memories based on what? A mere six weeks with him? She would be much better recalling the manner in which he had humiliated her at the end of that brief relationship. He had been cruel, unnecessarily cruel. Just as he was being now in a far more careless way.

'If you want me to make that last flight, I should leave now,' she heard Jon say.

Turning her head to glance at him in confusion, Glory only then realised that Jon had been addressing Rafaello, who was poised several feet away. She set down her glass and tilted up her chin, shutting out those dark golden eyes which could exercise such frightening power over her. 'I might as well catch a lift with Jon if he's going to the airport. I'm not staying.'

The younger man dealt her a startled glance before he walked back indoors, discreetly removing himself from the proceedings.

'You're not going anywhere, *cara*,' Rafaello delivered with formidable cool.

'And how are you planning to stop me?' Glory enquired tightly, hanging on to her temper and her pain with fierce concentration, determined not to betray either or to give him the satisfaction of knowing how much he had hurt her by allowing her to meet Fiona Woodrow.

'With brute force if necessary.'

Glory opened her violet-blue eyes very wide to show how unimpressed she was by that threat. 'You wouldn't dare. I'd scream the place down.'

'Noise doesn't bother me. Being ripped off does, though.'

The tension sparked like invisible warning flares between them.

'That's right, be a real gentleman!' Glory snapped. 'Remind me about the callous agreement you forced on me—'

A winged black brow was elevated. '*Forced?* Didn't you trek all the way to Montague Park on Friday night dressed like a tart just for my benefit?'

'I was *not* dressed like a tart!' Glory hissed at him in outrage.

'Isn't that just like a woman?' Rafaello jerked loose his tie and cast it on the table. Her gaze widened slightly as, having undone his shirt collar, he proceeded to shrug with fluid grace out of the jacket of his suit. 'Parade the bait and then go into pious denial when the victim bites—'

'You are no woman's victim, Rafaello Grazzini!' Glory was infuriated by his line of argument. She had been desperate. She had believed that temptation was the only means of persuasion within her power. But whose fault was it that she had felt that she had to lower herself to that level? Who had spelt out those demeaning parameters? Who had made it brutally clear that in his opinion her looks were her only currency?

'That's right,' Rafaello confirmed, his smouldering dark

golden eyes holding hers full force. 'Glad you've divined that fact. Do you recall how you tried to play me for a fool five years ago? Do you also remember how that ended? I wasn't the one who fled in tears.'

'You bastard...' Glory framed in shaken outrage and pain. The very last thing she needed just then was the recollection of how devastated she had been at eighteen when he paraded her replacement, the merchant banker's daughter, in front of her.

Rafaello discarded his jacket on the table alongside his tie. 'I don't let anyone call me that,' he intoned in a lethal low-pitched drawl.

'Well, I just got away with it!' Glory slung in helpless triumph.

'You're not getting away with anything. It's all going on an account to be rendered with your name at the top. *Dio mio*, you think I'm a fool?'

'Look, I'm not going to waste time arguing with you.' That unsettling reference to an account being rendered had chilled Glory to the marrow. 'I'll get a lift with Jon back to the airport.'

'I said no.'

'Oh, wow...' Glory sounded out with syllabic thoroughness and all the scorn she could muster.

'I warned you.' Striding forward with an expression of calm intent stamped on his lean, strong face, Rafaello settled his hands to her waist and swept her off her feet.

In furious disbelief Glory swung back her arm and attempted to land a resounding slap on one hard male cheekbone but he ducked his head before it could connect. 'How dare you do that when I want to hit you?' she raged at him.

'If you try to hit me again I might just dump you in the pool to cool off,' Rafaello threatened with immovable cool as he hoisted her over his shoulder to prevent her flailing fists from doing any damage.

'I can't swim!' Glory gasped in horror.

'I'll get into the water with you, then, but dip you I will,' Rafaello swore, striding through the vast lounge into the hall.

'I'll call the police if you don't put me down!' Glory threatened in a rising screech.

'What with? Alien antennae?' Rafaello enquired.

Another voice entered the proceedings. 'Rafaello...' It was Jon Lyons' quiet voice and he cleared his throat with pronounced hesitancy before continuing. 'Do you really think you ought to be manhandling your guest like that?'

'Don't mess with what you don't understand,' Rafaello advised his executive assistant, galling amusement audible in his dark, deep drawl. 'Glory and I go way back in time—'

'No, we don't!' Glory braced her hands to his muscular back to raise her head, but she still couldn't see Jon Lyons because he was standing out of view. So enraged was she by the ridiculous figure she had to be cutting that she was surprised that flames weren't pouring from her mouth.

'Glory was four years old when we first met. She was at a Christmas party for the estate workers' children. She thumped a little boy who was chasing her with mistletoe. She was tiny but she attacked like a lion,' Rafaello recounted, making Glory blink in bewilderment as she listened. 'I hauled her off him before she got hurt and she was swinging her fists and screeching, "Let me at him!" She hasn't changed much.'

'You just made that whole story up.' Glory had no memory whatsoever of the episode he had described, although she had certainly attended those festive parties as a child. 'That never happened!'

Rafaello started to mount the stairs. 'I didn't notice you again until you were about thirteen, but don't get excited at that news. It wasn't you who first attracted my attention. It was the incessant car horns being sounded by admiring male drivers while you stood at the bus stop in the morning and I was driving past. Then, after you moved into the gardener's cottage, I used to see you lurking in the rhododendrons beside the main drive, slapping on the paint before you could face the school bus.'

Glory was so stunned by that second even lengthier speech, her luscious mouth fell inelegantly wide.

'I can see I was out of line interfering...' From the hall below, Jon Lyons punctuated that retreat with a rueful laugh. 'When you said *way back* you weren't joking, Rafaello. It sounds like you two practically grew up together. I'll see you next week.'

As the front door thudded shut downstairs and silence enclosed them again Glory balled both hands into furious fists and struck at Rafaello's back again. 'What were you doing sneaking through the bushes when I was putting on my lip gloss?' she demanded for want of anything better to attack with at that moment.

'When I was back from university I used to go out running in the morning. You were such a vain little creature. You used to sit endlessly combing your hair like a mermaid on a rock.'

'You *spied* on me!' Glory accused shakily. 'I was not being vain!'

'I avoided the main drive after I saw you there a couple of times. Spying on little schoolgirls wasn't my style then or now.'

'Mum wouldn't let me style my hair or use make-up like my friends did, and I used to do myself up a bit before I went for the bus,' she protested with fierce defensiveness. 'I was *not* vain. Haven't you ever heard of peer pressure? Put me down, Rafaello!'

Rafaello lowered her to the carpet in a lovely bedroom. French windows stood wide on a balcony on the far side of the room. The silk curtains were fluttering in the gentle breeze. For an instant the unusual bed engaged her attention. The tall headboard had an ornate carved frame and what appeared to be tiny pictures with silver surrounds set into the polished surface. Frowning over her momentary distraction, Glory headed straight back towards the door through which she had been carried. 'You can stop acting like a caveman right now.'

Rafaello was lounging back against the door with folded arms. His white shirt open at his strong brown throat, his devastatingly dark and handsome face set with intent, he looked back at her with challenging golden eyes. 'So tell me, what made you *suddenly* decide to go home again?'

Glory stiffened and paled. 'If you think I'm willing to be another in the long line of your tarts, you'd better think again!' she launched back grittily.

'Welcome to the fold, *bella mia*.' Rafaello's delivery was as smooth as silk.

CHAPTER FIVE

'DID I just hear you say what I thought I heard you say?' Glory demanded with stark incredulity.

'I was hoping provocation would get you to the crux of the matter.' Rafaello's glinting, lustrous dark gaze rested on her. 'Fiona's parents own a villa just along the coast. She's a regular visitor and I wasn't expecting her. You're throwing a tantrum because Fiona was here when you arrived and she embarrassed you...or you embarrassed yourself.'

Glory's lovely face flamed as if he had lit a bonfire inside her. So much had passed between them in the last few minutes that she did not know where to begin in arguing or defending herself. 'I don't throw tantrums like some spoilt brat demanding attention. But, whether you like it or not, I do have standards—'

'But offer you enough cash and you drop them,' Rafaello slotted in with lethal timing.

'Oh...so we're back to the cheque I accepted when I was eighteen, are we?' Although Glory felt severely undermined by his referring to that episode again, she squared her slight shoulders and tossed her honey-blonde head high. 'I suppose it's time that I told you the truth about that. I let Dad have that money because he needed it. Your father forced me to leave my home.'

'And how did Benito do that?' Rafaello enquired with extreme dryness and the kind of outrageous aura of unspoken disbelief that made her want to scream and force him to listen to her with an open mind.

'For goodness' sake, Dad was drinking at the time. I know you never mentioned it but you must've known about

his alcohol problem,' Glory asserted in a strained undertone. 'Your father threatened to sack him unless I moved
away and broke off all contact with you. Dad would never
have stopped drinking if he'd lost his job and his home as
well.'

Silence had fallen. Rafaello was very still, his fabulous
bone-structure defined by hard tension. But his ice-cool
dark eyes were now bleak and unimpressed. 'How very
distasteful it would be if you were telling the truth. But I
have *very* good cause to know that Benito would never
have sacked your father or left him and your brother homeless,' he asserted with harsh conviction. 'You're talking
about blackmail. You're lying in your teeth.'

Although Glory had known that Rafaello would not easily credit her story, it was none the less a blow when he
rejected her version of events with such immediacy. Furthermore she neither understood nor believed his assurance
that Benito Grazzini would *never* have sacked her father
and put him out of the cottage. After all, any employer
would eventually sack a drunken worker and would feel
little need to defend their action. Why would Rafaello's
father have felt any different? Compassion only went so
far.

'Why try to wrap up what really happened?' Rafaello
was now studying her with derision curling his wide, sensual mouth. 'You got the offer to be a model and you
couldn't wait to grab at what you believed was your chance
for fame and fortune. You had already decided to leave
home, so you simply accepted the financial bribe my father
offered you.'

So that was how he had reasoned it all out to satisfy
himself as to her guilt and greed. It was a tidy reading of
past events but it was *not* what had happened. Then she
had been foolish to hope that Rafaello would even consider
accepting her word over his father's.

Letting his allegations lie unchallenged, for she saw no

good reason to continue a losing battle, Glory said flatly, 'I meant what I said downstairs...I'm leaving. If you're so keen to have a mistress, why don't you ask Lady Fiona? She seemed more than willing!'

'For no good reason that my brain can comprehend, I want you much more.' Rafaello strolled away from the door at a leisurely pace.

'I'm not getting mixed up with a man who is carrying on with other women—'

'As far as I can see, my bed's empty... Fiona and I have a history, but that's not something I intend to discuss with you, *cara*.' Rafaello came to a halt only inches away from her and reached for the long plait curling over her shoulder with a calm hand.

'What are you doing?' Glory spat, feeling threatened by his proximity.

'I like the mermaid hair loose.'

'Do you think I care what you like?'

'I believe you can learn if I give you lessons in easy stages, *bella mia*.'

She encountered sizzling dark golden eyes and her breath snarled up in her throat. His fingers were busy unravelling her hair. All she had to do to bring an end to that liberty was put some distance between them, but she stayed where she was. 'I'm no good at learning what I don't want to learn.' Glory recognized the edge of desperation in her own voice. 'Let me go home. This is not going to work, Rafaello—'

'Let me be the judge of that—'

'But you *said* you wanted an experienced lover,' Glory reminded him in a last-ditch attempt to persuade him that she was not the kind of woman he really wanted. 'I'm an amateur—'

'Well, I didn't want a professional,' Rafaello told her, quick as a flash with the repartee.

Her colour heightened. 'I'm a virgin.'

The lean fingers engaged in slowly disentangling her hair stilled. 'That's not even funny.'

She gritted her teeth. 'I wasn't trying to be—'

Rafaello cupped her elbows to hold her still in front of him. He gazed down at her with wondering eyes. 'If you were Pinocchio, your nose would reach as far as the front door. A virgin? *You?* Even five years back, I wasn't entirely convinced by the purity pleas but I gave you the benefit of the doubt. I could hardly argue.'

Glory breathed very deep. 'What makes you so sure that I'm not?'

'You're too sexy,' Rafaello responded without hesitation. 'You move, you walk and you talk like a woman who knows her own body—'

'I've lived inside it a long time—'

'Virgins are a rarefied species. I've never met one your age—'

'You ask every woman you meet, do you?' Glory snapped, out of all patience and increasingly offended and angry rather than embarrassed. As she pulled her arms free Rafaello settled his lean, strong hands onto her rigid shoulders instead. 'Well, it's about time you woke up to the fact that there are quite a few women who don't believe in putting sex on a level with having a takeaway—'

'I don't eat takeaways either. I am irredeemably attached to the gastronomic delights provided by my French chef. Tell me, are you trying to make me feel guilty about our arrangement? Is that why you're suddenly telling whoppers the size of Jonah's whale?' Rafaello enquired with sardonic bite. 'If I thought you were a virgin I'd run like hell. But I know you can't be. I know it the way I know the earth is round.'

That seemed fairly conclusive. But he had hurt her. It hurt her even more to realise that he had even doubted her innocence five years earlier. He was such a cynic, but more than anything else he was revealing that he had always seen her just as other men saw her: in the most demeaning light. As a blonde bombshell, a sure thing, not too bright and bound to be promiscuous. But at least he had explained Fiona Woodrow's presence to her satisfaction, hadn't he?

Glory worried at her full lower lip with her teeth and looked up at him in sudden Stark appeal. 'I just don't *want* to be your mistress—'

'You really ought to stop me taking your dress off, then. I warn you, once I catch a glimpse of delectable bare skin I will use every trick in the book to get you horizontal.'

So intent on her troubled thoughts had Glory been that she hadn't noticed that he had unzipped her dress. Now she gazed down in frank confusion as he eased the garment slowly from her shoulders and down over her slender arms, exposing the pouting swell of breasts cupped in white lace. 'Rafaello, n-no...'

'I can put my hand on my heart right now and admit that nothing has ever turned me on harder and faster than your gorgeous breasts,' Rafaello confessed with earthy male appreciation.

Conscious of him with every fibre of her being, Glory trembled. Unprompted, the dress drifted down over her hands and dropped to her feet. She recognized the burning hunger in his intent gaze and the most terrible physical weakness flooded her. All natural modesty was overborne by the realisation that he was admiring her, appreciating her. The wanton side of her nature adored that and thrilled to the reassurance that he liked what he was seeing. Then it was what she had always secretly sought from him. She had *always* wanted Rafaello to be her first lover, her last lover, her forever lover. Temptation was pulling at her hard. Why shouldn't she pretend that something other than the cold arrangement he had offered had brought them together again? Hadn't she spent five years fruitlessly seeking a male who could make her feel like Rafaello had once made her feel?

Rafaello gathered her up into his strong arms and carried her over to the huge bed. 'I have been waiting a very long time to do this.'

As he threw back the bedspread and settled her down on the crisp white linen sheet Glory whispered, 'Honestly?'

He plucked off her shoes and straightened with easy grace to stare down at her. '*Per amor di Dio*, how could you doubt that?'

Glory's look collided with his stunning golden gaze and her heart started to pound. Yet, lying down, she felt so much more self-conscious than she had standing. Her bra and panties might cover a great deal more of her than most beachwear but never had she been more aware of her own body and never had she felt less clothed.

'You're the only woman who has ever denied me. A clever move, that...' Rafaello was unbuttoning his shirt, a slanting smile on his beautifully shaped mouth. 'Perhaps that's why I want you so much, *bella mia*.'

Hurt tinged her growing apprehension. 'It wasn't a move. I wasn't trying to be clever—'

'Weren't you?' He cast off his shirt. 'It doesn't matter now.'

But it mattered to her that he should hold such an unrelentingly low opinion of her. Yet she could not retain that level of concentration, not when she was seeing Rafaello shorn of his shirt for the first time. Five years ago he had invited her to join him for a swim in the indoor pool up at the Park but she had made excuses not only because she couldn't swim but also because she had feared that folk would say that Glory Little was *really* getting above herself. She had endured enough cracks about 'mixing with the toffs', had soon learned that people were, at the very least, uncomfortable watching the gardener's daughter dating Benito Grazzini's son and heir. The very last thing she would have risked was being seen swanning round the Grazzinis' luxurious pool complex.

Now her mouth went dry as she focused on the hard, muscular planes of Rafaello's chest and the taut flatness of his abdomen. He was absolutely gorgeous, just as she had known he would be. His bronzed skin, rippling muscles and the haze of crisp black curls sprinkling his pectorals were overpoweringly male and sexy. She discovered that she could not take her attention from him for a moment lest she miss the chance to admire a different angle of view. Her face burned with colour at that acknowledgement. Pulling herself up against the pillows, she more covertly scanned his narrow hips and long, powerful thighs as he shed his well-cut trousers.

'I hope you're planning to do the same for me,' Rafaello drawled softly.

'Sorry?'

Rafaello, clad solely in a pair of black silk boxer shorts, sent her a wolfish look of all-male amusement. 'I can feel your eyes devouring me like fire.'

Glory reddened to the roots of her hair and ducked behind it, belatedly grateful that he had undone her plait and given her that amount of cover. 'Obviously you'd like to think so—'

'Lust can recognise lust,' Rafaello assured her, stripping off his last garment with a level of cool she could not credit, for certainly she could not mirror his self-possession.

There he was, totally revealed, and she was stunned. Naturally she had been a bit curious as to what a man looked like when... But wondering had not kept her awake at night. Indeed, in the past, registering that a man was physically aroused by her had always made her feel instinctively disgusted, only noteably that had *not* been her reaction to Rafaello. However, now seeing him in that naked state truly shook her, for she had never dreamt that he would be quite so intimidating.

'We're not going to fit.' Glory mumbled in a strangled voice, and then so appalled was she that panic had pro-

voked her to say such a thing and out loud, she shut her
eyes tight and cringed for herself in embarrassment.

'Is that a compliment, *bella mia*?' She could hear the
smile in his dark accented drawl, the satisfaction. He was
irrepressible, she thought in furious mortification.

'Even your little shell-like ears are turning scarlet,'
Rafaello noted with amusement.

'No, they're not!' Glory gasped, whipping up her hands
to touch the offending parts and discovering that they did
indeed feel rather warm and hurriedly pulling her hair over
them in concealment.

As the mattress gave slightly beneath her she realised
she had company on the bed and her eyes flew wide. She
connected head-on with eyes as golden as dazzling sunlight, all the more accentuated by the effect of his spiky
black lashes and the bronzed hue of his staggeringly attractive lean, dark face. It was like jamming her finger in
an electric current. His sheer sizzling appeal bereaved her
of breath and made her heart thump like a demented road
drill.

'Come here...' Rafaello urged huskily, lean hands closing on her forearms to tug her closer.

From that first moment, he gave no quarter. He caught
her mouth under his and plundered her soft pink lips with
molten hunger. She shivered in sensual shock, her breath
rasping in her throat and turning into ragged little gasps as
he continued that marauding assault at full pitch. His
tongue danced and mated with hers and then darted deep
with a rhythmic eroticism that she was defenceless against.
He had once taught her that just kissing could be incredibly
exciting, and his technique reduced her to the level of absolute compliance.

Rafaello released her swollen mouth and surveyed her
passion-glazed face with hotly appreciative eyes. 'We're
supposed to be seated downstairs enjoying a long and leisurely meal by candlelight—'

'I couldn't eat!' Glory exclaimed in dismay as if he was threatening her with that possibility.

'Later…' Rafaello seemed to taste the word as if he was savouring the far more entertaining alternatives currently available to him.

Only brute force could have dragged Glory from him at that moment. As she stared up into his mesmeric bright eyes he hooked an expert finger in the front fastening on her bra and the cups parted, releasing her full breasts into his reverent hands. Her throat closed over on the almost painful surge of sensation that assailed her as he touched her there for the first time without clothing to dull her own response. All Rafaello had to do was brush his thumbs over the throbbing pink peaks of her nipples and she was lost beyond redemption. She loosed a moan she could not restrain and her face burned hot with embarrassment because he was watching her.

'You denied us even this much five years ago,' Rafaello reminded her in raw-edged reproof.

As he rubbed the tender buds straining for his attention she was trembling beneath the rising strength of her own response. Had she had breath she could have told him that, with hindsight, her caution then had been very wise. Even now, she did not have the control to deny herself and would have had considerably less when she loved him. No matter how tough it had been to lose him, she knew it would have been ten times tougher and more demeaning had he succeeded in seducing her into bed with him.

'I'm going to drive you crazy with desire, *cara*.' It was both threat and promise combined.

'You already got there,' Glory framed unevenly, torn between exhilaration at her own intoxication and fear at the effect he was having on her.

Rafaello tipped her back and rearranged her to his satisfaction, fanning out her honey-blonde hair over the pil-

lows when it caught beneath her shoulder. 'I'm only beginning...'

He tugged up her knees and lifted her to extract her from
her panties in one smooth movement. And the very smooth-
ness with which he did that jolted her into wondering how
many other women it must have taken to develop that
amount of expertise. That hurt enough to make her think,
but then that arrogant dark head lowered. He captured a
rosy nub between his lips and proceeded to torment her
sensitive flesh without conscience. Before very long the
stroke of his wicked tongue and the glide of his even white
teeth had reduced her to a level where concentration was
an impossible challenge.

'I already knew you had a perfect body,' Rafaello
groaned, scanning her hectically flushed face with earthy
male approval. 'But I had no idea that you might also be
every man's fantasy of the perfect lover, *bella mia.*'

Challenged to speak as well as respond, Glory blinked
up at him, feeling she must have misheard him. 'A...
fantasy?'

'You heat up fast.' Rafaello extended, running an appreciative hand down over a slender thigh and employing a
judicious knee to deftly separate it from its partner.

Glory tensed, not so sure a fast heat-up rate was a compliment to be cherished. Suddenly she was feeling very
vulnerable, apprehensively aware of the boldness of his
arousal as he shifted against her hip, wondering if there
was even the remotest hope of waves beating on distant
sunny seashores in store for her. Or whether something like
the one or two more disturbing experiences she had heard
other women share with blunt amusement might be her lot
instead.

'If you hurt me, I'm not doing this again,' she warned
him tautly.

'*Accidenti?*' Rafaello dealt her a startled appraisal. '*Hurt* you? I'm not going to hurt you. I've never hurt a woman in my life!'

Grateful for that reassurance, Glory put up no objection to the sensually tender kiss he seemed to use to soothe her with action as much as words. Indeed, within a very short space of time she forgot her apprehension. True, she tensed when he let his fingers roam through the tangle of blonde curls at the apex of her slender thighs, but then he reached a place so impossibly sensitive to his skilful attentions that thinking about what came next was quite beyond her. She had never dreamt that she was capable of feeling what she felt then. Sunk into mindless pleasure and writhing uncontrollably with a hunger that felt wicked, greedy and utterly devouring, she ached and burned to a height of excitement that felt unbearable.

When she could no longer stand that gnawing ache for satisfaction Rafaello seemed miraculously to understand. But, just as he was hauling her under him with a degree of wild, needy impatience that she found even more exciting in the mood that she was in, he paused and stretched away from her to yank open the drawer in the bedside cabinet.

Entirely in the grip of her shameless, feverish hunger, Glory listened to him mutter a fierce imprecation in Italian and regarded him with blank eyes.

'Are you OK?' Rafaello ground out, staring down at her with what looked remarkably like a prayer in his gorgeous eyes.

He was asking her permission, she thought, which, considering that he was trembling with eagerness against her, seemed very considerate and sweet.

She raised her hand and let her fingertips trail in a caress beneath the taut line of his shapely mouth. 'Yes...of course.'

With an air of intense relief Rafaello claimed another passionate kiss and slid his hands beneath her hips to tip her back. She felt the hot, urgent probe of his shaft against

her most tender flesh and she was so driven by the tormenting ache for fulfilment he had roused in her, she urged
him on in a movement as old as time itself by rising up to
him and wrapping herself round him. He answered that
invitation with a driving thrust. For the first instant, she
was shocked by the sensation of invasion, and, for the second, overwhelmed by responsive pleasure to that incredible
intimacy. Then came a sharp, stabbing pain that wrenched
her from her sensual spell with a vengeance, and she cried
out.

Rafaello stilled and gazed down at her with an expression
of shattered disbelief. 'You *can't* be…' he whispered half
under his breath.

There was no mistaking the level of his shock at the
discovery that she had not been lying about the precise
extent of her experience. Stunned golden eyes gazed down
into hers.

Something perilously akin to smugness eased the dying
remnants of physical discomfort Glory was suffering. She
liked the idea that she had shattered his image of her and
proven it to be false.

'I'll stop…' Rafaello gritted, taking her aback with that
decision in turn.

Glory closed both arms round him, let her fingers delve
through the thick silk of his black hair, scanning the lean,
strong features so close to her own. 'Might as well finish,'
she mumbled, hot-faced, telling herself that she didn't want
him thinking she was a tease by calling a halt at what could
not be said to be a good moment for him.

'*Si…bella mia,*' he muttered with a flattering amount of
appreciation. '*Per meraviglia*…stopping now would kill
me!'

Generosity felt very good at that point. While she was
resigning herself to enduring the rest of it for his sake while
striving to explain to herself why she should feel so self-
sacrificing all of a sudden, Rafaello took her even more by

surprise. He surged into her with an immense gentleness that she found incredibly touching and then, to her astonishment, even more enjoyable. Her eyes opened very wide.

'I'll make it good,' Rafaello swore with roughened tenderness.

Her heart started accelerating to a hammer-beat again and everything she had been feeling before that brief instant of pain returned to her tenfold. Suddenly she was with him again, losing the power of thought and then control, arching up to match his fluid thrusts, discovering a pagan rhythm all of her own. Her breath coming in shallow pants, she gave herself up to the powerful excitement building higher and higher within her. He drove her, gasping, to a dizzy peak and nothing could have surpassed the sheer wondrous sensation that gripped her writhing body with an ecstasy of pleasure.

Glory drifted back to the land of the living to find herself still plastered as close to Rafaello as an extra layer of skin. Finding no fault whatsoever with that discovery, she snuggled even closer and could not control the dreamy smile stretching her mouth. Paradise was being in his arms, she decided, breathing in the hot, damp, sexy scent of him as if he was a drug she needed to survive. She felt amazingly tender and affectionate towards him and only just resisted an urge to smother him in loving kisses.

Rafaello tensed. 'Quit snuggling,' he told her drily.

Glory froze as if the roof had come down on top of her. Before she could even react to that apparent rejection that just seized her up with pain, Rafaello rolled her flat onto her back against the pillows and leant over her. He brushed her tumbled honey-blonde hair back from her brow, dropped an unexpected kiss on her reddened mouth and smiled down at her.

It was that glorious smile that finally convinced her that she had misread his signals. When he had urged her to quit he had been teasing, and her heart went crazy when she

recognised the easy humour curving the relaxed line of his
sculpted mouth. 'You have really shocked me,' he confided
huskily.

Glory kept on smiling. All was right within her immediate world. She was brimming full of happiness purely
because he was happy. By no means did he look dissatisfied
by his recent discovery that she was not the skilful partner
he had expected. And in no way was she dissatisfied with
him.

'I've got no excuse. I can't defend myself. I *should* have
listened to you, *bella mia*,' Rafaello conceded with an
amount of regretful humility she would never have believed
a male of his unquenchable assurance could display.

'Yes, you should've,' Glory agreed, but she was quick
to snake her arms round him again lest he think she was
withholding forgiveness.

'I'm just amazed,' Rafaello admitted, surveying her with
frowning fascination. 'You've been knee-deep in predatory
men all these years and you didn't succumb to one of them.
Yet you're not a cold woman.'

'You're more persuasive than the rest,' Glory confided
shyly.

'Evidently…' Rafaello rolled over and sat up. 'You've
just blown a great big hole in my image of you as calculating.'

'I guess…' Glory was now feeling so buoyant she was
vaguely surprised that she wasn't floating round the ceiling.
Flipping onto her side, she surveyed him. Dear heaven, just
looking at him made her feel dreamy and silly. She wanted
to ease back into physical contact with him but was afraid
of seeming too clingy. She wanted to hug him again. She
wanted to tell him he was wonderful…she wanted to tell
him she loved him. Odd how she had wanted to tell him
that before she had even admitted it to herself, she acknowledged in a daze. It was pretty naff, her still being so keen
on him after five years apart, she reflected ruefully. It didn't

say much for her ability to move on, did it? But then, it
was not something she planned to share with him.

'Although I confess to being very grateful that you were
sufficiently calculating to accept that we were going to end
up in bed sooner rather than later,' Rafaello was saying
while he toyed with a straying blonde strand of her wildly
tousled mane of hair.

Glory's brow furrowed. She wondered if she had missed
a line of explanation somewhere. 'Sorry...what do you
mean?'

Rafaello released a rueful sigh and tugged at her hair as
to reprove her for her evident lack of concentration. 'When
I realised that the only contraception I had was in another
room I was very relieved to discover that you were better
organised than I was, *cara*.'

Glory was now very still and when her voice emerged it
was rather strained. 'Better organised?'

'On my last stay here, this room was being decorated
and I used the one next door,' he explained.

Glory remembered his opening the drawer in the bedside
cabinet. Having only briefly wondered what he was looking
for, she now felt unbelievably stupid. Rafaello had been
reaching for protection.

'A virgin who takes care of contraception in advance is
a very sensible woman.'

To Glory, that statement seemed to hang there in the air
between them like a giant rock about to fall on her. Her
opinion of her own common sense dive-bombed. 'But...but
I didn't take care of contraception,' she admitted in a very
small voice.

'Run that by me again,' Rafaello breathed, abandoning
all play with her hair, his Italian accent screaming at her
the way it always did when he was very tense.

'I'm not taking any precautions or using anything,' Glory
clarified shakily.

Rafaello's hard jawline clenched. Narrowed dark eyes

scanned her anxious upturned face and an expression of incredulous fury slowly fired his gaze. In a sudden movement that made her flinch, he sprang out of the bed. 'But I *asked* you if it was OK to make love to you!'

A silence, fragile as a sheet of glass about to smash, stretched.

Her heart sinking, Glory gulped. 'When I said yes, I thought you meant that question literally...I didn't know you were asking whether or not it might be s-safe,' she stammered, ready to curl up and die as she realised how foolish she had been. 'I didn't think—'

'You didn't think. So you're trying to say that it was only a simple misunderstanding?' Rafaello ground out, glittering dark golden eyes smouldering with furious condemnation, his accent thick as molasses. 'Do you honestly think I'll believe anything that unlikely?'

'What else could it have been but a misunderstanding?' Glory was sincerely taken aback by his attitude.

'How about a textbook case of entrapment?' Rafaello shot at her with lethal contempt, his hard cheekbones prominent beneath his bronzed skin, accentuating his ferocious tension.

'Entrapment?' she repeated without comprehension.

'I really fell for it, didn't I?' Rafaello raked at her fiercely. 'And, knowing my luck where you're concerned, you'll probably fall pregnant—'

'I hope not...' It was a stricken whisper.

Shattered by his suspicions, Glory was frozen to the bed. How could he think that she would deliberately run the risk of unprotected sex? How could he believe that she would welcome an unplanned pregnancy? The mere prospect of such a development terrified Glory. She had an instant vision of unwed motherhood combined with horrendous poverty. One or two of her schoolfriends had taken that route within a couple of years of leaving school and had lived to regret the choice.

'Do you really? If I've knocked you up I'll be keeping you and the kid for the next twenty years at least!' Rafaello informed her in outraged conclusion. 'That's a bloody high price to pay for your precious virginity. I need a shower!'

As he strode into the connecting bathroom and the door slammed shut Glory felt gutted. Her happiness had been so short-lived that it now seemed like an illusion she had dreamt up. How could he imagine that she would sink that low? Was there no end to his distrust? What sort of an idiot had she been to think that she could so easily change his opinion of her? And wasn't she now getting exactly what she deserved for her foolishness?

Nothing was ever going to change. He was very rich. She was poor. There was no equality and there never would be. Without the equality, maybe respect and trust could not exist, she reasoned wretchedly. She was Glory Little, the gardener's daughter, the gypsy's daughter, the factory worker. He was Rafaello Grazzini, an extremely successful businessman and famed for his entrepreneurial skills.

He was *hurting* her again. How could she be letting him do that to her a second time? Didn't she ever learn? She had agreed to be his mistress. He had said he only wanted sex. She had given him what he wanted. End of story. What on earth had she been doing, clinging to him? *A textbook case of entrapment?* Glory shuddered, nausea stirring in her sensitive stomach. As if she was some greedy, scheming little tramp he had picked up off a street corner!

She threw herself off the bed and viewed the tangled bed-sheets with shamefaced discomfiture. Well, retribution had come even faster than she had warned. 'If you don't value yourself, no man will,' her mother had once told her harshly. So what had she expected to achieve when she had *sold* herself? Choking tears of regret clogging her aching throat, Glory knew she needed to get a grip on herself before she risked facing Rafaello again. But her dress was nowhere to be seen. Just as she was wondering if her dress

lay beneath the bedspread heaped on the carpet, she heard
the shower switch off and panic filled her.

As her case was still downstairs, she raced over to the
sleek built-in units that covered one wall and yanked open
a door. Seeing a row of shirts hanging, she trailed one off
a hanger and dug her arms into it at frantic speed. Within
ten seconds she was out of the bedroom and hurrying down
the stairs. Catching a glimpse of Rafaello's manservant
clearing a table in one of the ground-floor rooms, she realised that the only true sanctuary available was the outdoors.
As she sped out of the front door, emerging into the bright
path of the outside lights, she found herself in the very teeth
of a surprisingly strong wind. But she hesitated only a moment before she fled down the path to the beach and into
the cover of the tamarisk trees ringing the cove.

CHAPTER SIX

GLORY could not credit that she had come out to a fabulous, scenic Greek island in the month of June only to find herself fighting to walk through a howling gale with sand blowing in her face.

The sea was foaming like a cauldron, mirroring the seething tempest of emotion inside her. Rafaello despised her. He truly did. She had to accept that but she didn't want to accept that, couldn't *bear* to accept that, she discovered. All the messy feelings she had buried five years earlier were escaping their bonds. Taking shelter beneath an overhanging rock in the massive outcrop near the end of the beach, she sat down, closing out the angry surge of the surf. With those painful emotions came the memories...

Glory had left school at sixteen. She had wanted to stay on but her father had asserted that no Little had ever been academic, and she had found work as an office junior at the local auctioneers. By the time she reached eighteen, sightings of Rafaello had become rare events. After all, the Grazzinis had divided their time between their Italian and English homes and, having completed his business degree, Rafaello had bought a London apartment and only visited Montague Park occasionally.

Glory had taken a long time to come to terms with their first humiliating encounter when she was sixteen and the horror of having been delivered home to her furious parents like a juvenile delinquent. When, afterwards, Rafaello would drive past Glory and award her a nod or smile of recognition, she would barely raise her head in acknowledgement. Yet, in spite of the lack of encouragement, one

week after her eighteenth birthday Rafaello had raked his
Ferrari to a halt in the drive and offered her a lift.

'Chance would be a fine thing,' Glory had told him
through the window he lowered, straining every sinew to
play it cool while striving not to overdo it.

'How would you like to go out to dinner tonight?'

She had got into his passenger seat almost before he
finished speaking.

'That was the magic combination, was it?' Rafaello had
murmured with a slanting smile that turned her all-too-
vulnerable heart upside-down and left her dizzy.

'Maybe I'm just hungry.' The truth would have been that
she had *never* been invited out for a meal. The males she
met invited her to bars, clubs, sports fixtures and the cin-
ema.

For the following six weeks Glory had walked on air and
her feet hadn't touched the ground once. True, mixing with
his friends had sometimes been a strain. She had discovered
entire conversational topics that had previously been unknown to her. Winter skiing, opera, ballet, yachting and the
total agony of not being able to locate the latest must-have
designer handbag. While warning her that only grief could
be coming in her direction, her own friends had pooled their
clothes and loaned her outfits to wear. Dating Rafaello had
been something of a community effort.

The talent scout who had sighted her out at a club one
evening had tried to get her to sign up with a modelling
agency in the north. She had felt terribly flattered but
Rafaello had squashed any dreams she might have cherished on that score at source.

'You're too small to be a fashion model. The guy can't
be legit. Alternatively, you could find yourself fronting a
knitting pattern or some such thing.'

Which Glory had quite understood roughly translated
into the news that *he* did not want her chasing after a modelling career a few hundred miles away. Since the only

LYNNE GRAHAM   95

thing in her life she truly cared about at that time was *him*,
she had thought no more about that offer. Soon after that
Rafaello had persuaded her to let him give her a tour of
Montague Park, but before they had even completed the
circuit of the ground floor his father had interrupted them.
Glory had immediately recognised that Benito Grazzini,
though he made every effort to hide the fact, was very
much shocked to discover that his son was dating his gardener's daughter.

'He doesn't like me seeing you,' she had said to Rafaello
afterwards.

'He was just surprised. That's all. You're too sensitive,'
Rafaello had told her.

But that same week Benito Grazzini had called at the
cottage on Glory's afternoon off. Even worse, that same
day her own father was upstairs sleeping off his drinking
excesses, rather than out working as he should have been.
Ironically, Benito Grazzini had looked awful, his eyes sunk
in his head as if he hadn't slept for days and his greyish
pallor no more healthy. But he had wasted no time in spelling out his terms.

As soon as he had told her that her father would be
sacked if she did not do as he asked, she had known she
had no choice. If she appealed to Rafaello for support she
would only be making trouble which would rebound on her
family. Rafaello was close to his father but she had only
been dating him for a paltry six weeks, and, while she
might be in love with him, he had made no such claims.
Sobered up, Archie Little had fully supported his daughter's
decision to surrender and leave home.

Glory had decided that the easiest way out of her predicament would be to tell Rafaello that she was accepting
the modelling offer. At the time, Rafaello had been only
weeks off spending four months setting up a branch office
in Rome and she had already been afraid that that separa-

tion would end his interest in her. However, she *had* naïvely believed that they could part as friends.

The following afternoon that she spent with Rafaello had been one long, agonising torment for her to endure until she worked up the courage to tell him that she was going away as well.

'Let me get this straight...*you* are dumping *me*?' Rafaello had interrupted with a stunned look stamped on his darkly handsome features.

'No, it's not like that. It's just that I'm leaving and you're going to be abroad most of the time...I can't imagine when we'd see each other, so isn't a clean break better?'

'It's no big deal,' Rafaello had confirmed while he smiled steadily at her.

Then she had become the author of her own humiliation. It had already been arranged that they would join his friends for dinner that evening at an exclusive local restaurant. 'Can we still go ahead with tonight?' Glory had begged, desperate to spend every last possible moment with him.

'Why not?'

He had called her an hour before he was due to pick her up to inform her that he would be late and that he would meet her there instead. He had even sent a taxi for her and she had had not a clue what was waiting for her on her arrival. She could still remember that long, slow walk across the restaurant and her own stumbling, demeaning retreat from the sight of Rafaello kissing the very lovely redhead before he pulled away again.

As if it was a moment trapped in time she recalled how he had looked across the table at her with callous cool as though he didn't recognise her, as though she was nothing, nobody. It had felt as though everyone in the room was staring at her and laughing, and his friends had certainly been entertained by the scene of her downfall.

Rafaello hadn't changed, Glory reflected wretchedly as

her mind returned to the more pressing problems of the present. He always assumed the worst and he attacked without hesitation. Would he have been so quick to accuse a woman who came from his own privileged background? Of course not. But assuming that Glory could only be on the make came very naturally to him. She shivered, only then registering that the sea spray lashing off the rocks had soaked her to the skin.

'Glory!'

Hearing that shout, she tensed and saw Rafaello running through the surf towards the rocks. His pale shirt and trousers glimmered in the moonlight. Evidently he had come out in as much of a hurry as she had, for he was barefoot. The wind whipped his shirt back from his bronzed, muscular chest.

'*Glory!*' He sounded frantic and she felt childish hiding from him.

Slowly and stiffly, because her chilled limbs were numb, she emerged from her shelter. For a split-second, Rafaello stilled when he saw her and then he powered over to her at even greater speed. He caught her to him. 'When I couldn't find you I thought you had drowned,' he launched down at her in raw condemnation. 'Don't you ever do this to me again!'

Glory looked up at him in astonishment. Drowned? His lean, strong hands were biting into her slight shoulders. That he had been genuinely scared that something might have happened to her was etched into the fierce lines of his hard-boned features and the intensity with which he was staring down at her. 'Oh, you'd have managed to come to terms with me drowning,' Glory heard herself say none the less. 'After all, if I was pregnant my death would be a very cost-effective solution.'

'*Per amor di Dio*…how can you even say such a thing?' Rafaello dealt her a hard look of censure, dark, deep-set eyes scanning her with angry disbelief. 'What sort of a bastard do you think I am?'

'You said it,' Glory told him unsteadily, and she shivered.

'You're cold as ice…and you're wet.' Rafaello banded a strong arm to her spine and urged her back along the beach. 'The sirocco wind can kick up a storm in the space of minutes. If you had stumbled into the water at this end of the strand there's a steep drop just feet out. You can't swim. Naturally, I was worried.'

Unmoved, cold and weary, Glory said nothing. Typical that he should assume she was too stupid to stay out of a roaring sea, she thought grimly. At the foot of the sloping path he bent and scooped her up into his arms. 'You're exhausted,' he grated. 'Once you've had a hot bath and something to eat, you'll feel better.'

'Not as long as you're around,' Glory breathed.

His arms tightened round her. 'You're unhurt. That's all that matters—'

He contrived to carry her all the way back into the villa and right up the stairs with only the most minor irregularity in breathing. In the mood she was in, she would have preferred it if he had been winded and forced to abandon the macho stance and put her down. As it was, he deposited her on the chaise longue in the bathroom and proceeded to run water into the jacuzzi.

'Get in, *cara*…' Rafaello prompted when the bath was ready for her. Barefoot, his trousers drenched to the knees, his black hair tousled by the wind and his aggressive jawline darkened by a blue-black shadow of stubble, he was a far cry from his usual elegance.

She was ashamed that he still seemed wildly attractive to her. 'Only when you get *out*.'

His eyes flared gold. 'I'm not leaving you alone. You might faint—'

'You're too used to little, fragile women who get off on

big, strong men looking after them. I *don't*. It's your fault I went out in a storm to get away from you!'

Without further argument, Rafaello just picked her up and settled her into the jacuzzi. She sat in the water still wearing his shirt and stared down into the bubbles sent up by the jets. Her strained eyes were suddenly prickling with tears.

'If I've got you pregnant I'll marry you,' Rafaello asserted harshly.

Glory was stunned. She could feel her heart racing but almost as quickly it slowed and sank again. He wasn't serious, he could *not* be serious. Rafaello Grazzini marry the gardener's daughter just because he had got her in the family way? He sounded like a male being roasted on a fire to breaking point, and his tone spoke volumes for his true feelings. It was a reluctant proposal, powered by guilt. In terms of class, she was hardly his equal. He had to be cringing at the mere thought of having to take a wife from a background as humble as hers was. 'You can forget that option. I would never be *that* desperate,' Glory responded flatly, striving to sound wholly unimpressed by an offer that had momentarily made her foolish heart leap with joy. She played fair. He didn't love her. She knew better than to snatch at an impulsive proposal made for all the wrong reasons.

'I made the mistake. I take full responsibility for it. I'm sorry,' Rafaello ground out half under his breath.

'Sorry enough to let me go home tomorrow?' Glory whispered tightly, not looking at him, sick with disappointment that his last words should have totally confirmed what had prompted that surprising offer of a wedding ring.

The silence simmered.

'No…not that sorry,' Rafaello qualified in the most ludicrous tone of apology.

She hunched her shoulders. 'What are you getting out of this?'

'You.'

She rested back against the padded pillow surround and let the water jets buffet her weary body with warmth and relaxation. She had never felt so tired in her life. When she surfaced from her inexorable drift into sleep she was out of the bath, propped up against Rafaello, and he was stripping off the wet shirt. Before she could object he had folded her into a giant, soft towel.

'You can't see it now but we're going to be great together, *bella mia*,' Rafaello told her with stubborn conviction. 'When you wake up tomorrow the sun will be shining and you'll feel different.'

Unresponsive in her exhaustion, Glory sank into the wonderful comfort of the bed.

'You need to eat,' Rafaello told her.

'I couldn't.' She did not think she had the strength to lift a knife and fork. Her drowsy gaze flickered over the exquisite miniature portraits set into the headboard of the bed. 'Who are they?'

'Saints. Those are icons.'

Glory dealt him a shaken look. 'What are you doing with a bed with saints watching over it?'

'It's a Corfiot marriage bed. It belonged to my mother's family.'

Glory had forgotten that his late mother had been an Italian raised in Corfu. 'A marriage bed?' So dismayed was she by the thought of how inappropriate that choice of venue had been for an unwed couple that her superstitious nature came to the fore. 'We should never have been in it!'

'It's just a *bed*, Glory.' Viewing her with wondering dark eyes, Rafaello slowly shook his head at that comment.

Throwing him an exasperated glance that implied that he was downright stupid not to appreciate the natural order of things, Glory closed her eyes and went to sleep, but not before she had said her prayers.

Just as Rafaello had promised, Glory woke to sunshine.

She was alone in the bed and there was no telling dent in the pillow beside her own. She headed straight into the shower to wash out the sand still clinging to her hair. Wrapped in a towel, she emerged again to find that a maid was unpacking her case. Choosing a blue skirt and a white sun-top, she went back into the bathroom to get dressed.

The door she had left ajar was slowly pushed wider.

'Breakfast?' Rafaello stood on the threshold, heartbreakingly handsome in a black T-shirt and well-cut chinos.

'I could eat a horse,' Glory admitted, colour rising in her cheeks, her eyes not quite meeting his.

The table on the balcony beyond the bedroom was laid with an extravagant choice of breakfast dishes. Glory took a cushioned seat and reached for the jug of orange juice. In silence she then worked her way through a bowl of cereal.

Rafaello studied her with brilliant dark eyes that probed her evasive gaze. 'We start fresh today.'

'Do we?' Honey-blonde head downbent, Glory sampled two of the cooked dishes on offer and the toast. Fresh? As though last night had never happened? Was he joking? An intimate ache new to her experience was sufficient reminder of the intimacy they had shared. However, she was infinitely more worried about the risk of pregnancy. While she had been in the shower, counting and recounting the days of her cycle had given her no comfort. Rafaello had made love to her at what was supposed to be the optimum time for a woman to conceive. An even greater concern was her own inexplicable, bone-deep conviction that what she most feared had already happened and that right now deep down inside her tiny cells of human life were engaged in frantic baby-making activity.

'Glory…' Rafaello reached out and ensnared her fingers before she could reach for another slice of toast. 'Did you fast before you arrived? Or are you now eating for two?'

Slowly Glory raised her head, bright blue eyes stricken in her pale oval face. 'Is that really your idea of a joke?'

Rafaello sighed. 'I know the way your mind works, *bella mia*. You took one look at those icons on the bed last night and primitive superstition felled you right before my eyes—'

'I do not have primitive superstitions!' Glory snapped.

'No? If there had been a church within walking distance you'd have been in it all night on your knees,' Rafaello groaned in rueful amusement. 'Are you listening to me? We did nothing wrong…'

Compressing her lips, Glory dropped her head.

'And no dire punishment is about to come your way,' Rafaello continued with unshakable conviction. 'I doubt that there will be repercussions from a single encounter.'

'Got a hotline to mother nature too, have you?' Glory could not resist saying.

Thrusting back his chair, Rafaello reached for her hands and hauled her up into the circle of his arms. 'You're the most appalling pessimist. Do you remember that picnic we had years ago? You kept on saying that it was such a gorgeous day that it was sure to rain. I couldn't quite grasp that connection—'

'It *did* rain,' Glory reminded him, recalling that midsummer afternoon five years before when everything between them had seemed almost frighteningly perfect. Within forty-eight hours they had parted. 'It rained when we were on the way back to the car.'

'So you took the edge off the whole occasion, fretting about something you couldn't control?' Rafaello pushed up her chin and stared down at her mutinous face with dark golden eyes that sought and held hers. 'That's a waste of time and energy. Whatever happens, I'll look after you.'

In receipt of those particular words, Glory shivered. So she was superstitious, so she believed in ESP. She noticed that he was no longer assuring her that he would marry her, had naturally thought better of that rash statement. No doubt he was already grateful that she had not accepted his proposal. She was tempted to ask what 'looking after' would entail but suspected that she already knew the answer. When a guy also used terms like 'repercussions' and 'dire punishment' as euphemisms for pregnancy he was telling her far more about his own attitude than he realised. Very probably he would suggest that a termination would be the wisest solution. No way, not *her* baby, Glory thought fiercely.

But there was no denying that she did suffer from that innate belief that every wrong action was followed by a kind of retributive balancing act. Even so, it was plain crazy for her to be imagining that she might be pregnant within hours of making love, wasn't it? Once again, Rafaello was right. Conception was not an event she could influence. What was the point of worrying herself to death at this stage?

'Finish your breakfast,' Rafaello advised. 'It's a treat to be with a woman who has a healthy appetite.'

An involuntary laugh tumbled from her. 'I couldn't manage another bite...'

'Nor could I—'

'You haven't eaten,' she protested.

'I breakfasted while you were still asleep.' The dark timbre of his voice had taken on a husky edge.

A lean hand splayed across her hipbone. She collided with his amazing eyes. Hot, sizzling gold. The wild flare of sensual awareness made her tense. Her mouth running dry, it was she who moved closer, charged by her own shameless yearning. She stared up into that lean, strong face, reacting to the explosive tension and the weakening surge of heat awakening deep in her pelvis.

A shimmering smile of satisfaction slashed his beautiful mouth and she trembled. Her face burned as he let his hands slowly mesh into the fall of her hair, tipping back her head, letting his thumbs caress her earlobes, making her shiver. 'I could not have trusted myself in that bed with you last night,' he confided.

'No?' Glory snatched in an audible breath, so entirely in thrall to the magnetic spell of his sensual power that she was lost.

'You deserved a night of undisturbed rest, so I slept next door and I tossed and I turned and I had a cold shower around dawn.'

'Masochist?'

'A necessity. The very thought of you makes me *ache*...' Rafaello told her hoarsely, his breath fanning her cheek, his mouth taking hers in a hot, hungry surge of cruel brevity before he lifted his proud, dark head again. Linking his hands with hers, he drew her slowly back into the bedroom.

Glory was all of a quiver, shaken at how fast and how easily he could turn her from rational thought. It was as if her body had a fever that only he could assuage, but no longer did she try to deny that craving. She loved him and accepting that love had only made the wanting all the more powerful a force. She had been wrong, so wrong about its being a cold, callous arrangement, she told herself. Last night he had searched for her, shown his concern and his regret. That was enough, that was truly enough to silence her worst misgivings. Nobody got everything, she argued with herself. Lots of folk had to settle for less than what they had once hoped to receive.

'What are you thinking about?' Rafaello demanded as he drew her, unresisting, down onto the bed with him.

'Nothing...' Glory let her hands rise up over his warm, muscular torso in an exploratory foray that was her very first. He stretched like a lithe tiger being stroked, brilliant eyes narrowing in slight surprise. As he bent his head a secretive smile as old as the Sphinx curved her ripe mouth. However long it lasted, he would remember her *always*, she swore.

As if sharing that identical ambition, Rafaello ran his expert mouth down the extended length of her throat, and her entire body hummed on the gasp of response that he dragged from her. Even the feel of him, hard and ready through the barrier of their clothes, sent the flame inside her leaping higher and proceeded to make her melt. But settling for less, she decided on the peak of another tormenting assault on her sensitised skin, could well mean receiving more pleasure than she had ever dreamt possible...

Glory studied the exquisite silver and turquoise choker in the mirror and then her bright eyes widened to take in the whole of her reflection. She did not recognise that elegant, classy lady as herself.

In the space of three weeks, her appearance had been transformed. She had swallowed her pride and allowed Rafaello to buy her clothes. Why? She had very wounding memories of never, ever having had the right clothes when she was seeing him five years earlier. Telling herself then that such superficial things shouldn't matter had been cold comfort when she stuck out like a sore thumb in company. Neither she nor her friends had owned the kind of outfits worn by the women who were part of Rafaello's world: the casual but oh-so-smart separates, the fashionable but understated garments that none the less screamed their designer tags. She had been tortured by fears that her appearance and her visible inability to blend in was an embarrassment to him.

Now sheathed in a Versace dress, purchased from one of the designer outlets that Corfu town offered the rich who flocked to the island over the summer, she had no such fear. The sleek dress was a magical shade somewhere between green and blue and with every movement and change of light the wonderful fabric seemed to change colour. It made her feel like a million dollars and gave her confidence.

Her thick mane of hair had been tamed and styled to fall back from her face. While she was in that exclusive salon she had taken advantage of the opportunity to be made up and had watched and learned and bought everything that was used with the gold credit card Rafaello had given her. So now she knew all about highlighting her cheekbones and using a subtle glimmer of different shadows on her eyelids. What had amused her most was the discovery of just how much work was involved in attaining that sun-kissed and wholly deceptive natural look.

Silver drop earrings with turquoise inserts hung from her ears. A silver watch encircled her wrist. Now Rafaello was set on buying her an elaborate choker. He had tried to tempt her into gold and diamonds and she had just laughed. She loved silver, and when she left she could take the silver jewellery with her without feeling bad about it, for on his terms such items cost next to nothing even in the most expensive shops. But there would be precious memories bound up in her possession of every piece. Memories she would share with their child on some distant day in the future. Her lovely face shadowing at a reality she had only had confirmed beyond doubt the day before, Glory thought back to the daunting but telling exchange she had shared with Rafaello several days earlier...

That particular morning, she had wakened feeling off-colour. As her period had already been slightly overdue, the nausea she was experiencing had reawakened her fear that she might be pregnant but she had decided that there was no point in involving Rafaello in her worries before there was any actual proof. After all, she had heard friends say that even a change of climate or a different diet could interfere with a woman's cycle.

However, when Rafaello had teasingly called her lazy for lying in bed so late, stress had provoked Glory into a snappish reply. 'Look, I'm just not feeling that great… OK?'

'Is it that time of the month?' Rafaello had queried with a frown, his sudden tension pronounced.

By putting her on the spot like that before she knew how matters stood herself, he had disconcerted and embarrassed her. 'Probably…yes…' she had responded hurriedly, picking up on his tension and telling herself that in all likelihood she *was* worrying herself unnecessarily.

'Well, that's good news, isn't it?' Rafaello had commented with a brilliant smile that seemed to accentuate his relief with cruel efficiency. 'At least you're not pregnant, *bella mia.*'

Once he had made that assumption and once she had witnessed his relief, wild horses could not have dragged the real truth from her. Forty-eight hours afterwards she had made a covert visit to a doctor in town and had learned that she was indeed in the very early stages of pregnancy. In choosing not to tell Rafaello, she had made the right decision, she told herself bracingly. Neither marriage nor a termination was on the cards and no way would she put him through the hypocrisy of attempting a supportive role in a pregnancy which he had so patently *not* wanted to happen. That would hurt her too much. After all, what did she really have left but her pride?

'Glory…?' The laughter in Rafaello's dark, deep drawl dragged her back to the present.

Pasting a determined and bright smile back onto her downcurved lips, Glory finally turned away from the shop mirror.

'I gather you like it.' Rafaello sent her a vibrant smile of amusement and she realised that, having interpreted her long silence as sheer appreciation, he had already paid for the choker.

'It's really beautiful.

But not one quarter as beautiful as him, Glory reflected

helplessly, scanning his lean, dark, devastating face with dreamy eyes of appreciation. Not once in five years had she known such happiness as she had experienced with him in recent weeks. She could not bring herself to destroy what had been a time of enchantment with the brutally realistic and unwelcome announcement that she was going to have his baby.

So if she was a bit sad now it was only to be expected. What goes around comes around. She had been right, he had been wrong and, whether he knew it or not, their time together was slowly running out. Her body was already changing with pregnancy. The speed of that development filled her with both fascination and fear. Her breasts were tender and the mere smell of certain foods made her nauseous. But surely she could manage to conceal those facts for another few weeks?

Linking sure fingers with hers, Rafaello walked her down the steep steps outside the shop and back into the colourful lively crowds passing through the narrow street. She adored Corfu town: the legacy of tall Italianate buildings adorned with shutters and balconies left behind by four centuries of Venetian rule, the buzz of the streets and cafés, the array of fascinating shops filled with silver, olive wood, needle-work and leather-craft items. Even the locals came out to promenade round their town during the long evenings.

'I suppose now we head for your favourite place,' Rafaello commented lazily.

'If you don't mind...'

A Frenchman had built the Liston as a copy of the Rue de Rivoli in Paris. The arched façade filled with fashionable cafés overlooked a lush green cricket pitch surrounded by trees. She adored sitting there to watch the world go by with Rafaello by her side.

'Why do people keep on staring at us?' she had asked uncomfortably on her first visit.

'You are a very beautiful woman.' His amused but appreciative smile that she should even ask such a question had dissolved the insecure feelings she always struggled to hide from him and made her heart sing. She had a desperate need to believe that she *could* look like the sort of woman who belonged with him.

While Rafaello ordered wine for himself Glory pored over the ice-cream menu to make her selection. Then she rested back in her comfortable seat to survey him, torn between pain and pleasure. He was a visual joy to her from the crown of his gleaming dark head to the soles of his feet. Nothing about him jarred. She was so much in love with him, she could have shouted it from the rooftops. But, denied that outlet, she burned with inner intensity and quailed in torment at the prospect of tearing herself from him.

Suppressing that miserable awareness, Glory made herself dwell instead on the wonderful days they had shared and the endless nights of mutual passion. One day drifting into the next, seamless, timeless, marred by only the rarest disagreement and resealed by the fastest reconciliations on record. He had taught her to swim but had made several biting comments when he finally realised that she *still* preferred drifting round the villa pool in a large plastic ring like an overgrown child or just sitting at the foot of the Roman steps, submerged but safe. Only when he had appreciated the fear of deep water that she had overcome initially only for his benefit had he appreciated the level of her achievement. He thought her ring was cute now. He didn't laugh when she just paddled down on the beach either.

She would carry away memories of wandering through the cool, shaded orchards that surrounded the villa, endlessly talking while they picked a path through the lush green trees laden with velvety peaches, tangerines and cherries beneath the burning blue sky. She would remember the glittering white of the sand-dunes at noon and the dark atmospheric richness of the church dedicated to the island's

revered St Spyridon. But most of all she would cherish the
reality that he had never once called her his mistress or
treated her with anything less than respect.

'If you don't start talking soon about what's bothering
you, *cara mia*,' Rafaello murmured with his lustrous dark
golden eyes fixed to her with magnetic probing force, 'I'm
likely to get annoyed with you.'

Glory froze as if he had turned a gun on her, dismayed
that her façade of contentment had not been as good as she
had imagined. It really shook her that he had evidently
noted a change in her behaviour.

'Not *that* annoyed,' Rafaello groaned with rueful amusement.

'I just don't know why you should think there's anything
bothering me,' Glory said tautly and she shrugged for good
measure, but one of her hands had found its way down to
her still flat tummy under the table.

'You are not a naturally silent woman but for the last
few days it's been as though you're not quite with me any
more, *mia preziosa*. So what's wrong? Is it your family?
You never mention them but possibly that's because you're
missing them.' Rafaello regarded her expectantly.

Glory turned scarlet with discomfiture. She never mentioned her family, not only because she could not bear to
recall the arrangement that had brought her out to Corfu in
the first place but also because she dreaded any further
reference to that five thousand pounds which had branded
her as mercenary in his estimation.

'If you're discreet I don't see why you shouldn't phone
them,' Rafaello proffered with the air of a male making a
generous gesture.

'But…but I've been calling them every few days since
I got here,' Glory admitted in some bewilderment.

Rafaello tensed in evident shock.

Glory frowned. 'I didn't think you'd mind. I didn't stay
on the phone long.'

'Let me get this straight,' Rafaello breathed in a charged undertone, golden eyes smouldering. 'Even though I asked you to be discreet, you have been chattering your dizzy head off to your father and your brother every few days?'

Glory paled and stiffened and then slowly nodded, wondering why on earth he was looking so angry.

Rafaello vented a single foreign word that sounded as though it might be a rude word.

Glory gulped and wondered if her own excusable omissions lay at the heart of his annoyance. Feeling horribly guilty, she muttered, 'You know, I never thanked you for being so very kind to Sam...I just didn't want to discuss all that stuff that happened. I'm sorry, I—'

'Shut up,' Rafaello urged not quite levelly, evidently striving to get a grip on his temper and not one whit cooled by her sincere offering of gratitude. Almost simultaneously he rose from his seat, tossed some banknotes down on the table and strode down the steps to await her.

Her own temper rising, Glory moved to join him at slow-motion speed.

'Have you the *smallest* conception of what you have done?' Rafaello ground out in a raw undertone.

'Don't you talk to me like I'm a brick short of the full load!' Glory warned him in a sideways hiss.

'I hate to state the obvious, *bella mia*...' Rafaello countered grittily, grasping her hand and resisting all her covert attempts to pull free of his hold '...but if you have cheerfully let your family know that you're out here shacked up with me—'

'Of course I haven't done that!' Glory snapped even as pain stabbed her at his use of that particular description of their relationship.

Rafaello stopped dead and turned to survey her. 'You...*haven't*?'

'Dizzy I may be sometimes but not downright thick. You think I'm proud of being here with you? Well, you think wrong and I'd be *ashamed* to let my father or my brother know how low I've sunk!' Glory completed in a shaking but fierce undertone.

Rafaello stared at her, his fabulous bone-structure prominent beneath his bronzed skin, his hard gaze darker than the blackest night. He said nothing and it was Glory who turned away first and began walking back in the direction of the car again. She was feeling sick. Her legs didn't feel strong enough to hold her upright either.

He unlocked the passenger door of the car first. She climbed in, her lovely face pale as marble and as expressionless, but inside herself she was just dying. She had not meant to say all that but he had hurt and provoked her. He swung in beside her and the horrible silence pulsed.

She laced her hands together to stop them trembling. 'Dad and Sam just think I've moved and they haven't asked the address because they don't write me letters. They assume I'm using a public phone with a number they can't call me back on. I didn't have to tell any lies,' she explained in tight voice. 'Neither of them has ever visited me in Birmingham, so they don't really have much curiosity about my life there.'

'I'm sorry. I misunderstood,' Rafaello breathed with icy cool, but there was an underlying roughness to his accented drawl. 'I employ your father. I thought your brother was a decent kid. I asked you to be discreet for *their* sake and yours, not my own.'

'No point advertising that you're slumming on a temporary basis, is there?' Glory heard herself say nastily. 'After all, now you've dressed me up in the designer togs, nobody could possibly tell that you took me off a factory floor!'

If the previous silence had pulsed, the one that followed that blunt and inflammatory response fairly sizzled. Again Rafaello said nothing, which really infuriated her. She knew she would have been better saying nothing too but entire speeches that would rip him to shreds were trembling in readiness on the tip of her tongue and holding them back tortured her. He drove off. She would have liked him to grate through the gears and jerk the wheel to demonstrate emotional upset but he drove as if he had just come through an advanced driving test with pronounced care and caution.

She kept quiet for a whole ten minutes and then it got too much for her. 'I really *hate* you, Rafaello Grazzini!'

'Naturally you do,' he murmured flatly. 'Sex and debt are hardly a satisfactory basis for any relationship. My choice, my mistake.'

Tears drenched Glory's eyes in a tidal wave. She squeezed her eyes shut, hating herself for tearing away the barriers and leaving them both without defence. But at the same time she was powerfully tempted to kick him. Why was he making things worse? Was he fed up with her, bored already? But what did it matter if he was? Wasn't she leaving anyway? For how could she stay with him when her waistline was going to vanish?

Back at the villa, she locked herself in the bathroom. Ripping off her clothes, she got into the shower and turned it on full so that she could sob to her heart's content. It was an hour before she crept out, eyes stinging from all the cold water she had splashed in them. Mercifully the bedroom was unoccupied. She dug into a drawer for a nightdress, the first she had worn since her arrival, and crawled into bed.

Somewhere in the early hours when she was lying there sleepless, drowning in buckets of self-pity, the bedroom door opened. She froze. She had not bothered to close the curtains and in the clear moonlight she saw a bronzed male silhouette. It was Rafaello, only a white towel knotted round his lean hips. She shut her eyes tight and seconds later noted the slight give in the mattress as Rafaello sank down on it.

She rolled over and arrived on his side of the bed only

a moment after he did. Expelling his breath in a slightly startled hiss, Rafaello closed his arms round her. 'We have to talk…'

Panic assailed Glory, for she did not want to talk. He might not appreciate it but the die was already cast. Nothing could be resolved, nothing could be changed. Gliding up over his lean, hard, muscular body in the circle of his arms, she pressed herself close and found his mouth for herself. For a horrendous instant as he tautened in surprise at the blatant invitation she thought he might push her away. Then, just as suddenly, he reacted by pinning her beneath him and deepening that kiss with a driving hunger that shook her.

In the moonlight he threw up his head again and scanned her with fathomless dark eyes. 'I want you *but*—'

Glory had no desire to hear what came after. Sinking desperate fingers into the black hair still damp from the shower, she drew him down to her again. A throaty groan escaped him but she was stronger when it came to the wiles of a temptress. She knew what he could not resist. She knew what drove him wild. Within minutes he was as much the prisoner of his own hunger as she was and way past rational speech.

There was none of the long, teasing rise to gradual excitement with which they had wiled away many a long afternoon. She had unleashed a storm of fierce passion that was well out of her control. He sank into her with delicious driving force, sent her out of her senses with pleasure, and every time she reached a peak it would all start again. A seemingly endless cycle of raw excitement and ecstatic satisfaction left her drained and rather shell-shocked around dawn, when he finally fell into a much-deserved sleep of exhaustion.

Glory lay beside him, questioning what had been different apart from the silence, and then it came to her: he had been saying goodbye to her. He knew it was over. He had decided that before he even came to bed, probably expecting her to be sound asleep. He wanted out. Only not because he was bored with her or because he no longer desired her. Earlier this evening things had got messy, and Rafaello did not like messy scenes. Perhaps it had finally dawned on him that, far from hating him, she loved him.

And, if he hadn't already guessed just how deep her emotional involvement already went, what had just happened between them would have got the message home to him fast. She had *thrown* herself at him like a brazen hussy. Not in a subtle, seductive way either. She cringed for herself and then swithered feverishly between fear and uncertainty. Stress about being pregnant and her own insecurity could be making her oversensitive, she reasoned. Maybe she was just *imagining* that she somehow knew what he was thinking.

But later that same morning she seemed to receive her answer to that question. Fully dressed, Rafaello wakened her. In a lightweight jacket worn with a dark blue shirt and teamed with faultlessly tailored beige chinos, he looked so gorgeous, he took her breath away.

'I have to go out,' he told her flatly. 'Jack Woodrow called me last week to ask for investment advice and I still haven't taken care of it.'

The first week of her stay Rafaello had taken her over to dine at the Woodrows' palatial villa. The prospect of being entertained by a genuine earl and his wife had made Glory feel quite sick with nerves. However, the scornful Fiona had been nowhere to be seen and the brunette's parents, Lord and Lady Woodrow, had turned out to be a delightful and charming older couple. They had greeted Rafaello with fond affection and welcomed Glory to their summer home without the smallest sign of discomfiture.

Rafaello sent her a veiled glance, his tension pronounced in the hard angles of his strong profile. 'Look, we'll talk when I get back but you should pack. We're flying back to London this afternoon.'

Well, she wasn't hanging around for that denouement, Glory told herself steadily. She would save them both from an embarrassing final encounter followed by an even more painful three-hour flight back home. No doubt he would try to ditch her with courteous consideration. What had got into him five years earlier she would never know, for the callous indifference he had shown towards her feelings then had not been his style.

At her request, Rafaello's manservant, Hilario, took her to the airport an hour later. But as soon as Hilario had departed again Glory got into a taxi and travelled back into town. She had seen several casual jobs advertised in cafés and bars. If Rafaello was leaving Corfu, why should she? Back in England, she no longer had either a home or a job. Furthermore, she had very little money. Nor could she face the prospect of returning to the gardener's cottage on the Montague Park estate. Her pregnancy would distress and embarrass her father a great deal and gossip might even carry the news of her condition right back to Rafaello. No, she was on her own and it was time she got used to that idea…

CHAPTER SEVEN

STANDING beneath the awning that shaded the empty tables in the narrow alleyway, Glory took the opportunity to rub at the small of her back where the ache was worst. Late afternoon the bar attracted little passing trade, but no matter how quiet it was she was not allowed to sit down.

Eight weeks had passed since Glory had walked out of Rafaello's villa to save face. She had soon lived to regret that impulsive decision, for nothing had gone quite as she had planned. Renting a room in Corfu town had proved to be much more expensive than she had naïvely expected and she had used up all the money she had before she had finally got a job as a waitress. Indeed she had only recently managed to save up enough to cover the purchase of an air ticket back to London.

In addition, now that the summer crowds of tourists were thinning, temporary bar staff were being laid off, so she was unlikely to have a job for much longer. When she finally flew back to England she would still be very short of cash. Staying on in Corfu had not been a good idea. Back home she would have had a better chance of finding employment while she did not look pregnant, she reflected ruefully. Now she could only get into trousers with elasticated waists and her once flat tummy was beginning to protrude, no matter how hard she tried to hold it in.

So why had she let Rafaello escape the consequences of their short-lived affair? In retrospect, her own behaviour seemed foolish and short-sighted. Recognising his tension that day when he had asked her whether she was feeling unwell because it was that time of the month, she had said yes out of an instinctive need to lessen his obvious concern.

117

Unfortunately, her recognition of his relief in receipt of the premature reassurance had sealed her fate and left her with the pretence to maintain. But, naturally, Rafaello had been relieved, Glory told herself miserably. Sex was sex but babies were something else entirely to the average male. She had heard that some men actually got broody just like women did. However, it had seemed pretty obvious that nature had so far left Rafaello untouched by a craving for fatherhood.

But it would have been more sensible for her to have steeled herself and told him the truth: that she was expecting his child and that she intended to have her baby. Why had she felt so guilty about that decision? Even more to the point, why on earth did she miss Rafaello so unbearably? It was madness for her to be missing him when he had been on the brink of ditching her anyway. After just three weeks too. All that romantic holding of hands, all the compliments, the charm, the seemingly insatiable level of his desire for her…and what had all that been worth at the end of the day? Feeling her eyes prickle, Glory blinked back the tears that of late seemed to come all too easily to her. No doubt wiser women than she was had been fooled by men, but how many of them had been taken in *twice* over by the same guy?

Glory suppressed a groan as she thought of the effort she had made and the pride she had dumped just to look classy for him. She should have gone for really tarty clothes and embarrassed the hell out of him every chance she got. That was what he had deserved. But oh, no, Glory Little had acted like a bimbo right to the fall of the final curtain. Remembering how she had passed that last night in Rafaello's bed made her shrink with mortification. Here she was, pregnant, poor, miserable and alone, and she had not even the consolation of knowing that she had told him where to get off!

Out of the corner of her eye she finally registered that

one of the tables at the far end of the bar's pitch had been taken. After two steps in that direction she recognised the angle of that arrogant dark head, the mysterious fluid arrangement of that lithe, lean body that, even seated, contrived to put out an impression of cool command and wealthy exclusivity. Her feet faltered and her heart leapt into what felt like the foot of her convulsing throat.

Rafaello removed his sunglasses. Lustrous, dark deep-set eyes zoomed in on her. His hard jawline clenched. Even wearing that grim and tense expression and clad in what appeared to be a formal business suit, he looked incredibly sleek and sexy.

A seriously debilitating wave of love and lust gripped Glory. She wanted him to smile. Why did he look so bleak? After all, what had she done? Taken herself off without fanfare? Hardly a hanging offence. Indeed, a lot of men would have been grateful to have been spared the inevitable messy and awkward scene of their parting. She tilted her chin but felt the hot betraying colour of awareness flood her cheeks.

'Sit down,' Rafaello suggested.

'I can't. I'm not allowed to,' she said unevenly, wondering wildly if he had missed her too and if he had sought her out to tell her so. Gripped by so much desperate hope that she could no longer look him in the face, she added jerkily, 'What would you like to drink?'

'Either sit down or tell me where you're staying and we'll go there to talk,' Rafaello countered tautly.

'How did you find me?'

'With the greatest of difficulty.' Lines of strain girded his wide sensual mouth as she stole a glance at him from beneath her lashes. 'But Sam was of some help—'

'*Sam?*' His reference to her kid brother in that line bewildered Glory.

'Glory...I have news that you are likely to find distressing.'

Her own fantasy that he might be making an approach to persuade her back to him burned into her soul like acid. By no stretch of the imagination could he believe that such a proposition would qualify as 'distressing'.

'Nothing you could tell me would distress me, and if you don't want a drink I'm not hanging around here to chat.' Employing that scornful assurance in an effort to conceal her own pitiful sense of disappointment, Glory began to turn away again.

'*Santo cielo!*' Rafaello gritted in a driven undertone and he thrust back his chair to rise to his full commanding height. 'Your father is ill…'

Glory jerked into the stillness of complete shock and gaped at him.

'I'm here to fly you home so that you can be with him,' Rafaello explained, temper back under control again, his voice level and quiet.

Her skin had turned damp and chilled and her head was starting to swim. She blinked at him. 'Ill with…what?'

'He had a brain tumour,' Rafaello admitted after a pronounced hesitation. 'He…'

Horror engulfed Glory. *A brain tumour?* Dizziness swept over her and, as she lurched towards one of the seats with the belated intent of sitting down, everything blacked out and she fainted.

Surfacing with a muzzy head again, Glory discovered that she was lying on the narrow bed in her room on the floor above the café. Her employer's wife was chattering excitedly to Rafaello in Greek and nodding with approval as though impressed by his responses. Her dad was *dead*, Glory recalled with stricken recoil. That was the news that Rafaello had been trying to break gently to her, only obviously he had not wanted to make that announcement in a public place.

'Did Dad just go like Mum did? Suddenly?' Glory whispered sickly.

Rafaello wheeled round, his brow indented with a frown. 'Your father's *not* dead,' he assured her immediately. 'He's had surgery, major surgery. He's holding his own...just.'

Pale as parchment paper, Glory attempted to follow that explanation but her brain was slow to comprehend, for she was numb with shock. She had reacted to Rafaello's arrival on a very personal level, only to discover that he had sought her out again for another reason entirely. She felt completely disorientated. 'Dad's...alive?'

'Yes, but I'm afraid he hasn't recovered consciousness as yet.'

'I was talking to him on the phone only a few days ago,' Glory protested as she pushed herself up on her elbows and sat up.

Rafaello sank down on the edge of the bed so that they were on a level. His brilliant dark eyes were very serious. 'It happened very fast and with little apparent warning. Your father developed a severe headache and simply collapsed. Sam called an ambulance and he was rushed to the local hospital and from there to a larger facility where scanning equipment was available.'

'But the medics operated, so there's hope,' Glory said, more for her own benefit than his. 'That's what I've got to concentrate on.'

'I'll wait downstairs.' Rafaello slid upright again. 'If you can pack quickly we can be in London by late evening.'

Glory was frantic with concern for her father but she appreciated the fact that Rafaello had not offered her empty reassurances. She knew that he was afraid that her parent might not survive the night.

'Did you have business over here?' Glory asked on the drive to the airport, belatedly wondering how he had become involved in the situation.

'No. I came for you. Sam could only tell me that you were working somewhere in this town in a bar. I put my staff on the phones. Bar owners rarely register casual workers and only personal enquiries were likely to receive an honest response.'

'I should have given Sam my address. I'm so sorry,' Glory mumbled, appalled by the trouble and inconvenience he had been put to in his efforts to locate her. He had flown all the way out to the island purely for her benefit.

'I flew out on spec, hoping that you would be traced by the time I arrived. Jon Lyons struck lucky when I was halfway here,' Rafaello completed, tight-mouthed.

Gritty tears lashed the backs of Glory's eyes. Willing them back, she thanked him again and fell silent. He had to be furious with her and she could not blame him. Grateful though she was that he had found her, she was recognising once again that unfortunate extra dimension to her relationship with him. He was her father's employer and the Grazzinis had always prided themselves on being good to their employees. Sam was only sixteen and someone had had to take responsibility in the crisis. It cut her to the bone that the adult forced to take that no doubt unwelcome responsibility had been Rafaello.

She fell asleep during the flight. Rafaello wakened her about an hour before the jet landed and she went to freshen up. When she returned a meal awaited her, and although she had small appetite she did her best to eat in the hope that food would give her more energy. But never had Glory felt more miserable. Even in the midst of fretting about her father, she was horribly conscious of the change in Rafaello's attitude to her. While being concerned, polite and in every way supportive, he was also maintaining a detached and impersonal approach.

'I can manage to get to the hospital on my own,' Glory said tightly as soon as they arrived in London. 'Thank you. You've been wonderful.'

'I'm coming with you. Try to persuade Sam to take a break. He's exhausted,' Rafaello urged. 'You'll also find my housekeeper keeping a vigil by your father's bed—'

'Maud Belper?' Glory glanced at him in surprise.

'I understand that Archie asked her to marry him last week.' Registering her astonishment at that information, Rafaello sighed. 'I gather Sam didn't keep you up to speed on what was happening on the homefront.'

He guessed right, but when Glory thought that development over it became less of a surprise to her. Her father and Maud Belper had known each other all their lives. If long-standing friendship had finally warmed into something more, she ought to be happy for them both. After all, her parent had been a widower for a long time, she reasoned, striving not to feel hurt and excluded at the news that her father had decided to remarry without even mentioning his plans to her. But then, why should he have done otherwise? For a long time she had lived only on the periphery of her father's life.

She looked at Rafaello but only when he was not looking at her. It struck her that his hard-boned features had fined down since she had last seen him. He was so tense as well. He was obviously hating every moment of their enforced proximity, she thought painfully.

'I'm so sorry about all this,' she muttered as she hurried into the hospital lift in advance of him.

As the lift doors whirred shut, Rafaello surveyed her with impenetrable dark eyes, his lean, strong face taut. 'Please don't misunderstand me when I say that I don't feel comfortable with your gratitude. You don't owe me any apologies either. I did what I had to do. It wasn't much. Let's leave it at that.'

Glory lowered her wounded gaze to the floor. She so badly wanted to feel his arms around her again but she knew that that was not going to happen. A gulf the challenging depth and width of an ocean now separated them. Sam was in the waiting room. He rushed to greet her with relief but the whole time he was hugging her his every

conversational sally was addressed over her shoulder to
Rafaello.

'I can't believe that you got back here with Glory so
fast!' Sam was saying. 'I knew you said you would but I
thought there would be delays and stuff. Most of the time
I've just let Maud sit with Dad—'

'I'd like to see him,' Glory slotted into her brother's
fraught flood of speech.

'Maud will have to come out,' Sam told her. 'Only one
person is allowed by his bed in the ICU. There just isn't
the space for more.'

Rafaello vanished from the doorway.

'He'll sort it,' Sam muttered, his lanky length sagging
into a weary slouch. 'He's done everything. Dad would be
dead right now if it wasn't for Rafaello. Did he tell you
that the surgeons here said they couldn't operate on Dad?'

'No…'

Her brother explained that the only surgical procedure
capable of giving their father a fighting chance of survival
had not been done in the UK before. Rafaello had had to
fly in a top-flight neurosurgeon from New York to perform
the operation. This was the same guy who could not stand
to be thanked, Glory reflected wretchedly. Rafaello had
moved heaven and earth to help her and her family.

Ushered into the ICU by a kindly nurse, Glory focused
on her father and all the machinery surrounding him and
then breathed in deep. She stopped thinking about herself
and her own problems and started praying instead and willing the older man to come through. Around dawn her father's vital signs began showing a marked improvement
and, revitalised by that information, Glory went in search
of her brother.

But it was Maud Belper who hurried forward when she
entered the waiting room, Maud, whose existence Glory
had entirely forgotten. In a guilty rush at that awareness,
Glory shared the good news. Tears of release from severe

stress swam in the older woman's red-rimmed eyes. She gripped Glory's hand. 'Would you mind if I went back in for a while?'

'No, I've been very selfish. Go ahead,' Glory encouraged. 'Where's Sam?'

'Mr Grazzini took him back to his city apartment. Sam was out on his feet. Will you phone them?' Maud begged, her impatience to be back by the side of the man she so obviously loved palpable.

Lingering only long enough to pass on the phone number, Rafaello's housekeeper disappeared. Glory called. Rafaello answered almost immediately and agreed that her news was wonderful but he also insisted that Sam should be left to sleep for as long as possible. She was taken aback by that insistence on the score of her own brother but was too drained to argue. Curling up in a corner seat, she waited out what remained of the night hours.

Mid-morning, Rafaello brought Sam back to the hospital. By then the general prognosis was that Archie Little was on the road to recovery. He had regained consciousness, squeezed Maud's hand and recognized his daughter with a weak smile. As Sam hurried off to take her place by his father's side, Rafaello studied Glory. 'You can come back to my apartment now and sleep—'

'No, thanks,' she said tightly.

'Don't make this more difficult than it already is,' Rafaello told her with a look of reproof. 'Are you planning to kip on a park bench just to score against me?'

Glory folded her arms with a jerk. She was so close to tears, she could not trust herself to speak. She felt frankly surplus to everyone's requirements. From the doorway of the ICU she had watched her father look at Maud's wan but smiling face and had appreciated that he took much greater strength and comfort from the older woman's presence than from hers. Then there was Sam, rushing in beside Rafaello, bopping about like a very large, clumsy puppy and then punching Rafaello's shoulder in that exclusive all-male way to bid him goodbye and barely awarding his sister a second glance.

Sam seemed to have succumbed to a severe case of hero worship where Rafaello was concerned. Indeed, Glory was amazed to see Sam, who could be so very reserved with strangers, so relaxed in Rafaello's company. After all, they hardly knew each other. Obviously her father's illness had brought down barriers but Sam was not behaving in what she considered to be an appropriate way. Rafaello was their father's boss, for goodness' sake, not a best mate or a big brother or something!

'I'm not trying to score against a-anybody.' Glory faltered to a charged halt at the rise of the sob that made her stammer.

Rafaello banded an arm round her hunched shoulders, swept up the handbag lying on the seat she had vacated and walked her into the lift. Too busy fighting to keep the tears in check, Glory was rigid for fear that she might suddenly succumb and fling herself against his chest and start sobbing all over him. Her family no longer needed her. They had got used to getting by without her. She was the needy one and Rafaello was busy supporting all of them like a positive saint. Yet he didn't want her thanks and she didn't want to *have* to be grateful. If she couldn't have his love, she wanted nothing to do with him.

Rafaello tucked her into the limo with careful hands. 'You're wrecked. You need rest. Have a good cry if it makes you feel better.'

'Stop being so *nice!*' Glory gasped accusingly, throwing herself over to the far corner of the rear seat and ducking down her head.

Without warning, a pair of lean and very determined hands settled round her waist and dragged her inexorably across the space she had opened between them. Glory

loosed a strangled squawk like a chicken on the run from
a meat cleaver. Rafaello brought his mouth crashing down
on hers and her hormones seemed to erupt like a volcano
in response. She went from raging emotional turmoil and
tears to raw excitement within seconds. Instantly she was
kissing him back, running her hands over his shoulders, his
hair, any part of him within reach, and her heart was hammering and breathing was a luxury no longer required.

It felt *so* good to be back in his arms, she had no control,
no thought of what she was doing. Only the elemental surge
of her own love and desperate hunger guided her. The pleasure was explosive, primal, almost too hot to bear. When
he threw back his head and deprived her of that connection
she suffered a cruel sense of loss.

Rafaello stared down at her, golden eyes shimmering like
bright sunlight in his lean face, dark colour accentuating
the fierce slant of his cheekbones, his jawline clenched
hard. 'My only excuse is lack of sleep and a low patience
threshold. My apologies, *cara*,' he breathed in a gritty undertone. 'But if it happens again, try pushing me away.'

Trembling and disorientated by a similar amount of sleep
deprivation, Glory could not meet his gaze. Her cheeks
fired up but that final comment of his filled her with rage.
Yet *still* she had an almost overwhelming urge to haul him
back to her, to lose herself in that wild heat and excitement
where she did not have to think but only feel. Her emotions
were all over the place. A combustible mix of love and
hatred was tearing her apart.

'Are you letting Maud stay here too?' she asked as she
entered the penthouse apartment, trying not to gape too
obviously at the large expanses of polished floor stretching
off in every direction.

'No, I believe she has a sister in Clapham.'

'Then why's Sam staying with you and not with her?'
Glory watched him still and tense at that enquiry and her

vague sense that something was not quite right was increased by his reaction to what she saw as a perfectly natural question. 'Maud *is* going to be his stepmother—'

Rafaello gave her an expressionless look. 'Maud has
scarcely left the hospital since your father arrived there.'

He strode down a wide corridor, thrust open a door into
a bedroom and told her where she would find a spare key
for the apartment. She felt that he could not wait to get her
out of his sight. She relived her own passionate response
in his limo and let the tears come, the tears of stress, which
she had held back for so many hours. Slumped on the bed,
fully clothed, she fell asleep.

Wakening in the afternoon in her crumpled garments, she
felt like an itinerant. The *en suite* bathroom was a dream
of glossy tiles and spacious luxury but all too many mirrors.
She grimaced at her shadowed eyes and tousled hair. A
long shower made her feel much more human. A towel
anchored round her, she rubbed at the ache in the small of
her back. Ever-conscious of her changing shape in recent
weeks, she had begun hunching her shoulders, aware that
when she practised good posture her swelling stomach was
much more obvious. But enough was enough, she decided
ruefully, straightening her shoulders with determination as
she padded back into the bedroom.

She stopped dead: Rafaello was in the act of walking in
through the bedroom door. 'I did knock…I assumed you
were still asleep,' he proffered. 'Sam's back and he tells
me that your father is asking for you—'

'Honestly?' Glory exclaimed, touched and pleased by
that news. Turning away from him, she headed straight for
the case sitting at the foot of the bed. 'I'd better get dressed
and get over to the hospital.'

She heard Rafaello draw in a sharp breath. A frownline
indenting her brow, she glanced at him again. Rafaello was
as still as a graven image, his attention fully lodged to his

view of her body in profile as delineated by the unforgiving cover of a fleecy towel stretched to capacity.

'*Per meraviglia*...' he breathed raggedly in the simmering silence. 'You look like a fertility goddess.'

As a schoolgirl, Glory had once seen such a statue in a museum. Being compared with an extremely rotund female from prehistoric times was the kind of compliment she would have gone some distance to avoid. Cringing inwardly, her colour rising, she sucked in her tummy in an effort to make it meet her backbone and forced herself to laugh. 'You're not supposed to tell women when they've put on weight, Rafaello. But then, you know how much I enjoy my food and if I want to be big and beautiful—'

'And...pregnant?' Rafaello dragged his stunned gaze from the no longer visible swell and raked it up to her stricken face.

'*Pregnant?*' Glory parroted shrilly, most of her oxygen supply engaged in the effort it took to keep her tummy in. 'Are you nuts?'

'Let's see. Take the towel off and start breathing again!' Rafaello strode forward, looking very much like a guy with a mission to prove his point by any means available.

Glory backed off, aghast. Shorn of the towel, all would be revealed: her vanishing waist, her increasingly Rubenesque curves.

'Glory...I want the truth,' Rafaello growled, intent golden eyes clashing with hers.

Glory swallowed hard.

'The baby has to be mine,' Rafaello continued, fiercely scanning her pale, strained face for answers. 'It's *got* to be! You're at least a few months along.'

'OK...you win,' Glory whispered through compressed lips, and she dropped her head because she could not bring herself to retain visual contact when she told him. 'Or maybe I should say, mother nature won. Yes, of course it's your baby—'

'So why did you go out of your way to convince me that there was nothing to worry about in Corfu? Was that an honest mistake on your part?' Rafaello demanded in a low driven undertone, his dark deep drawl no longer level. 'Did you only discover that you were carrying my child *after* you'd walked out on me?'

'No.' Suddenly Glory was feeling very guilty and confused. 'One of the days I said I was getting my hair done, I also went to see a doctor. It was confirmed then.'

Rafaello absorbed that confession with bleak, dark-as-midnight eyes. 'So why didn't you tell me?'

Tears gritted up her eyes and she blinked furiously. 'You didn't *want* to know—'

'That is not true.' The contradiction was lethally quiet.

'I *saw* how relieved you were when you believed I wasn't pregnant!' Glory argued chokily.

Briefly Rafaello closed his eyes as if he was praying for patience and then he swung away, the bunched muscles of his powerful shoulders betraying the ferocious level of his tension. 'I was relieved because that was not the way I wanted it to happen. History repeating itself...I didn't want it to *be* like that between us—'

'History repeating itself?' Glory echoed, totally at sea as to his meaning.

Rafaello swung back to her, his darkly handsome features clenched hard. 'Something similar once happened in my own family.'

'Oh...' Weak from stress, Glory sank down on the corner of the bed. 'I really didn't know what to do when I found out I'd fallen pregnant. Maybe I have a bad habit of wanting to tell people what I think they want to hear.'

'That's no excuse.' Disconcertingly impervious to that mode of appeal, Rafaello shot her a look of angry derision.

'You're tough enough when you want to be. All over me like a rash one moment and doing a vanishing act the next. But this is something else again, this is my baby too. I would've married you in Corfu but you were quick enough to tell me that you weren't *that* desperate!'

Struck by the revealing rawness of that final sentence, Glory gave him a shaken appraisal. It was almost three months since he had made that offer and he had never mentioned it again. But only now did she see that she had actually hurt and offended him. When he had voiced that grim assurance that he would marry her if she conceived he had been serious, much more serious than she had given him credit for being. And how had she reacted? She asked herself with a sinking heart. Offered what she most desired in the world but believing it was the most grudging of proposals, she had shot him down in flames.

'You're not being fair,' she argued shakily. 'I was angry and upset that night. I honestly didn't believe you were serious! But I have to admit that I still wouldn't want to marry anybody *just* because I was pregnant—'

'Well, what you want and what you get aren't always the same thing in this life,' Rafaello drawled with icy precision. 'But I can assure you that we are getting married just as fast as I can arrange it. We don't have a choice.'

Glory took a very deep breath and then another. Maybe he was just really hopeless at proposing. In fact, he was a walking disaster on that subject, but on this occasion she had no urge whatsoever to utter a stubborn, proud refusal. She loved him to bits and he was the father of her baby and she was very, very willing to be convinced that they could marry and share a future together. Indeed, there was nothing she wanted more but at the same time she did not want Rafaello opting for that choice solely on the basis that she was carrying his child. 'I can't really agree that we don't have any other choice. I just think I need to hear you

give me some reasons *why* you think you should marry
me—'

'We're in a bloody tight corner!'

Glory was bitterly disappointed by that response. He was
gorgeous, he was clever, he was impatient to do 'the right
thing' about two decades after so many men had abandoned
such moral niceties, but being in a very tight corner was
not the kind of reason she so much needed to hear. Were
he to say that he still found her madly attractive or even
fun company, she would be happily convinced that their
marriage would have a chance of success. But then, possibly he did not think or feel either of those things and her
being pregnant was truly his *only* motivation in proposing,
she conceded wretchedly.

'You want me to help you out, Rafaello? Babies have a
right to know who their father is—how about that?' Without the smallest warning, Sam's voice broke in on an aggressive rising note that froze both Glory and Rafaello into
stillness, for both of them had forgotten that the teenager
was in the apartment and neither had noticed that Rafaello
had neglected to close the door. 'Why don't you try that
one out on my sister? That reason would be a real good
laugh for a Grazzini!'

Glory barely had the time to absorb Sam's startling interruption before her brother launched himself off the
threshold and literally threw himself at Rafaello. As she
had never seen her easy-going brother even lose his temper
before, she could not credit the violence that just seemed
to explode from him. Sam hurling abusive swear words was
another new experience for her and she sat there, rigid with
shock at that physical assault, terrified that Rafaello might
lose his temper and fight back.

'Sam...please, *no*!' Glory pleaded brokenly, torn apart
by guilt at her brother's distress at what he had overheard.

'I trusted you!' Sam shouted at Rafaello. 'I thought you were different from your—'

'I *am*.' Breathing heavily as he finally got a restraining grip on Sam, Rafaello was strikingly pale beneath his bronzed complexion, his strong bone-structure hard-edged, his dark eyes mirroring the reality that Sam's aggression had shocked him every bit as much as it had shocked Glory. 'I was just being a smart-ass, Sam.' Forced to pin her struggling brother against the wall in an effort to cool him down, Rafaello was suddenly talking very fast. 'I *love* your sister...OK? I really do want to marry her!'

Sam's still furious dark gaze was nailed to Rafaello as if he was searching for the proof of those far-reaching reassurances. 'Glory doesn't need you *just* because she's having a baby...'

'No, but I need her,' Rafaello stated with hard conviction.

As Rafaello stepped back and released Sam, Glory could not look at either of them. She was aghast that her brother had overheard their conversation and horribly ashamed that her behaviour and her condition should have upset him to such an extent. Rafaello was equally shaken and naturally he had endeavoured to come up with the *only* sort of response likely to calm Sam down.

'You needn't think I'm apologising for trying to hit you either!' Sam hurled in a last burst of defiance in Rafaello's direction before he backed warily out of the room as though he was still waiting on some form of violent retaliation.

Sam left a silence in his wake that seemed endless.

'I'd better go and talk to him,' Glory muttered tightly.

'No, let him cool off for a while. He's too upset to handle either of us right now. Anyway, your father's waiting for you,' Rafaello reminded her, raking a not quite steady hand through his luxuriant black hair in a gesture that revealed just how shattered he still was by what had occurred. 'I think we need a special licence, *bella mia*—'

Glory squeezed her anguished eyes tight shut. 'Rafaello—'

'We've done enough damage. Sam's right. Every baby has a right to know who his father is,' Rafaello said with a quality of raw regret in his dark deep drawl that cut her sensitive soul to the bone.

And, on that note, he left her.

CHAPTER EIGHT

ARCHIE LITTLE had been moved out of the ICU into a private room.

Maud Belper was waiting outside that room with a troubled look on her face. 'Could I have a word with you before you go in, Glory?'

'Dad's all right, isn't he?'

'Yes, he's doing fine.' The older woman sighed. 'But Archie's taken it into his head that he must talk to you now. It's a lot to ask but, for *his* sake, could you try to stay calm whatever he tells you? He's still very weak.'

Glory stared at her and then nodded, her colour heightening. No matter how hard she tried not to, she resented Maud's interference. She also felt uneasy about the obvious fact that the other woman was already acquainted with what her father wished to discuss with her. In the awkward silence, however, a sudden rueful smile of comprehension flashed across Glory's face and she leant forward and gave the older woman an impulsive hug.

'*Of course*, we haven't yet discussed the fact that you and Dad are going to get married! I'm really pleased for you both. I'm not saying I wasn't a bit taken aback when I first heard,' Glory admitted with her usual frankness. 'But when I saw you and Dad together, and realised just how much you care for each other, I was truly happy for him.'

'You're a dear girl.' In spite of her answering warmth, Maud's tension remained undiminished 'But I can't let you go in there thinking that that's what Archie wants to get off his chest. It's not.'

Glory had no time for mysteries and she had not forgotten Maud's cryptic remarks that night at Montague Park three months earlier. Was the older woman one of those personalities who revelled in making mountains out of molehills and who enjoyed uttering dire hints and warnings? Embarrassed by that suspicion, Glory hurried into her father's room before her future stepmother could say anything more.

Archie Little looked so much better with a little colour in his cheeks. Settling down into the seat by the bed, she smiled at him. 'You're looking good, Dad.'

'I had to see you and get this over with.' Her father released a troubled sigh. 'But I know that what I have to tell you is going to upset you—'

Get what over with? Glory wanted to question, but instead she cradled his hand where it lay on the bedspread between both of hers and tried to soothe him. 'I'm not that easily upset.'

'It's about Sam. Sam...well, Sam's not mine,' her father said haltingly.

Glory kept her widened gaze focused on his anxious expression, convinced she must have misheard him, and then she said uncertainly, 'You mean...Sam's adopted?'

'No. Your mother...' The older man grimaced. 'She got mixed up with another man—'

'You're pulling my leg,' Glory told him in a teasing tone of disbelief. '*Mum*...with another man?'

'You were only a kid of seven when Sam was born,' Archie reminded his daughter heavily. 'For a long time after that your mum and I lived like strangers.'

Even as he said that, Glory's memory was stirred. Only at that prompting did she recall that her mother had shared her bedroom for a while when she was around that age. Her parents had been sleeping apart, she realised in dismay, shaken that until that moment it had never occurred to her to put that knowledge into its adult context and question what that separation had meant. Her tummy muscles clenched. 'But you and Mum were happy,' she heard herself say as if she was still that young child and begging for reassurance. 'I remember you being happy—'

'Later we were again. But Sam is Benito Grazzini's kid and Rafaello's half-brother,' her father framed, tiredness and stress visible now in his lined features. 'I never would have told you, Glory. I didn't want to tell you. I didn't want to hurt you or spoil your memories of Talitha.'

'It's all right...' Glory managed to say but she had to release his fingers because her own hands were trembling.

No, it could not be true. How could her mother, who had preached purity to her own daughter for so many years, have engaged in an adulterous affair? Worse still, given birth to her lover's child? Her mother and Benito Grazzini? Sheer madness! Where had her poor father picked up this crazy story? Was it in his own head? Something to do with the surgery? Was he getting all confused about people and mixed up about the past?

'I forgave her but she never got over the guilt or the fear of you or Sam finding out,' the older man muttered heavily. 'It was one of those things that nobody could've stopped. I was there the first time Benito Grazzini saw her at an estate party. He and your mum...they couldn't take their eyes off each other and that was the start. It went on all that winter.'

Glory was now straining to catch every word and her refusal to credit what she was being told was being challenged. What was it Maud had said to her that night at Montague Park on the subject of how Archie Little would feel about his daughter being involved with Rafaello? 'You're getting into a situation you don't really understand.' She shivered, chilled inside and out. If Benito Grazzini had fathered Sam it meant that her brother was Rafaello's brother too. Was it possible? She did not *want* it to be possible.

'I'm sorry, Glory. I've not been fair to you either.'

'How?'

'When Benito Grazzini made you give up Rafaello when you were eighteen I was pleased because I didn't want the two of you getting together either.'

There was a horrible ring of truth to her father's discomfited admission.

'But how could you bear to keep on working for Benito Grazzini?' Glory asked, struggling to keep her mounting incredulity out of her voice.

'Because I won. I kept your mother,' Archie Little muttered with a rich satisfaction that seemed undimmed by the passage of years. 'He did everything he could to take her away from me but he *lost*!'

Glory blinked at that most unexpected conclusion. She was in so much shock at what she had learned that she simply sat there, staring into space. When she finally parted her lips to speak again she discovered that she had waited too long to do so, for her father had fallen asleep. As it was unthinkable to wake him up and bother him with further questions on such an issue, she lurched out of his room on legs that were wobbling. Maud was waiting outside.

'Dad's asleep...quite happy,' Glory told her stiltedly. 'You knew, you *knew* all along, didn't you?'

'I didn't know for sure about Sam until your father told me this year. But yes, I knew about the rest,' the older woman confirmed wryly, guiding Glory into the greater privacy of the waiting room. 'I've worked at the Park for the best part of thirty years and I've not missed much of what went on there.'

Glory was still in a shattered state of nerves. 'How could Mum *do* that to Dad?'

'I don't think she meant to hurt anybody—'

'He was a married man,' Glory muttered in a shaking undertone. 'And she was married to Dad...'

'I reckon they both paid a steep price for what they did,' Maud sighed. 'Anyway, your mother came to her senses

when she fell pregnant. She told Mr Benito to get lost and
that was that.'

'Was it? Dad had to bring up another man's child.' Try
as Glory could, she could not square the memories of the
mother she had loved with the woman who had irrespon-
sibly indulged in an affair that had damaged her marriage,
her husband and the whole future of the son she had
brought into the world.

'That was Archie's decision. He adored your mother. He
felt he'd come off all right.'

'I've been so slow to catch on,' Glory mumbled, momentarily closing her eyes as if willing herself to get a grip
on a brain that was shooting in too many directions at once
and throwing up far too many different thoughts. 'Rafaello
knows Sam is his brother—'

'Sam knows too, Glory. When Archie realised that Mr
Benito had told *his* son, he decided that he had to tell Sam
the truth as well—'

'Everybody knew but me,' Glory whispered thickly. 'I
think Rafaello found out that night I was at the Park. His
father came to see him—'

'He wouldn't have had much choice. When Rafaello told
his dad that Sam Little had been charged with theft it
must've put Mr Benito in quite a sweat. So he finally
owned up.'

The more the ramifications of what she had learned sank
in, the more distraught Glory could feel herself becoming.
Parting from the older woman with an embarrassed apology, she left the hospital.

Everything was falling into place for Glory but she
shrank from the picture that was emerging. In all likelihood,
Rafaello had had a flaming row with his father that evening.
He must have been as shocked by the revelation as she was
now but he hadn't breathed a word to her, had he? No, he
had packed her off back to Birmingham, ensuring that she
remained ignorant of that secret connection between her

family and his own. Then he had gone down to the gardener's cottage to take a closer look at the brother he had never known he had and had stayed until after midnight...

In fact, the sole point Rafaello had in his favour was that he evidently did want to acknowledge and form a family connection with Sam. Or *did* he? Perhaps events had got out of his control and her own father had accidentally forced that issue by finally telling Sam the truth about his parentage. Once that cat had come out of the bag, there had been no putting it back. No wonder Sam was in such a volatile frame of mind. Yet Sam had also been showing every sign of being delighted by the discovery that he had an older half-brother. As opposed to a sister? A *half-sister*, Glory acknowledged reluctantly, liking even less a distinction that diminished the blood ties between herself and the brother she loved. Was that why Sam had more or less treated Glory like the invisible woman since her return? Stung by that hurtful reality, which she had tried to ignore until that moment, Glory splurged on taking a cab ride back to Rafaello's apartment.

What seemed like the ultimate betrayal finally struck her. Even knowing that there was no way on earth that he could possibly prosecute his own brother, Rafaello had *still* held Glory to the deal they had made. He had still swept her off to Corfu to become his mistress. Not once had he been tempted or even shamed into telling her that her little brother was also his little brother!

But only as Glory made it into the lift in Rafaello's apartment block did she make what was for her the most distressing connection of all. No longer did she need to wonder why Rafaello had been so quick to offer marriage even in advance of discovering that she was pregnant! Regardless of his own feelings, there was a family dimension to be considered now. It was bad enough that their respective parents had had an affair and that Sam should have been the result, but the fallout from Rafaello's getting

Glory into the same condition would be all the greater precisely *because* of that background. Sam had been quick to
think the worst and Archie Little would be equally sensitive. The mere suggestion that Rafaello was treating an expectant Glory with anything less than respect would be sufficient to create an all-out war of loathing and resentment
where the men in her family was concerned.

As Glory entered the penthouse Rafaello strode out into
the hall to greet her. The sheer effect of his stunning dark
good looks combined with his lithe, powerful physique hit
Glory really hard. He was just so gorgeous. She was out
of her league, *way* out of her league and always had been
with him. The instant he had mentioned marriage she
should've realised that there was something strange going
on. Entrapment? He hadn't been joking. A terrible sense of
pain and rejection filled her and she blanked him out, fighting to retain control of her seething emotions, but all the
time the anger inside her was rocketing.

'Where's Sam?' she demanded, stalking past him into
the contemporary lounge. 'I want to talk to him in private.'

'I'm afraid he's gone—'

'I beg your pardon?' Taken aback, Glory spun round.

'Sam has opted to go and stay with his friend Joe's family for the next few days—'

'And you just let him walk out of here in the mood he
was in?' Glory prompted in disbelief.

'Sam's already missed the first week of the new school
term,' Rafaello pointed out levelly. 'He discussed his plans
with your father this morning. Sam will be fine, Glory.'

'I just bet you wanted him gone before I got back!' Glory
launched at him furiously.

'Now, what has put you in this mood?' Rafaello mused,
shrugging back his wide shoulders and viewing her with
enquiring dark golden eyes.

'Can't you guess?' Glory flung him a livid look and she
was so mad, so worked up, she couldn't stay still and she

walked all the way over to the window before spinning back again. 'Why didn't you tell me that your lousy father seduced my mother and just about wrecked my parents' marriage?'

Rafaello stilled, spiky black lashes semi-screening his keen gaze. 'So you *know*—'

'No thanks to you!' Glory snapped, outraged by that almost calm reaction to a revelation that had virtually torn her apart. 'Just when were you planning to tell me that Sam has rotten Grazzini genes in him?'

Rafaello's gaze shimmered and then flashed. 'Cut it out, *bella mia*…or I might just hit back.'

'I'm not afraid of anything you could have to say. In every way possible your father has caused enormous distress to my family!' Glory condemned.

'My mother had a nervous breakdown when I was thirteen. I never knew why until I found out about Sam three months ago,' Rafaello admitted, shocking Glory into silence. 'She was a very reserved woman. She tried to pretend the affair wasn't happening, but when my father confessed that there was going to be a child she fell apart. Did you imagine that wealth and position protected my mother from being as hurt as your father was?'

'I never thought about her…maybe because I don't ever remember seeing her.' A hectic flush on her cheeks, Glory was momentarily ashamed of the way she had tried to hurl blame without appreciating that, one way or another, everybody involved had suffered. But conceding that point in no way lessened the bitter sense of betrayal she felt.

'My mother never returned to Montague Park and Benito admitted that, but for Sam's existence, he would have sold the estate. Let's face it, between them, my father and your mother made a hellish mess but the only real victim now is Sam,' Rafaello murmured flatly. 'My father always knew that Sam was his son. However, he had *no* idea that Archie knew as well, so he had no choice but to keep his distance.'

'I guess not,' Glory was forced to admit.

'Now that the truth is out, Benito very much wants to get to know Sam,' Rafaello admitted. 'But Sam needs time to adjust to that idea.'

Rafaello had given Glory another shock and one she could have done without. Benito Grazzini wanted to get to know his illegitimate son? Why did the obvious always have to be spelt out to her? For here was yet another powerful reason why Rafaello *had* to marry her. If Rafaello didn't marry her, his father could kiss goodbye to any hope of Sam's warming to him in the foreseeable future. Devastated by that further realisation, Glory tried to shut it out again because she shrank from the challenge of speaking such humiliating thoughts out loud.

Her lovely face tight and pale, her anguished eyes screened, she said hoarsely, 'You found out the truth about Sam that night I was with you but you didn't *tell* me—'

'How could I tell you? At that stage, I believed your father didn't know he'd been raising another man's son,' Rafaello countered in blunt exasperation. 'However, Archie disabused me of that idea the minute Sam went up to bed that evening. He said that, although he might've been willing to tell Sam the truth, he couldn't do it because he didn't want *you* to know that your mother had had an affair!'

'You still should have told me,' Glory retorted stubbornly.

'It wasn't my secret. To be honest, I didn't think your father would *ever* tell Sam, so it would have been wrong for me to interfere,' Rafaello stated with immovable conviction. 'But while we were in Greece Archie decided that if my father could tell me that Sam was my brother then Sam had the right to the same information.'

'But I was *still* left out of it, even by my own family,' Glory said bitterly, struggling to hide her hurt.

'It's not exactly the kind of news people want to break on the phone.'

'And it's certainly not the sort of news *you* were likely to share when you were using Sam and those theft charges to make me agree to become your mistress!' Glory flung back in fierce condemnation.

Rafaello threw back his arrogant dark head and stood his ground in silence.

'Even knowing that there was *no* way on earth you would have let those charges stand against your own half-brother, you went ahead and dragged me into bed!' Glory continued in a rising crescendo. 'How low can a guy sink?'

'If he wants a woman as much as I wanted you... probably even lower,' Rafaello conceded with disconcerting frankness, brilliant dark eyes bleak, hard jawline clenched. 'I am not proud of what I did, *cara*.'

'That didn't stop you, though, did it?'

Pale beneath his bronzed skin, lean, powerful face taut, Rafaello surveyed her steadily. 'I got pretty much what I asked for. You walked out on me again—'

'*You* were about to dump *me*—'

'No, I wasn't,' Rafaello stated.

'Why are you lying about it?' Glory shot at him shrilly. 'You think my being pregnant means you can't be honest any more?'

'No...' Rafaello responded. 'I think your being pregnant means that I'm not going to fight with you. It can't be good for the baby.'

Off-balanced by what struck her as a shockingly smooth and devious sidestepping of the major issues she was striving to confront him with, Glory experienced such a surge of unfettered rage that she felt light-headed. 'Just you leave my baby out of it—'

'It's my baby too—'

Her teeth gritted on that unarguable point. 'You used me in Corfu—'

His expressive jawline took on a more aggressive slant,

his dark eyes suddenly flaring gold. 'Don't you dare try to tell me that you didn't want me. Don't you *dare*.'

'Is that how you excused yourself?' Glory was impervious to that warning intonation and accelerating tension in the air.

'You were the one who needed the excuse. I won't let our parents' mistakes tear *us* apart—'

'How did *I* need an excuse?' The atmosphere was humming, setting up a chain reaction in Glory's own trembling length.

Rafaello strolled closer, all dominant male, all confident threat. 'An excuse to enjoy the passion,' he drawled soft and low and insolent as all get-out. 'I gave you that excuse, that outlet, that freedom. As long as you could blame me for forcing you into that arrangement, you didn't have to feel guilty. You were no unwilling mistress!'

Outmatched by that demanding reminder of her own weakness, Glory turned scarlet, unable to think of anything to hurl back which would not be an outright lie. Infuriated and embarrassed, she tried to brush past him but Rafaello caught her to him. Trapping her struggling slim body into the unyielding strength of his hard, muscular frame, he crushed her mouth beneath his with passionate force. Sensual shock lanced through Glory in a debilitating wave. In the midst of her raging turmoil she felt her own desperate hunger for that physical connection pulling at her with talon claws, but she fought it.

'Don't do this to us,' Rafaello lifted his dark head to demand in ragged appeal. 'Don't make me so mad that I'll say things that will hurt you, *bella mia*.'

Encountering the blaze of those smouldering golden eyes, reacting to that disconcerting note of masculine urgency, Glory was mesmerised into stillness. It was as if he pressed a magic button and the rage went out of her. She quivered, shifting inexorably into closer contact. The magnetic attraction of that lean, powerful physique of his

against her own softer feminine curves was immense. She
was madly aware of the hard contours of bone and sinew
beneath the formal business suit, and the thrusting promise
of his undeniable arousal. Between one breath and the next
she was lost to temptation, all resistance beaten down by
the answering ache of her breasts and the moist heat stirring
between her thighs.

'Rafaello…' she muttered in desperation, fighting to call
a halt to her own susceptibility.

Rafaello dealt her a scorching smile and hoisted her up
into his arms without another word. He carried her out of
the lounge. You can't do this, you *mustn't* do this, cried
her conscience on a frantic note. But she ignored that inner
voice, pushed her face into a wide, solid shoulder, letting
her nostrils flare on the familiar scent of him, feeling every
skin-cell she possessed switching onto a higher frequency
in response. He laid her down on a bed in an unfamiliar
room and plucked off her shoes. Straightening with easy
grace, he removed his jacket and tossed it aside.

Glory sat up, flushed and stiff. 'We were fighting—'

'This beats the hell out of fighting, *amore mia*,' Rafaello
pointed out with husky conviction.

Her hands were shaking and she wound them round her
upraised knees while she fought to find the strength to get
back off the bed again, reinstate control and common sense.
But her defences weren't working, weren't there to call
upon. Her whole world had begun to cave in around her
when her father had started speaking a couple of hours
earlier. The bricks and mortar of her childhood stability had
taken a heavy hit. Little memories were still sneaking up
out of her subconscious and striking hard: the phone con-
stantly ringing but never answered, her mother taking it off
the hook, pacing the floor, back and forth in tortured circles,
hands knotted as if she was praying, tears running down
her face as she shooed her curious little daughter into the

kitchen and suggested she set the table for supper. A woman fighting temptation, a woman craving the man she loved but denying herself. And just as Talitha Little had loved Benito Grazzini, Glory loved his son.

'Forget them...forget *all* of it,' Rafaello urged with angry impatience as if he was attuned to her very thoughts.

But how could she forget when that was *why* he would marry her? Then would she rather do without him? Would pride be any consolation when she denied herself what she most wanted? Rafaello on any terms. Any way she could have him, she conceded painfully, recalling those wanton weeks on Corfu. Any excuse. He knew that but she was only now facing that same fact that pride had a lesser hold on her than he had.

She connected with his blazing golden eyes, sensing his anger, his frustration and mercifully his desire. Desire was there in the smouldering caress of his gaze as it roved over her, lingering on her full mouth, the pouting thrust of her breasts beneath her buttoned cotton top. Even without the fancy frills of the right make-up and the right clothes, he was hungry for her.

'I am so hot for you, I am burning up,' Rafaello growled, throwing his shirt aside, exposing the hard hair-roughened expanse of his muscular torso and the hard bronze slab of his flat stomach.

'Yes.' Acknowledgement escaped Glory's already parted lips in a sighing breath for she was melting just watching him strip. Total weakness, total lack of resistance, that was what she was feeling and it was running through her like a burst dam of susceptibility. With hands that were all thumbs she began to pull at the pearlised buttons on her top. Then, losing patience, she tugged it over her head and emerged in time to see him strip off his boxer shorts. She caught her breath and her mouth ran dry at the potent virile proof of his male hunger for her.

Arrested bright blue eyes pinned to him, Rafaello padded over to the bed and reached for her. He took about five seconds to extract her from her combat trousers. Kneeling on the bed, he pulled her to him and let his tongue slide once, twice into the moist depths of her mouth in an erotic penetration that sent the blood thundering through her veins in helpless response and left her trembling.

'You're so sexy,' she whispered unevenly.

'And you have the most divine body I've ever seen,' Rafaello husked, depriving her of her bra, freeing the ripe swell of her breasts from confinement, shaping his hands to her burgeoning curves with near reverent care.

Is that *all*? she almost asked, needing to be so much more, but that pained thought was as quickly lost in the rush of pleasure induced by his caressing fingers brushing over her distended pink nipples. The sensation was so intense as to be almost unbearable and she shut her eyes in embarrassment as a moan escaped her.

'You're even more sensitive now, *amore mia*,' Rafaello murmured thickly, impatient hands dispensing with her panties and then rearranging her so that she lay fully exposed to his plundering gaze.

In dismay she opened her eyes wide, and she moved her arms to cross them protectively over herself. He caught her hands in his and settled them back either side of her. 'Rafaello!' she gasped strickenly, painfully aware of her changing shape, needing and wanting to conceal those alterations from too close a scrutiny.

'*Dio mio*...you excite the hell out of me,' Rafaello ground out, raw appreciation in the fascinated appraisal he dealt her prone figure, releasing one of her wrists to run a satisfied hand over the slight swell of her stomach and splay his long fingers possessively there. 'Those Grazzini genes you insulted are inside you, part of me, part of you—'

'Pushy genes,' Glory mumbled, not really knowing what to say because his attitude had taken her by surprise.

Rafaello dealt her a scorching smile that sent her vulnerable heart racing. 'Strong and assertive, *cara mia*,' he countered with amused agreement.

He really *did* want their baby. For the first time she recognised that reality and, even as relief coursed through her, it brought pain in its wake; for his warmth seemed directed at the child she carried, rather than at her. His child lay at the very heart of his wish to marry her. So when he kissed her there were tears in her eyes, but when he touched her quivering body she could no longer retain such thoughts. Indeed, she was all the more eager to forget and find the only true oblivion she had ever known.

Excitement took her in a fiery rush as he found the throbbing peaks of her breasts, lowered his proud, dark head and tasted the swollen buds, laving them with his tongue, delicately grazing them with his teeth. He was setting her on fire, rousing a tight aching feeling deep in her pelvis, making her gasp at the slow-burn effect of his knowing touch on a body too long starved of sensation.

'I do want you...I *always* want you!' she moaned in sudden shame at her inability to control the wild hunger he had ignited.

Rafaello leant over her like a dark avenging hero, hot golden eyes flaming over her, primal satisfaction emanating from every hard angle of his darkly handsome features. 'And all I want to do is torture you with pleasure until you beg...'

Shock momentarily stilled the upward rise of her hips, the squirming invitation she could not prevent that close to his lean, powerful frame. Rafaello claimed a devouring kiss from her swollen lips, sending an electrifying current through her sensitised body, and gazed down at her again, connecting with the bewilderment in her passion-glazed eyes. 'And beg...and beg...until you're enslaved, *amore mia.*'

Glory tried and failed to swallow, staring up at him like a rabbit caught in car headlights, certain of destruction but hypnotised. 'S-sorry?'

Rafaello ran an expert hand down over her quivering length to the very heart of her, where she ached for the merest hint of a touch, and her entire body rose in an eager movement as unstoppable as a tidal wave. Something akin to anger burned in his intent scrutiny as he watched her respond helplessly to that provocative power-play. 'I was a bloody fool when you were eighteen. I should have taken you to bed. I don't believe that anything could have parted us then!'

'R-Rafaello...?' Glory was startled by the angry regret and bitterness that he made no attempt to hide from her.

'But we're together now, *amore*,' Rafaello growled, capturing her mouth again and shifting a hair-roughened thigh over her to hold her captive.

'I love you...' she gasped, lost in the tormenting hunger he had ignited.

Rafaello tensed and then vented a harsh laugh, scanning her with blistering golden eyes that emanated anger like a forcefield. 'If you say that *one* more time I'm walking out on you forever!'

Glory stared up at him, utterly intimidated by that threat. She could feel the tears of rejection welling up. With a roughened imprecation in Italian he curved his hands to her cheekbones and he followed the track of one salty tear with his lips in a disorientatingly tender salutation that bemused her even more. 'It's OK...' he soothed not quite levelly. 'Really, it's OK...'

All shaken up, she lay there quivering under him, scared to speak, scared to do anything in case it was the wrong thing. It was as if her whole life was up for grabs, there to be lost or gained on a single shake of the dice, for that was what *he* meant to her. In Corfu, when she had been without him, every day had stretched like an endless grey sea in front of her, empty and without colour.

He kissed her breathless and she clung to him, her own need surging higher than ever, instantly recalled, instantly reawakened. He teased the most sensitive spot in her entire body until she cried out, wanting more, driven by impulses much stronger than she was and a need that was more than she could bear. He shifted in a lithe rearrangement and employed his expert mouth on her instead.

From that point on, thought was too great a challenge and she was enslaved by her own frantic, feverish responses, her hands twisting through the thick silk of his hair, helpless cries breaking from her throat. By the time he rose over her, settled his long, muscular frame between her spread thighs, excitement had deprived her of all control. He entered her with a sure, forceful thrust and sent her spinning into a convulsive climax. Out of her senses with that sudden, shocking overload of pleasure, she cried out his name at the peak of ecstasy.

'And now you do that again, *cara*,' Rafaello instructed thickly as she came drifting back down in a sensual daze into her own body again.

'Again…' Glory echoed, 'I can't—'

'You *can*.' He surged deeper into her again, all virile male and hungry dominance. Her tender flesh was so sensitive she moaned out loud. The raw excitement snatched her up again, her heart thundering in her ears as he drove her back into the grip of pure, mindless pleasure where nothing mattered but that he not stop, where all that guided her was her own overwhelming need. And, without feeling she had anything to do with the development, she hit another shattering climax that totally wiped her out.

*　　*　　*

Glory stirred and lifted heavy eyelids to focus on the bed-side light burning at what appeared to be a very low setting.

Never quick to regain her wits on first wakening, she lost a minute or two computing the fact that she had never seen that particular lamp before. She was in Rafaello's bedroom in his penthouse apartment. The recollection of their pas-sionate lovemaking made her face burn, but she turned cold again almost as quickly as she recalled the angry, bitter frustration he had revealed and the manner in which he had rejected her impulsive declaration of love.

Rafaello felt trapped. Of course he did. Her gabbling like some dizzy teenager about love probably made him feel even more trapped, she thought wretchedly. He might still find her attractive and he might want their baby to have a father, but that was a long way from wanting to *marry* her. But what other choice did he have? If Benito Grazzini was so keen to establish a relationship with Sam, relations be-tween their families would have to be good and smooth. Glory's being pregnant by Rafaello and unmarried would make relations exceedingly rocky.

The sound of a door opening startled her. She rolled over to see Rafaello emerging from the bathroom. He was freshly shaven but with his hair still damp from the shower, and his sheer masculine impact took her breath away. He was already dressed in a crisp cotton shirt and dark tailored trousers. His back to her, he paused in front of a dressing mirror to fix his tie, his bold bronzed profile taut, half in shadow, half in light.

'What time is it?' she whispered.

Rafaello tensed and only half-turned to flick her a glance. 'Almost seven. I was about to wake you. Marcel is making dinner for you—'

'Marcel?'

'My chef. He'll travel down to Montague Park with you

when you decide to leave town. He has instructions that you have to eat three times a day minimum—'

Glory eased herself up slowly and clutched the sheet as if she was cold. 'Where are *you* going?'

'I have urgent business in Rome tomorrow. My life's been on hold for the past week,' Rafaello reminded her. 'Unfortunately, Grazzini Industries doesn't run itself. On the way to the airport I'll call in with Archie to announce our nuptials—'

'Our...what?' Glory could feel the distance in him again and she was super-sensitive to that rather sardonic edge to his cool drawl.

'Our wedding. I applied for the special licence this afternoon and I've booked the church down at the Park for ten days from now—'

'Ten...days?' Glory parroted in shock and then she pinned her lips shut again, for she had no desire to argue on that timing.

'The sooner we're married the better. I spoke to your father's consultant earlier as well,' Rafaello revealed, reaching for his jacket and swinging round to face her. 'By the time I get back from abroad, Archie should be up to attending our wedding in a wheelchair at least.'

'But I haven't even said I'll marry you yet...' Glory believed he ought to take note of that point and hoped it would puncture his cool.

'I rather took agreement for granted, *cara mia*.' Rafaello focused on the tumbled bedsheets with suggestive intensity before skimming his glittering dark gaze back up to her hotly flushed face. 'But, of course, if you're willing to watch World War Three break out between our families, go ahead and turn me down. This is one decision you have to make on your own.'

The silence simmered. Her tummy flipped. He was hitting her on her weakest flank. Love and hatred twinned inside her. 'You *know* I'm not going to turn you down.'

In an abrupt movement he swung away from her again, his jawline set at an aggressive angle as he made what seemed to her a quite unnecessary further adjustment to the knot on his silk tie. 'Do I?'

'Just tell me…what do you get out of marrying me?' Glory asked tightly.

'Great sex and a baby. As long as you leave the love stuff out of it,' Rafaello drawled with cutting clarity, 'I'll have no complaints.'

At that reminder, she flinched.

'Jon will be in touch with you about the wedding arrangements,' he continued. 'He'll sort out the caterers et cetera. All you have to do is buy something brilliant white and float down the aisle in it looking like an angel—'

'I can't wear white in *this* condition!'

Rafaello rested exasperated dark golden eyes on her. 'I want to see you in white…OK? Your father's a conventional man. I was planning to save the news that his first grandchild is on the way until he's feeling rather more resilient. As he's not even aware that we've been seeing each other, I should think the announcement that we're getting hitched is quite enough for the moment.'

Slowly, grudgingly she nodded in receipt of that argument. 'You have a point.'

'I also want you to move into the Park itself once you feel you can leave your father to Maud's devoted care,' Rafaello delivered.

Glory glanced at him in dismay. 'Not *before* the wedding—'

'The cottage hasn't been your home in five years, and if you can lure Sam under the same roof it might make breaking the ice between Sam and Benito easier when the time comes.'

'When is that time coming?'

'When and if Sam agrees, not before,' Rafaello told her levelly. 'My father would be over here right now if he thought Sam would be willing to meet him but he knows he has to be patient.'

And then what? But she turned her troubled thoughts back to her own problems. So, regardless of how Rafaello felt about her, she was still going to marry him, wasn't she? Coward, you spineless coward, piped up the voice of her subconscious. What he had said to her in bed, about sex on their very first date being more her style than the candlelit dinner he had romanced her over, would haunt her forever more. She shuddered. That was what Rafaello *really* thought of her. A sexy wanton with few sensibilities and even fewer morals. All right for slaking his high sex drive on, all right as an incubator for the next Grazzini but not much use for anything else.

'Well, it must give you a real kick to think that the mother of your child and your future wife is a greedy, gold-digging little tart,' Glory said grittily.

Not unnaturally, she took Rafaello entirely by surprise with that out-of-the-blue attack. He stared at her, brilliant eyes dead-level and serious. 'I *don't* think that.'

'No?' Glory widened her bright blue gaze, steeling herself to go a step further. 'Then you now accept that your precious father blackmailed me into leaving you five years ago—'

'If I thought that, I'd probably kill him,' Rafaello murmured without hesitation. 'But I don't think it or accept it, and as for the rest of it...' A rather bleak laugh fell from his lips. 'I know money's not that important to you. I got that message in Corfu.'

Reminding her that he wanted to call in with her father before he headed for the airport, he left without fanfare and she sat there, staring at the space where he had been, thinking that no matter how much she loved him she would never, ever understand what went on in that dark, complex head of his. Why did the man who was about to marry her look almost regretful when he agreed that she was not mercenary? Why did he react to the word 'love' as if it was a term of abuse?

CHAPTER NINE

'JOE thinks that finding out I'm an illegit Grazzini is on a par with winning the National Lottery!' Sam said, tight-mouthed with discomfiture.

It was Glory's first meeting with Sam since he had left London, and from the instant of his arrival she had been unsettled by her kid brother's likeness to Rafaello. The more she studied Sam, the more amazed she became that she had never once noticed the resemblance between man and boy. That black hair, those dark, deep-set, dramatic eyes. Her mother had never been that dark. The sculpted cheekbones and the newly aggressive tilt of Sam's jaw were pure Grazzini. How could she have been so blind to what was staring her in the face?

'I mean, *look* at all this stuff!' Sam spread a censorious and uneasy glance over their surroundings. They were in the rear sitting room at Montague Park, one of the less opulent rooms but still much too grand in her brother's estimation. 'Like I said to Rafaello, living like royalty is not about to go out of style with the Grazzinis around. Take that snuff box...sixty grand, and there's homeless people starving on the streets!'

Glory could not feel that Rafaello, a capitalist to the backbone, could have much enjoyed that particular lecture. 'You can knock what they've got and how they live but don't forget that Grazzini money saved Dad's life.'

'Of course, I appreciate that.' Sam kicked at the tassle fringing on a nearby chair before stuffing his equally restive hands into the pockets of his jeans and turning away. 'But I can't think of him as "Dad" any more. He said it would be OK to call him Archie if I wanted to—'

'Oh...*Sam*!' Glory was dismayed by the thought of how much that request must have hurt the older man. 'He's acted as your father for sixteen years. Isn't that worth something?'

'Yeah, but he's never loved me like he loved you. No, don't you argue about that because it's true and you can hardly blame him for feeling that way,' Sam warned her with sudden force, flipping back to face her, dark eyes full of a pain that saddened her. 'I grew up knowing I *wasn't* the son Archie Little wanted. Why do you think I play all that sport when I hate it? Only to be what *he* thought I should be. Have you any idea what it's like having it dinned into you that five generations of Littles have been gardeners here?'

Glory swallowed back impulsive words in her father's defence. Sam had to talk to someone and she was grateful that he was willing to discuss his feelings with her. Arguing with his every statement would only silence him.

Sam breathed in deep and then shrugged. 'Do you know what my first thought was when Archie told me I wasn't his kid?'

Glory shook her head.

'Thank God I don't *have* to be a gardener...can you believe I was *that* superficial?'

Glory was concealing her steadily growing shock at what she was hearing. The quiet and affectionate but always reserved eleven-year-old boy she had believed she knew so well five years earlier had turned into a young man she needed to get to know all over again.

'I was a misfit. Even Mum...' Sam muttered uncomfortably. 'Always telling me only sissies want to sit drawing pictures all the time! Narrow people with narrow minds.'

Glory paled and bit her lip. 'Sam...*please* don't talk like that—'

'You were bright enough to stay on at school and they made you leave and take a rubbish job because that was

our place in life. Bottom of the pile and no room for ambition or imagination,' Sam shot at her with angry resentment. 'If you must know, it was a relief to find out I wasn't
a Little!'

'Yes,' Glory conceded because she could truly see it had
been for him. Those Grazzini genes, those strong and assertive Grazzini genes had been buzzing about below Sam's
deceptively tranquil surface just waiting for the opportunity
and the freedom to erupt. He was clever and he was deep
and he had loathed that yoke of low expectations.

'Only problem is...' Sam gave her a rueful lopsided
smile that tugged at her heartstrings. '...I'm not sure I'm
up to the challenge of being even an illegit Grazzini—'

'You only need to be yourself.' Glory gave him a supportive hug and sighed. 'I love you loads, Sam. I just want
you to be at peace with yourself and happy again—'

'No teenager would ever admit to being happy, Glory,'
Sam mocked. 'Look, I've got a stack of work to do for my
art project. Show me where I'm to kip and I'll get on with
it and see you later.'

She was delighted that he was staying the night without
argument. When Joe's father had dropped him off Sam had
set his suitcase prominently by the front door and indicated
extreme unwillingness to take up residence under the same
roof as her.

Her brother followed her upstairs and then, steps slow-
ing, he drifted away from her on the landing, drawn by the
paintings lining the walls.

'Who's this?' Sam demanded, stopping dead in front of
a canvas of an elderly man.

'Could be one of your ancestors...but I haven't a clue.
Rafaello could tell you—'

'Yeah...but I bet this old guy was another super-
achieving Grazzini,' Sam grimaced and accompanied her
to the room she had selected for his hopeful occupation
earlier that day. 'I'm never going to fit in anywhere, Sis.

This lot are all money mad and into big business, and I want to be an artist.'

'Why shouldn't you fit?' Glory protested. 'At least the Grazzinis appreciate art.'

Looking thoughtful at that obvious point in their favour, Sam glanced at her. 'Glad you're putting Rafaello out of his misery by marrying him.'

'How do you mean?'

'I talk to him on the phone most days,' Sam admitted. 'I still feel bad that I went for him that day in London, because once he explained how things had *been* with you two—'

'He did...what?' Glory folded her arms and surveyed her brother with a martial glint in her enquiring eyes.

'Glory...you've really given Rafaello the run-around. Be honest about it,' Sam urged. 'Of course the guy's insecure. You keep on ditching him. He's not even sure he can depend on you to show up at the church on Friday!'

'Is that a fact?' Glory absorbed this very different viewpoint of her past history with Rafaello with some difficulty.

'Why else did he suggest I should move in here if not so that if you took some crazy notion of legging it before the wedding I could warn him?'

Glory walked slowly downstairs again. Rafaello, afraid that she might get cold feet? Her susceptible heart flowered as though the sun had come out to warm it. Rafaello had been abroad for a solid week and she had left London only the evening before. He had flown from Rome to New York, where he seemed to be working eighteen-hour days. He called her most days but their conversations had been horribly impersonal. Furthermore, Rafaello had not referred to their wedding once since she had told him to mind his own business when he had asked her if she had bought a white dress. But oh, yes, Glory was eager to think that Rafaello might *care* enough about her to feel even a tiny bit insecure.

Then, as more rational thought kicked in, her face fell at dramatic speed. Of course, Rafaello *wasn't* insecure. But what a wonderfully devious and touching story he had dreamt up to persuade Sam to move even temporarily into Montague Park. Sam had until now been insisting that when he left Joe's house he wanted to return to the cottage even though it was currently empty. Yet in one easy move Rafaello had got their mutual brother beneath a Grazzini roof by lowering the macho front and asking for help and support that he didn't need!

Archie Little would not be released from hospital until the day before the wedding. Maud had stayed on in London by his side. Both her father and her future stepmother had accepted the early-retirement package that Rafaello had offered them. Not his idea either but Maud's. Rafaello had already thrown a team of workmen into a house in the village owned by the estate. A cosy home all on one floor. He was planning to sign it over to Archie and Maud when they married along with a small car. He was very generous, very thoughtful, Glory acknowledged, dashing tears from her eyes. She had to be the most spoilt woman in the world to think she could have love as well as passion, romance as well as kindness.

Here she was with a sheaf of gold credit cards, the ability to move between three different dwellings that she knew of and very possibly more, and he *was* gorgeous and she loved him to death. So what if he still believed she had sold him down the river for five thousand pounds when she was eighteen? He no longer seemed to care. And if he had been telling the truth when he had said that he would kill Benito if he believed her version of events was the correct one, well, there were enough family divisions without that development, weren't there?

Mopping her damp face with a tissue, she sat down with a maternity magazine to read articles about future motherhood that were now of absorbing interest to her. While she was scrutinising outrageously expensive but very cute items of baby apparel with dreaming eyes she heard the front door slam and then voices filtering in from the echoing hall. She stuffed the magazine behind a cushion because she was embarrassed about what had become a serious secret fix.

'*Santo cielo!*' thundered an intimidating masculine voice. 'I am Benito Grazzini. Are you trying to tell me that I am no longer welcome in my son's home?'

Glory's blood ran cold in her veins. Almost falling off the sofa in her haste, she raced over to the door to peer round it in horror. The new housekeeper, engaged by Jon Lyons, was striving to apologise and soothe. 'It's only that Mr Grazzini doesn't want Miss Little to be disturbed—'

'I'm not going to disturb her…I only want to *see* her!' Benito Grazzini growled, hoving into view like a big, burly silver-haired bear. 'Surely she's not in bed at this hour?'

Glory plastered herself up against the wall behind the door and stopped breathing. She did not even have to think about hiding—the urge came entirely naturally. So it was a further shock when the brief silence that fell was broken by yet another infinitely more familiar voice…Rafaello's, raised in anger. *Rafaello?* Where had Rafaello come from? At that moment, Glory did not care. As far as she was concerned, he was like the cavalry, riding to her rescue. She recovered the courage to peek round the door again. By that time, Rafaello and his father were exchanging staccato bursts of charged Italian in anything but a friendly way. The sight distressed her, for she knew how close they had been, and she had to intervene.

'Look…I don't know what all this is about but please stop it,' Glory pleaded anxiously, and in the abrupt silence that fell both men wheeled round to stare at her, wearing remarkably similar expressions of discomfiture. 'Sam's here and I'm sure you don't want him to hear you shouting at each other like that.'

'Are you kidding? This is as good as a soap opera. Family life in the raw, Grazzini-style!' Sam mocked from his vantage point halfway down the sweeping staircase, his attention fully lodged on the older man. But her brother was very pale, one hand gripping the bannister so tight she could see his knuckles gleaming white beneath his skin.

Sam must have been drawn by the racket. Glory almost groaned out loud, for she could not have pictured a worse way for Sam to meet his birth father for the first time.

'Just typical.' Rafaello shot his silenced parent an exasperated appraisal. 'You come in like a bull at a gate in spite of all my advice.'

'Don't be so pious. I'm finally getting a good look at my younger son for the first time in my life,' Benito said hoarsely, studying Sam where he stood with unashamed intensity and moving forward to address him direct. 'Always when I've seen you before I was afraid to stare in case I betrayed myself. I didn't even know you were here in this house. I came to talk to your sister this evening.'

Rafaello expelled his breath in an impatient hiss. 'I've already told you how I feel about that—'

'Your father can talk to me if he wants to,' Glory cut in. 'Anything's got to be better than all this bad feeling and awkwardness.'

'Yes, Rafaello.' Benito Grazzini backed her up. 'No need at all for you to fly home and come racing down here to protect Glory. We're all family now, or we will be by Friday, and we've got to mend fences as best we can. Come down and join us, Sam. But if you don't want to, that's all right too.'

'You talk even more than Rafaello does.' Sam surveyed his birth father with grudging fascination. 'It must be hard to get a word in edgeways.'

'Why do you think I shout?' Rafaello groaned, curving an arm round Glory's slight figure, and only then as he drew her back against him did she realise that she was trembling. 'Sorry, didn't know you were within hearing distance. I just didn't want Benito upsetting you, *cara*.'

One by one they all filed into the drawing room, where there was lots of space for people who might not want to be too close together. As soon as Glory had seated herself, Benito sank down on a sofa. Sam hovered way back by one of the windows and Rafaello took up what could only be described as a combative stance by the imposing fireplace. In his well-cut dark pinstripe suit, his black hair slightly tousled, his stunning eyes semi-screened by his lush black lashes above his smooth olive cheekbones, Glory really had to work hard at dredging her attention from him.

'So where and how do we start?' Benito enquired.

'I'd like to know the truth about you and Mum,' Glory told the older man, her strained gaze skimming over him fast and away again. 'She's gone and I can't ask her. But please be honest.'

'Are you out of your mind to be asking that?' Rafaello demanded.

'If I'd had the guts I'd have asked for her.' Sam sent his sister a wry glance of appreciation.

Benito squared his broad shoulders. 'Talitha and I both had what we thought were happy marriages. Then we met and discovered that there was more. She was the love of my life and with her I felt complete.'

'Are you serious?' Glory lifted her head to prompt, utterly taken aback by that speech.

The older man was watching Rafaello, whose shaken expression was revealing, and with a troubled frown he turned his attention back to Glory. 'We *did* love each other, and for a while the rest of the world just did not exist. We were very selfish and I can't pretend otherwise. When Talitha told me she was carrying my child I asked Rafaello's mother, Carina, for a divorce and perhaps only then did I appreciate how much pain I had already caused.'

'Oh…' Glory stole an anxious glance at Rafaello to see

how he was taking what appeared to be news to him as well. His father had been prepared to divorce his mother? Her heart went out to the man she loved when she saw his eyes veil and his strong bone-structure clench tight. 'I don't think we should talk about this. I was stupid even suggesting that we did—'

'No.' This time it was Rafaello who disagreed. 'I need to hear this too. I only wish I had heard the whole story three months sooner,' he told his father.

'You were too furious to listen. As I confessed to you then, Carina had a breakdown,' Benito said in weighted continuance, scrutinising the rug on the floor with fixed interest, guilt and grim regret emanating from him in waves. 'I can't even say I saw my duty then. It was Talitha who said we must finish, that we had no right to cause so much pain, that we each had children to consider…and, no matter how hard I tried to change her mind, she wouldn't see me or speak to me again.'

'Mum was like concrete when she made up her mind about anything,' Sam conceded in the strained silence that had fallen.

'You got ditched by a Little too,' Rafaello drawled in the most curious of tones, surveying his brooding parent with an air of surprise and sympathy.

'I thought you were a sleazebag who hit on my mother just for fun,' Sam told Benito in an embarrassed rush. 'But I can see it wasn't like that. You got hurt too.'

Benito rose upright and threw back his shoulders. Fixing his attention squarely on his eldest son, he said bluntly, 'Before I wear out my welcome I must admit to what I did to Glory five years ago—'

'Oh, never mind about that,' Glory broke in hastily, feeling that Rafaello had had a ghastly enough experience being forced to listen to how *his* mother, Carina, had only held on to Benito because *her* mother had ended their affair.

Rafaello pulled away from the fireplace, lean dark features taut, dark eyes glittering. '*I mind...*'

'You're getting into stuff that's nothing to do with me.' Sam spread an uneasy glance round his tense companions. 'I'll be down robbing the fridge if anyone wants me. I'm starving.'

Some of Benito's tension ebbed. 'Does Sam know?' he asked Glory.

'No, and I won't tell him.'

'You *did* threaten to sack Glory's father, didn't you?' Rafaello studied the older man with incredulous contempt. 'Glory's been telling the truth all along and you lied to me. *Why?*'

Benito grimaced. 'Your mother was still alive. I couldn't face your bringing Talitha's daughter home to meet Carina. She couldn't have coped with that. It was too close. There was the secrecy over Sam too. I was afraid of everything coming out and of Sam's home-life being wrecked...and I panicked.'

'What right did you have to visit your mistakes on *my* life?' Rafaello derided.

'None,' his father admitted heavily. 'But you and Glory had been dating such a short time, I thought that you'd soon forget each other. Obviously I was wrong on that score and probably I believed what it suited me to believe.'

'If I can't trust my own father, who *can* I trust?' Rafaello shot at him in complete disgust.

Benito was grey with strain. 'I'm sorry. I was afraid that you would turn against me if you found out about Talitha and Sam.'

As Benito walked heavily from the room Glory looked at Rafaello with pained eyes. 'Go after him. My father wasn't any keener on us dating back then. If I can forgive Benito, you can too. What are you so angry about anyway? You didn't exactly break your heart when we went our separate ways!'

'Do you think *all* Grazzinis wear their broken hearts on their sleeves?' Rafaello demanded with a bitterness that took her aback. 'My father destroyed our relationship. He lied to me about you and he threatened you...I could never forgive that!'

'Then think of Sam,' Glory told him in dismay. 'Sam relies on you and he trusts you. If you're at odds with Benito he's going to want to know why.'

'I am in no mood to overlook what we suffered through no fault of our own five years ago.' Rafaello framed each word with harsh, angry clarity. 'I *loved* you...I was devastated by what happened between us!'

Glory gazed back at him with very wide eyes. 'You...loved me? But you *smiled* at me when I said a clean break was the best idea—'

'The more I feel, the more I hide.' Brilliant dark eyes grim, Rafaello lifted his proud dark head high. 'Do you think I would have let you see that you were hurting me? You spoke as though we'd only been casual friends, behaved as though I had never meant *anything* to you—'

'I didn't know how else to behave.' Tears clogged Glory's response, for it savaged her to think that she had hurt him without even realising the fact and tore her apart to credit that he too had cared. 'I knew I loved you but we'd been together just a few weeks.'

'A few weeks was long enough. That night I delivered you home when you were sixteen, your mother actually warned me off,' Rafaello revealed, his wide sensual mouth twisting at the memory. 'As I was leaving I could not resist urging her not to be too hard on you and she saw through me—'

'Mum warned you off?' Glory exclaimed in astonishment.

'I didn't need the embargo. I didn't need to be told that you were too young for me when I had seen it for myself.

But your mother wanted to be sure that I knew that *she* knew I was interested in you even then—'

'You were thinking about me that far back...?' Glory was enchanted by that admission and she wound her fingers round his with a possessive confidence that she had never before felt with him. 'I used to hide behind trees and watch you on your motorbike. All my mates knew I was mad about you. When I saw you that night in the bar—'

'You made a real ass of yourself...but it was kind of sweet because it was all for my benefit,' Rafaello commented. 'And very funny—'

'Funny?' Glory had swallowed that first less than tactful comment but was unable to tolerate that final term.

Rafaello sent her a sudden wicked grin. 'You looked so beautiful but you hadn't a clue how to flirt and it was like watching a ten-year-old trying to be a vamp, every move wildly exaggerated—'

'It was the drink did that.' Glory's cheeks were scarlet. 'But to get back to what you were saying earlier...if you loved me when I was eighteen, why did you set me up so horribly at the restaurant that night? Letting me turn up and see you snogging that redhead—?'

'And I wouldn't have been at all surprised had you sat down at the table with us and wished me well with her,' Rafaello admitted without the remorse she had been hoping to hear. 'That was one of the worst nights of my life—'

'Well, it wasn't exactly the best night of mine!' Glory pointed out with some heat. 'And I'm still waiting for an apology because you were really cruel!'

'*I* was cruel?' Rafaello exclaimed in astonishment. 'You ditch me and then you really turn the screw by expecting me to still spend the evening with you as though absolutely *nothing* has happened?'

Glory thought about that angle and winced. 'I just wanted to spend every last possible moment with you. I didn't ditch you because I wanted to,' she reminded him.

'But I didn't *know* that. A real coward would've said no to the prospect of that evening but I was set on proving that I could be as cool and unfeeling as you appeared to be...' Rafaello hesitated, slight colour springing up over his taut cheekbones. 'So I went home and got very, very drunk. I'm a Grazzini to the backbone where love is concerned. That night I was convinced my life was *ruined*—'

Glory found his other hand, finding her hold on one was insufficient to demonstrate her need to proffer support and comfort. 'You got...drunk?'

'I arrived at the restaurant in advance of you, sat down and informed the entire table that I was planning to d-drink myself under it.' Rafaello's dark deep drawl shook with sudden amusement at the memory of that melodramatic announcement. 'So all my friends were feeling hugely sorry for me and your name was being taken very much in vain. The redhead saw you arrive and just grabbed me. I suppose she was trying to help me save face—'

'Rafaello,' Glory muttered shakily, her hands releasing his fingers to work up his sleeves in little comforting squeezes. 'I was stupid. Because I didn't know you cared, I didn't realize what I was putting you through. I can't bear to think I hurt you—'

'But I got healthily furious when Benito told me about the five grand a couple of days later.' Rafaello gazed down at her with lustrous dark golden eyes that made her heart skip a beat. 'And of course my father's lies ensured that I wasn't tempted to go after you—'

'I just can't believe that you loved me then.' Her lovely face mirroring the strength of her regret, Glory released an unhappy sigh. 'In fact, I just can't bear that you loved me and we *still* lost each other—'

Linking her caressing fingers round his neck, Rafaello backed her down onto the sofa. 'It makes a big difference to me that you didn't throw up what we had by choice, although I still don't understand why you didn't just tell me what Benito was threatening to do.'

'I didn't have enough confidence to do that. It seemed to me that, no matter what happened, it would be my family that suffered, so it seemed wiser just to keep quiet. I love your eyes...' Glory confided, her mind travelling off in another direction entirely as he rearranged her against the cushions. She was blissfully lost in the smouldering dark golden depths trained on her with hungry but tender intensity. 'We're going to be married in forty-eight hours and I can't wait—'

Rafaello stilled as though something in that reference to time had ensnared him, and then he froze and levered himself back from her. '*Dio mio*...what am I *doing*?'

'Nothing I don't want you to do,' Glory was quick to assert, slim fingers closing round the parted edges of his suit jacket as she attempted to ease him back to her.

Rafaello surveyed her beautiful expectant face and the inviting curve of her pink mouth and groaned out loud in frustration. 'I have to fly straight back to New York—'

'*What?*' Glory sat up fast and linked imprisoning hands round his neck, fingers spearing into the thick black silk of his hair.

'This was a literal flying visit, *cara mia*. I only came over because I realised my father was set on approaching you this evening and I knew you were scared of him—'

'Not any more...don't go,' she begged.

'I have to.' He drew her hands down, pressed a fervid kiss of regret to one of her palms and then sprang upright again. 'We've got Sam in the house too. We really can't consider cavorting on a sofa like randy teenagers—'

'No...' she agreed in some embarrassment at that reminder, but her voice wobbled, for she could not stand letting him go.

Rafaello made it to the door and then he swung round, hauled her into his arms and claimed a passionate kiss

which sent her temperature rocketing. 'Forty-eight hours...'
he reminded her raggedly, pulling away again and backing
across the hall in the general direction of the front door,
not removing his attention from her for a second.

'Are you all right?' Glory gasped as he banged his shoulder off the edge of the marble hall fireplace.

'Aching more in places I wouldn't like to mention, *bella
mia*,' Rafaello groaned.

He departed and she went off in search of Sam, but the
kitchen was in darkness. Only when she went back up to
the ground floor again did she hear her brother laughing.

Closer investigation revealed that Sam was in the games
room. Benito had not departed as she had assumed. His
jacket doffed and a cue in one hand, he was instructing
Sam in the noble art of billiards. After a covert glance in
at father and son getting on so well, she tiptoed away again,
leaving them in peace.

Well, she told herself dizzily, Rafaello had been in love
with her when she was eighteen and that was really encouraging to find out. What he had managed once he could,
with careful encouragement, manage again. Now that she
had time to think about it, she was even more heartened by
his admission that he had been devastated when they broke
up back then. He had cared, *really* cared about her after
just six weeks...and no sex. Maybe if she had contrived to
stay out of his bed in Corfu for more than an hour after
her arrival she might have reanimated those warmer feelings.

So, in retrospect, even though she would have been very
willing to make love on the sofa, she was frantically grateful that the demands of business had made that impossible.
Maybe resisting him was the secret, maybe he needed a
challenge, only it was rather difficult to work out how she
could meet that expectation once they were married...

CHAPTER TEN

THE next two days were incredibly busy for Glory. She tidied and aired the cottage for her father's return from hospital. She visited the vicar who was to conduct the service, enjoyed half a dozen lengthy visits from former schoolfriends, who were surprised and delighted at their receipt of wedding invitations, and finally she welcomed her father home.

'Sam's taken to Benito Grazzini, then,' Archie Little gathered within ten minutes of his return, having learned that Rafaello's father was still staying at the Park.

'Does it bother you?' Glory asked awkwardly.

'It's only what I expected. Sam's been one of them from birth,' the older man remarked with a wry smile of acceptance. 'I tried to make him into a Little, goodness knows I did, but even as a little kid he had all his own ideas. But it's not his fault he was a cuckoo in the nest.'

He was a practical man and she supposed it was just as well, for there was already talk of Sam going over to Benito's home in Tuscany for his half-term break, and Benito was talking about the possibility of buying a house in London. For the foreseeable future, Sam was going to be dividing his time between two families and two very different lifestyles.

Rafaello got back to Montague Park on the night before the wedding. He was not overjoyed to discover that Glory was spending her last night of singledom at the cottage and much, much too busy even to see him. 'See you at the altar!' she told him cheerfully on the phone.

'I just want to see you for five minutes—'

'No, I'm sorry. I promised Dad I would devote myself

172

to him tonight and if I see you, well, you *know* it's not going to be for just five minutes.'

Ten minutes later, the knocker on the cottage door went. Rafaello was on the doorstep.

'Wedding gift,' Rafaello drawled, shoving a slim parcel into her startled hands.

'Oh…oh—er—thanks!' she exclaimed in surprise, momentarily deflected from literally eating him up with her eyes.

'Engagement ring.' Rafaello settled a small box on top of the first package and then a second box as well. 'Eternity ring—felt I might as well get it all over with at once,' he imparted as he met her astonished gaze.

Glory thrust the gifts on the dresser to one side of the door and was just within an ace of throwing herself exuberantly into his arms when he backed off in an exaggerated step, both lean hands rising as if to hold her at bay.

'I can play hard to get too, *bella mia.*' A sizzling smile slanted his darkly handsome features, his stunning eyes full of pure gold mockery. '*Buona notte!*'

And with that he sauntered back to his red Ferrari, all fluid grace, cool and extreme sexiness.

Lacking that subtle touch, Glory raced down the path in his wake. 'You can come in if you like—'

Rafaello paused with one hand on the open door of his car and skimmed her a glance of vibrant amusement and satisfaction. 'I wouldn't dream of it. I almost forgot…' he murmured smoothly. 'Don't be late at the church. It's two minutes away and I will just come and fetch you—'

'It's tradition for the bride to be a little late!'

'Stuff tradition,' Rafaello enunciated, springing into the Ferrari. 'I want you there on the stroke of the hour.'

Glory shot between him and the car door and yanked his keys out of the ignition. 'OK…what's going on?' she asked anxiously because, although she was charmed by his won-

derfully light-hearted mood, she was disconcerted by the
alteration she sensed in him.

'What's going *on*?' Rafaello laughed. 'I'm just happy!'

'Oh...' As that was news that could only please any
woman the night before their wedding, Glory returned his
car keys to him.

But Rafaello climbed out of the car, pushed shut the door
and lounged back against it. He breathed in very deep. 'I'm
happy because when we were in London you told me you
loved me and I'm hoping like hell that you meant it...'

Taken aback by that blunt admission, Glory reddened.
'Of course I meant it.'

His brilliant eyes gleamed and he startled her by snatching her up off her feet, striding round the bonnet and stow-
ing her in his passenger seat.

'For goodness' sake, what are you doing?' Glory yelped.

'I'm kidnapping you,' Rafaello asserted, swinging in beside her and firing the engine before she could do anything
about it.

'Are you crazy? I was about to make Dad's supper—'

Having accelerated back down onto the lane, Rafaello
jammed on his brakes and lifted his car phone to stab out
a number. 'Sam? Yes, I told her I was kidnapping her but
she's not impressed by the dramatic gesture—she's more
concerned about Archie's supper—'

Glory's cheeks flamed at that proclamation. Rafaello replaced the phone and dealt her an amused appraisal. 'Sam
will ensure that your father eats...OK? Can you relax
now?'

It was a beautiful early-autumn evening. He parked the
Ferrari below the beech trees that lined the woodland walk
that followed the river through the estate. Closing a lean
hand round hers, he tugged her out of the car. 'I had to talk
to you before the wedding, *bella mia*.'

'What wouldn't keep until tomorrow?' Glory teased.

Rafaello came to a halt. 'It crossed my mind on the flight

back home that although you had heard me telling Sam that I loved you, I had never actually told you...at least, nor properly.'

'Not properly...' Glory repeated unsteadily, her attention resting on the decided colour that had risen to accentuate his fabulous cheekbones. 'Are you trying to say that you were serious when you said that to Sam in London? I thought you were just saying it to calm him down—'

'I'm not that good a liar in moments of crisis where you're concerned. If you hadn't done a runner on me in Corfu I would have told you I loved you then.'

Glory was desperate to believe that he loved her but afraid to credit that what she most wanted could already be hers. 'But that last morning we were together at the villa you were so grim and tense with me...that's why I got the idea that you were going to dump me!' Glory explained awkwardly. 'I don't want you feeling you have to rewrite history just because I got pregnant and you want to make me feel better about our getting married.'

His lean strong face clenched hard with tension. 'I don't believe this. I've never told a woman I loved her in my life, and the minute I do you start telling me I *don't*! But then, how can I blame you for that when I've made such a hash of everything? I *always* get it wrong with you—'

Colliding with the raw emotion in his lustrous dark eyes, Glory started really listening instead of doubting. 'You don't—'

'Yes, I do. Even when you told me that you loved me, I screwed up!' Rafaello ground out, swinging away from her and raking his fingers through his black hair in a movement of violent frustration. 'I thought you were only saying it because you had guessed that I was crazy about you and you were feeling sorry for me. That stung my pride—'

Dumbfounded by the revelation that Rafaello could be that insecure, Glory closed her hands round one lean clenched fist and drew him back to her again, but he was so busy talking, he hardly seemed to notice. 'There's *never* been anyone else for me but you,' he was telling her aggressively. 'When I first saw you again I went haywire and came up with the mistress idea. I just wanted you back on any terms I could have you without losing face.'

As Rafaello paused for breath Glory was starting to smile. 'Without losing face?' she encouraged.

'Then I wrecked things again by coming off with that rubbish about you trying to trap me by getting pregnant,' Rafaello informed her with a guilty grimace. 'I was in shock at finding out you were still a virgin, but by the time I got out of the shower I had actually quite warmed up to the idea that you might conceive my child—'

'You…*had*?'

'Then I realised you'd gone out in the storm, and I don't *ever* want to relive that panic you put me in, *cara*,' Rafaello confided with a positive shudder of recollection. 'By the time I got you back up to the villa, I knew I had much deeper feelings for you than I had been prepared to admit—'

'So you proposed marriage to me when I was in the bath. Trouble is, I didn't think you meant it—'

'I'm not like my father. I was really impressed listening to him giving forth about your mother and without a shred of self-consciousness admitting that she was the love of his life. I'm just not great with the words,' Rafaello interrupted with raw regret, strained dark eyes holding hers as if he was willing her with every atom of his being to believe in him. 'But I just looked at you and my feelings…well, they just *overwhelmed* me and I know it wasn't the most romantic proposal *or* the best place to propose—'

Glory was so shaken by that disjointed burst of confidence that her eyes stung with tears. 'And I rejected the idea straight off. I'm so sorry I didn't listen—'

'No, it was my fault, throwing it at you like that,' Rafaello insisted, gathering her close and snatching in a sustaining breath. 'I realised that I had to try to prove to you that we could be happy together—'

'You succeeded—'

'But I didn't have the guts to sit down and trash the mistress arrangement straight off in case you just upped and walked out there and then,' Rafaello confessed in a charged undertone of embarrassment. 'Then that last night we had that stupid argument and you said how mortified you'd be if your family knew what you were doing with me...I honestly thought you despised me for being such a jerk—'

All those brains, Glory reflected in silent fascination, and he could not see the wood from the trees when it came to her feelings for him. 'I was just saying that because I was angry with you—'

'But I felt so guilty and ashamed. Then when I came to bed thinking you would be asleep, you turned out to be awake,' he reminded her. 'And I was dreading saying what I knew I *had* to say...'

'Which was?' Glory prompted.

'That I was sorry that I had forced you into becoming my mistress but that I had never once thought of you that way because I loved you and still wanted to marry you—'

'Why on earth were you *dreading* saying that to me?' Glory demanded in some bewilderment.

Shimmering golden eyes assailed hers in a head-on collision and his hard jawline clenched. 'I was scared you would just pack your bags and go—'

'But I was nuts about you too!' Glory exclaimed. 'I suppose you were so tense the next morning because you were *still* thinking that but, you see, I thought you were warming up to dumping me. How on earth could you think I would walk out on you after the way I'd behaved in bed with you?'

'Passion didn't mean you wouldn't grab the first chance you got to have your freedom back.'

'I hope you know different now. Passion and love go together for me,' Glory informed him gently.

'When I got back and found you gone I was shattered,' Rafaello muttered heavily. 'I assumed you'd gone back to England and I hired an investigation agency to search for you—'

'You...*did*?' Glory was shocked by that admission.

'Then your father fell ill and I was finally able to find you after two months of hell—'

'But you were so distant—'

'Even the most stupid guy would get the message that he was unwanted after being ditched twice over, *bella mia*,' Rafaello pointed out defensively. 'And the way you kept on thanking me all the time for doing what I could for Archie made me feel even worse. I was also feeling very uncomfortable with the fact that *I* knew Sam was my brother but *you* didn't.'

Glory's bright blue eyes shone like stars as she gazed up at him. 'You never have been unwanted by me in your entire life, Rafaello Grazzini,' she swore with a slight break in her voice. 'You love me, you *really* love me—?'

'So much I can't keep my hands off you in public places.' Registering that he was on a decided winning streak, Rafaello hauled her even closer and kissed her with hungry passion, breathing raggedly in the aftermath. 'I can't wait to marry you, I just can't wait...'

They didn't stay out long. He took her home and they parted and Glory went indoors and gave her brother a big hug. 'You're even cleverer than I thought you were,' she told him.

Sam laughed but he was bewildered. 'Why?'

'Sorry, can't explain. But you were right about something that I am incredibly happy to have been *wrong* about,' his sister said with an ecstatic smile that left him none the wiser.

It was her father who reminded her about the gifts which

Rafaello had brought. Glory discovered that the slim parcel contained a jewel-case which contained an exquisite diamond and platinum necklace and drop earrings. She was overwhelmed by Rafaello's generosity but it all meant so much more to her now that she knew she was loved. Her engagement ring, the gift which most touched her heart, was an equally beautiful diamond solitaire, and the eternity ring, a narrow matching band.

The next morning, the day of the wedding, she was up early and had only just gone upstairs when she heard a car pulling up outside. Maud, who had come over to help her get dressed, called up to tell her that she had a visitor.

Glory was disconcerted to be told that Rafaello's father was waiting to speak to her. Maud had shown him into the rarely used front parlour. The reason for Benito Grazzini's visit shook Glory even more. He had come to give her a very beautiful diamond tiara that had belonged to his own mother.

'I always planned to give this to Rafaello's bride but it took me until this morning to work up the courage to offer it to you,' Benito admitted anxiously. 'I very much want to repair the damage I have done to you and to Rafaello and I also wish to welcome you with a whole heart to our family.'

Recognising the depth of the older man's sincerity, Glory thanked him and told him that she had already forgiven him and that Rafaello would soon feel the same.

Maud exclaimed over the tiara but was even more impressed by Rafaello's gifts. 'He's certainly pushed the boat out and no mistake!'

'It's just so extravagant…all this for me.' Glory fingered the gorgeous necklace with reverent fingers. 'It's like a dream.'

'Just like a wedding ought to be,' the older woman said with warm approval.

An hour or more later, when Glory studied her reflection

in the mirror, a glow of incredible happiness consumed her. The instant she had seen the dress in an exclusive wedding store in London she had fallen madly in love with it. The neckline was off the shoulder and elegant and the intricate bodice of silver beaded and embroidered silk ended in a flattering V-waistline. The sleeves were tight but flared out into a fall of exquisite lace at the elbow. The satin-silk skirt opened at the centre to reveal a panel of the same gorgeous beaded silk as the bodice. Having set aside the pretty fake tiara she had intended to wear with her Chantilly lace bridal veil, she had replaced it with the diamond tiara that Benito had given her.

Glory went downstairs to join her father, Maud having already left for the church. Leaning on the stick that gave him the extra support he needed while he was still slightly unsteady on his feet, the older man looked very well. But as she reached the hall Glory's brow indented. 'What's that noise? It sounds like horses…'

'Strewth…' Archie Little gasped in astonishment at the sight that met his eyes when he peered out of the front door.

Rafaello had sent not a car to collect her and her father but an open carriage lined in sapphire velvet, driven by a coachman in a full regalia and pulled by four white horses ornamented with elaborate plumes. Glory was thrilled to bits.

'The boy's certainly doing you proud,' was all her shaken father could think to comment when a wildly impractical white carpet was unrolled to pave her entry into the church.

Glory alighted on the white carpet and smiled for the photographers and floated along the carpet into the church and down the aisle to join Rafaello at the altar in a blissful daze.

'You look like a fairytale princess,' he whispered, shimmering golden eyes riveted to her in heart-stopping admiration. 'Just as I always imagined, *bella mia*.'

After the marriage service they travelled back in the carriage to Montague Park, where the wedding breakfast was to be served. The ballroom had been transformed with glorious flower arrangements into the most magnificent backdrop for the occasion. In the afternoon the bride and groom departed, but not before Glory had thrown her bouquet and her future stepmother had caught it.

They were to spend their honeymoon in the Grazzini home in Tuscany. Arriving there at dusk, Rafaello carried her over the threshold and straight upstairs to a gorgeous bedroom, where he finally got his bride into his arms without an audience.

'I have had the most wonderful day,' Glory informed him, gazing up at him with shining eyes of love and contentment.

'It's been the happiest day of my life, *amore mia*.' Rafaello framed her lovely smiling face with possessive fingers, studying her with passionate tenderness. 'And, if I have anything to do with it, *every* day you spend with me will be the same...'

Just over a year later Glory tucked their infant son into his cot. At almost six months old, Lorenzo had silky black curls and big blue eyes. He was a friendly, cheerful baby with a wonderful smile who slept well, ate well and loved being cuddled.

They had flown out to the villa in Corfu only that afternoon. The night before, they had celebrated the first anniversary of their marriage with a special family dinner at Montague Park. Glory was thinking how happy she had been to have her father and Maud, Sam and Benito all at the same table with nobody seeming to feel the slightest bit awkward any more. The divisions between their families had been healed and Rafaello had long since regained his former closeness with his father.

Archie and Maud had got married a couple of months after Glory and Rafaello and had then surprised everyone by taking over the village shop and embarking on a pretty busy lifestyle which seemed to suit them very well. Sam had lived with them in their new home in the village until he completed his school year and was able to sit his exams. He had then spent most of the summer in Tuscany with Benito and had returned with a good grasp of Italian. Determined to stay in advance of her kid brother, Glory had started taking lessons to learn the same language faster. Sam was currently studying for his A levels at a London school and he spent regular weekends with Archie and Maud. Benito had bought a city apartment, where Sam had come to grudging terms with living in the lap of luxury, but only after being made to appreciate how much the Grazzinis gave to charitable causes.

Glory had enjoyed a blissfully happy first year of marriage. She still wondered why it had taken her such a very long time to realise that Rafaello adored her. He had shown her his love in Corfu those first weeks they had been together, shown her in so many ways while her father was ill, but her own low self-esteem had blinded her to what she was seeing. In the same way, the strength of her love had enabled her to respect the sacrifice her mother had made in giving up Rafaello's father for the sake of their respective families. And she finally understood all the harshly offered moral principles which her parent had endeavoured to instil in her daughter. Giving way to her own passion for Benito Grazzini had ultimately caused Talitha Little great unhappiness, and she had undoubtedly wanted to protect Glory from making a similar mistake.

'Lorenzo's not asleep *already*, is he?' Rafaello demanded in disappointment as he strode into the nursery and sprang Glory from her thoughts.

She watched her tall, dark and undeniably gorgeous husband stare down ruefully into the cot where his baby son was indeed sound asleep, long lashes lying smooth on his peaceful little face.

'You were on the phone to Benito for ages,' Glory reminded him.

'I don't get enough time to play with our son,' Rafaello lamented. 'He's out like a light every night by eight. I thought babies were supposed to be night owls—'

'We don't *want* him to be a night owl,' Glory assured her husband, trying not to laugh at the tenor of his complaint. 'I don't think you'd be too pleased if he was crying in the middle of the night.'

Rafaello processed that alternative option and gave her a sizzling smile of comprehension that warmed her cheeks. 'As always where our son is concerned, you are right, *bella mia*. Such a shame that you never got to use all that knowledge you acquired reading at least a thousand magazines on what to do with a crying baby. By the end of our honeymoon, I knew more about babies than ninety-nine out of a hundred first-time fathers-to-be and we had hit every baby shop in Tuscany at least twice—'

'Stop teasing me,' Glory warned him, rather embarrassed by the reminder of how obsessive she had been in those pursuits during her pregnancy. 'Why were you on the phone so long to your father?'

'Benito has volunteered to become chairman of a charity for the homeless—'

Glory struggled not to smile. Sam's social conscience had evidently stretched to enclose his birth father. 'That's good news, isn't it?'

'Yes. He has too much energy to settle into full-time retirement and he has a huge number of contacts to offer.' Rafaello reached out to bring her slim body into connection with his big powerful frame, his mouth curving with satisfaction as she gave a faint little quiver of response.

Dio mio, cara mia...' he breathed huskily, lustrous dark golden eyes gleaming over with a wealth of tender appreciation and warmth. 'How come you married a guy who tied himself up in knots just trying to tell you that he loved you?'

'I had high hopes of how he would turn out,' Glory teased, stretching her arms up to link them round his neck, looking up into his darkly handsome features with an accelerating heartbeat and the sensation that she was one of the luckiest women in the world. 'You can actually say, "I love you" without blushing like mad now!'

'Are you ever going to let me forget that?' Rafaello groaned.

'No chance...' It was one of Glory's most tender memories. His love was all that more special and precious because he had never said those words to anyone but her. That one small fact alone made up for the years they had spent apart.

'I adore you, *bella mia*,' he murmured, his stunning eyes telegraphing the same message into hers and making her melt inside and out. 'I think you're a wonderful wife and a fabulous mother and the most incredibly loving and sexy woman alive—'

'I love you too,' Glory told him breathlessly, and while Lorenzo slept on in perfect tranquillity his parents kissed and exchanged mutual compliments which grew increasingly excessive in nature. Eventually, Rafaello swept Glory off into their bedroom next door where they sealed their love with the passion that never failed to fill them both with renewed joy and contentment.

DAMIANO'S RETURN

Lynne Graham

CHAPTER ONE

EDEN was in the changing cubicle pinning up the hem on a customer's skirt when she heard the shop door open.

'You're always very busy,' the older woman commented. 'I suppose people just don't have the time to do their own alterations these days.'

'I'm not complaining.' With a rueful smile, Eden eased the last pin into place and rose upright. Five feet four inches tall and slightly built, she wore her thick golden hair twisted up into a clip. Her heart-shaped face was dominated by her clear green eyes.

Emerging from the cubicle, she looked in some surprise at the two men in business suits, who in company with a young woman were talking to her middle-aged assistant, Pam.

'These people are looking for you, Eden.' Pam could not hide her curiosity.

'How can I help you?' Eden asked.

'Eden James?' The older of the two men double-checked.

Conscious of the keen appraisal she was receiving from the trio and also of the indefinable tension they exuded, Eden nodded slowly.

'Is there somewhere we could talk in private, Miss James?'

Eden's eyes widened.

'Perhaps upstairs in your apartment,' the young woman suggested briskly.

She both looked and sounded like a police officer,
Eden reflected, her anxiety increasing. But usually the
police identified themselves first. Aware that her two
employees and single customer were a captive audience,
she flushed and hurriedly opened the door that led into
the short passage which gave entrance back out onto
the street.

'Could you tell me what this is about?' Eden
prompted tautly then.

'We were trying to be discreet.' The older man now
extended an official identity card for her inspection.
'I'm Superintendent Marshall and this young woman is
Constable Leslie. This gentleman with me is Mr Rodney
Russell, a special advisor from the Foreign Office. May
we go upstairs to talk?'

Somehow, Eden found herself responding automatically to that calm note of command. What did they
want? The police? A senior policeman too. The Foreign
Office? *The Foreign Office?* Her mind blanked out with
sudden horror and her hand started to shake as she stuck
the key into the lock on her front door. Damiano! For
so long, she had waited for such a visit but here it was
catching her totally unprepared. When had she stopped
fearing every phone call, every ring of the doorbell?
When? Guilt-stricken dismay at that discovery about
herself froze her to the spot.

'It's all right,' the female police officer asserted, contriving to gently urge Eden out of her paralysis and over
the threshold. 'We haven't come here to break bad
news, Mrs Braganzi.'

Mrs Braganzi? The name she had left behind when
the cruel spotlight of press intrusion had become more
than she'd been able to handle. So many reporters had
wanted to ask her what it was like to be the wife of an

important man who had simply disappeared into thin air. Refused those interviews, tabloid interest in Eden Braganzi had taken a nastier turn.

Not bad news? Eden blinked, mind briefly focusing again. How could it *not* be bad news after five years? There was no good news possible! And then natural common sense exercised its sway and steadied Eden a little. Was this yet another official courtesy call; was that it? Just letting her know that the case was still open but unsolved? It had been some time since anyone official had requested actual face-to-face contact with her. She herself had gone long past the stage where she continually phoned them, pushing, pressuring, finally hysterically begging for some action that she had only gradually come to appreciate they could not offer her. And only at that point had she begun finally to give up hope...

After all, Damiano's brother, Nuncio, and his sister, Cosetta, had given up hope of his survival within a month of his disappearance. Damiano had been in the South American republic of Montavia when a military coup had taken place. In the street violence which had followed in the capital city that day, Damiano had simply disappeared. He had checked out of his hotel and climbed into a limousine which should have taken him to the airport and his flight home. But that had been the last reliable sighting of him alive. The bodyguards in the car behind had been blown off the road by an explosion. Unhurt but with their vehicle wrecked, they had lost the limousine. Damiano and the limo and the driver had all vanished without trace.

During the subsequent enquiries, the new dictatorship had not been particularly helpful, but then by that time opposition to the coup had been spreading and a full-scale civil war had been threatening Montavia. The overstretched authorities had had little interest in the disappearance of a single foreign national and had pointed out that, during the fighting which had raged a full week in the city, many people had died or disappeared. There had been no trail to follow and no witnesses had come forward. But neither had there been any evidence found to actually *prove* that Damiano had been killed. It had been that appalling lack of proof of any kind which had tormented Eden for more years than she could bear.

'Please sit down, Mrs Braganzi,' some one of the three prompted her.

Didn't the police always ask a person to sit down when there was a nasty shock coming? Or was that only how actors portrayed the police in television productions? Still finding it impossible to concentrate, but slightly irritated at being ordered around in her own home, Eden sat down in an armchair and watched the two men settle themselves on the small couch opposite. The frown-line on her brow deepened. Their faces were taut, flushed, almost eager.

'Constable Leslie was telling you the truth, Mrs Braganzi. We're not here to break bad news but to give you extremely good news. Your husband is *alive*,' the police superintendent informed her with firm emphasis.

Frozen within the armchair, Eden stared at him in shaken disbelief. She parted dry lips. 'That's not possible...'

The other man, Russell, from the Foreign Office started to speak. He reminded her that at the outset of Damiano's disappearance a kidnapping had been suspected. But only along with every other possible crime or reason under the sun, Eden recalled, her dazed mind momentarily straying back five agonising years.

'After all, your husband was...*is*,' Russell corrected himself at speed and continued, 'a very wealthy, influential man in the international banking fraternity—'

'You said alive...' Eden broke in shakily, her face stricken as she surveyed the men in instinctive condemnation that they should dare to try to raise hopes she did not believe she could stand to have resurrected. 'How could Damiano still be alive after so many years? If he's alive, where has he been all this time? You've made a mistake...a dreadful, dreadful mistake!'

'Your husband is alive, Mrs Braganzi,' the superintendent spelt out with measured care and confidence. 'Naturally coming out of the blue as it has this is a considerable shock for you. But please believe what we are telling you. Your husband, Damiano Braganzi, is alive and well.'

Eden trembled, searching their faces and then suddenly shutting her eyes tight. She was struggling to overcome disbelief and simultaneously offering up a prayer of desperate hope to God. Let it be true, let it be real, please don't let me wake up if it's a dream—for over the years there had been many such dreams to torment her.

'Your husband surfaced in Brazil almost two days go,' the Foreign Office advisor divulged.

'Brazil...' Eden echoed shakily.

'He has spent over four years in prison in Montavia and on his release he had the good sense simply to slip quietly out of the country again.'

'P-prison?' Eyes shattered, Eden stared at the younger man with ever-mounting incredulity. 'Damiano's been in prison? How...*why*?'

On the day on which Damiano had disappeared, he had been kidnapped and taken to a military camp in the countryside. A military camp? She frowned at that unexpected information. A few days later, with civil war raging through the tiny republic, rebel forces had attacked the camp and in the ensuing battle Damiano had received serious head injuries. Finding a wounded prisoner in the aftermath, the rebels had quite naturally assumed that he was one of their own.

'Your husband is a fluent Spanish speaker. That and his quick thinking saved his life. He received treatment at a field hospital in the jungle. He was only just beginning to recover when he was picked up by the government soldiers, cleaning up the last pockets of resistance. He was imprisoned for being a member of the guerrilla forces.'

Damiano was alive…Damiano was *alive*! Eden was beginning to put faith in what she was being told although still every sense screamed at her to be cautious. She was fighting so hard to concentrate but she found that she just couldn't. She felt stupid, numb, disbelieving.

'Naturally you are wondering why your husband didn't immediately identify himself when he was captured,' the bland-faced Russell continued. 'He believed that admitting his true identity would be signing his own death warrant. He was aware that he had originally been kidnapped by soldiers loyal to the current dictatorship in Montavia. He knew that the kidnapping had been bungled and that, from that point, there had never been any intention of letting him go alive…'

Eden blinked, struggling to focus on the Foreign Office advisor and absorb what she was being told. Her blood was chilling in her veins, her tummy turning queasy. Damiano had been kidnapped, *hurt*... Her own worst imaginings had come true.

'Appreciating that his survival would be a severe embarrassment to the Montavian government, your husband decided that he would be safer retaining his assumed identity and accepting the prison term. On his release, he headed for the border with Brazil and from there to the home of a businessman called Ramon Alcoverro—'

'Ramon...' Eden whispered, slowly shaking her pounding head, lifting her hand to press her fingers against her damp, taut brow as if to aid her thinking powers. 'Damiano went to college with someone called Ramon.'

'About an hour from now, your husband will be landing on English soil again and he is keen that his homecoming should be kept from the media for as long as possible. For that reason, we have been discreet in our approach to you.'

Damiano alive, Damiano coming home. *Home?* To his family, of course, but *not* to her! In sudden, raw, shaken turmoil, Eden sat there, experiencing simultaneous joy and agony. These people had come here to make their announcement because she was still legally Damiano's wife and next of kin. But Eden was painfully aware that her marriage had virtually been over by the time of her husband's disappearance. Damiano had never loved her. He had married her on the rebound and lived to regret the impulse.

When had she forgotten that reality? When had she begun living in her own imagination? For Damiano would never return home to *her*. Had circumstances not cruelly intervened, he might well have come home to ask her for a divorce five years ago. Hadn't his own

brother suggested that? And now, after the ordeal he
had suffered, he would be anxious to get on with his
life again. Indeed, in all likelihood, after hearing what
had happened during his absence, Damiano would make
no attempt to see her and any contact made would be
through a divorce lawyer.

'Mrs Braganzi…Eden, may I call you Eden?' the superintendent enquired.

'His family…the Braganzi, his brother and his wife,
his sister…' Eden framed dully. 'They must be overjoyed.'

The senior policeman's face stiffened. 'As far as I
understand the somewhat limited information that I
have received, your husband's family received a call
from Ramon Alcoverro and immediately flew out to
Brazil on their private jet.'

Eden froze at that disconcerting news, what colour
remaining in her cheeks draining away to leave her
deathly pale. Damiano's family had already flown out
without even bothering to contact her and give her the
news of his survival? She dropped her head, sick to the
stomach at such cruelty.

'At times such as these, particularly where families
have become estranged, people can act very much without thought,' the older man commented in the taut silence. 'We only became aware of the situation when the
embassy in Brazil contacted the Foreign Office. They
required certain information before they could issue a
replacement passport to your husband so that he could
travel home.'

Eden still said nothing. She was studying the carpet
with eyes that ached. Nuncio had probably already told
Damiano why he had not brought Eden out to Brazil
with him. Those dreadful lies that had been printed

about her in that newspaper only three months after Damiano had gone missing! The scurrilous gossip and opprobrium that had finally broken her spirit and forced her to leave the Braganzi home for the sake of her own sanity.

Rodney Russell took up the explanation in a brisk tone. 'By that stage, your husband was demanding to know why you had not been informed, unaware that his own family had failed to keep us up to date on developments.'

Eden blinked and looked up very slowly. 'Really?'

The superintendent gave her a soothing smile. 'I gather Damiano made it very clear that he can't wait to be reunited with his wife—'

Eden studied him with strained eyes of disconcertion. 'Damiano can't wait to see…me?' she whispered in faltering interruption, certain she must have misheard him.

'He's flying into Heathrow at noon and then he's taking a helicopter trip to an airfield just outside town. We'll convey you there. Obviously the hope is that it will be possible to evade any media attention.'

'He wishes to see *me*?' An almost hysterical little laugh escaped Eden's convulsed throat. She twisted her head away and lowered it, feeling the hot, stinging rush of tears hitting her eyes.

She wanted privacy but instead she had strangers watching her every reaction. Strangers who had to be well aware just what a charade her marriage had become by the time Damiano had gone missing. She ought to be used to that reality now, the knowledge that nothing had been too sacred to commit to an information file somewhere. But then the behaviour of Damiano's family in recent days spoke louder than any volume of words.

Nonetheless, after Damiano had vanished, there had been a full-scale investigation by both the British and the Italian authorities. Financial experts had gone in to check that the Braganzi Bank was still sound. They had looked for fraud or evidence of blackmail or secret accounts. They had even looked for links between Damiano and organised crime syndicates. Then they had turned their attention to his own family circle to see if anybody there might have employed a hitman to get rid of him while he was abroad.

No stone had been left unturned. No opinion had gone unsought. No question had been too personal or too wounding to ask. Damiano had been too rich and way too important to just disappear without causing muddy ripples of suspicion to wash over everybody connected with him. And nobody had suffered more than Eden, the wife his snobbish siblings had secretly despised, the wife who had swiftly become the target of their collective grief and turmoil. Nuncio and his sister, Cosetta, had turned on Eden like starving rats on prey. She had even been blamed for the fact that Damiano had gone to Montavia in the first place.

'In situations such as this, we normally arrange specialist counselling and a period of protective isolation for the victim,' Rodney Russell remarked, 'but your husband has categorically refused that support.'

'I believe Damiano said he would prefer prison to counselling,' the superintendent said with wry amusement.

A cup of tea was settled on the low coffee-table in front of Eden. 'You've had a major shock,' the female constable said kindly. 'But you're going to be reunited with your husband this afternoon.'

At that staggering reminder, Eden rose in one jerky

motion and walked into her bedroom several feet away. She closed her eyes again, fighting for some semblance of composure. Damiano was alive; Damiano was on his way home. To *her*? She scolded herself for letting her thoughts slide once again in the wrong direction. A selfish direction. If Damiano wanted her now, she would be there for him. Naturally, obviously. In fact, if Damiano had asked for her, nothing would keep her from his side!

Had Nuncio kept quiet about her supposed affair, after all? Yet if he had, what excuse had he given Damiano for his failure to bring Eden out to Brazil with him? And what was Damiano likely to say when he came back? How was she to explain why she had left the Braganzi family home? Shed his name to hide behind another name? Built a new life far from what had so briefly been hers?

Struggling to suppress her mounting fears, Eden focused on the framed photo by her bed. Damiano smiling. All sleek, dark good looks and cool Italian charisma. It had been taken on their honeymoon in Sicily. But they had only been together seven months in total. Long enough though for her to see him withdraw from her, for her to stop expecting the connecting door between their bedrooms to open again, for him to start spending more and more time abroad on endless banking business. Long enough to break her heart. Love like that didn't go away. Love like that just *hurt*.

A light knock sounded on the ajar bedroom door. 'Are you all right?'

Mastering concerns which were pushing her close to panic at what should have been a most ecstatically happy moment, Eden turned a pale, tear-wet face to the young female officer. 'What now?'

'We'll leave for the airfield in half an hour. If I were you I'd shut up shop for the day and just think about what I wanted to wear.'

Wear? Eden swallowed a shaken laugh. Damiano... Damiano. What had he suffered? Kidnapped, his life threatened, seriously injured, locked up in some primitive foreign prison. Damiano, whose life had not prepared him in any way for such an ordeal. Damiano, born to wealth, command and supreme privilege. Once he had liked to see her in green. That thought just popped up out of nowhere and spawned a second, no less trivial recollection. Green had been his favourite colour.

She ransacked her wardrobe with suddenly frantic hands. Maybe he only wanted to see her to say, 'Hi, I'm back *but...*' without his precious family hanging around in the background. And Annabel, his first love, his true love. How could she have forgotten Annabel? Annabel Stavely, Damiano's ex-fiancée, who in the years since had had a child by a father she had refused to name but who remained single. Eden raised her hands to her face. Her hands were shaking, her palms cold and damp. She was a basket case with an out-of-control mind and the most desperate crazy desire to shout and scream with excitement and fear at one and the same time...

The phone rang barely a minute before Eden and her escort left the apartment.

'Eden?' It was Damiano's younger brother, Nuncio.

Shaken that her brother-in-law should finally call her after so many years of silence, Eden literally stopped breathing. She was instantly afraid that he was ringing as his brother's messenger to say that Damiano would not, after all, be flying on to see her and she whispered strickenly, 'Yes?'

'I have told Damiano nothing. How do I welcome him home with such news?' Nuncio demanded in a tone of bitter condemnation. 'I was forced to lie and say that we had lost contact with you after you moved out. But you had better tell him the truth for I will not stand by and see my brother made to look a fool by my silence!'

The truth? As Eden replaced the phone again with a trembling hand her own bitterness almost prompted her to pick it up again and call Nuncio back. But it was the temptation of a moment and swiftly set aside. In any case, he would never believe her, would he? Neither he nor anybody else would believe or indeed even *want* to believe the real truth, which was that her two best friends had betrayed her and ultimately left her to carry the can.

'You must understand that the man you remember *won't* be the man who will be coming home to you,' Rodney Russell informed her with daunting conviction as they sat in the back of the unmarked police car on the way to the airfield. 'It will be a great strain for both of you to rebuild your relationship—'

'Yes...of course.' Wishing he would stop winding her up with such warnings, Eden listened with veiled and ever more anxious eyes. The lecture about post-traumatic stress syndrome had been scary enough.

'Damiano is returning to a world he lost five years ago. It will be a challenge for him to adjust. He will suffer from mood swings, frustration and a sense of bitter injustice at the years that have been stolen from him. At times, he will crave solitude, but at other times he may relentlessly seek out company. He may be with-

drawn, moody, silent or he may put on the macho-man
act of the century but it won't *last*—'

'No?' she queried tautly.

'Try to appreciate that however your husband reacts
now will not be a fair indication of how he'll be when
he has come to terms with what has happened to him.
This will be a transition period for Damiano.'

'Yes.' That last assurance had sent her heart sinking
like a stone. She wasn't stupid. Was he warning her that
Damiano might be seeking her right now but that in a
few weeks he might walk away again? Did he think she
fondly imagined that paradise might now be miraculously reclaimed from the debris of a marriage foun-
dering five years ago? She was not so simple, nor so
foolishly optimistic. She expected nothing, would ask
for nothing from Damiano. She just wanted and desperately needed to *be* there for him. But she was challenged to believe that Damiano might need her.
Damiano Braganzi had never been known to admit a
need for anybody or anything.

It had been she who'd said, 'I love you,' but he had
never said those words. Yet once he had said them to
Annabel, hadn't he? Or at least he had had them etched
on a beautiful gold necklace: 'All my love, Damiano.'

'I think some fresh air would do you good, Eden,'
the superintendent cut into her increasingly frantic
thoughts and she realized only then that the car had
arrived at the airfield.

'Yes…yes, it would.' She slid out of the car and
breathed in deep in an effort to steady herself. 'How
much longer?'

'Maybe ten minutes…' The older man had no need
to ask what she meant.

Ten minutes to wait after five years? She was such a

bag of nerves. She paced the Tarmac, ignoring the door
open in welcome at the small passenger terminal. She
smoothed trembling hands down over the fine green
wool dress which was absurdly warm for a summer day
but all that she still possessed in that colour.

'Russell is only doing his job as he sees it,' the senior
policeman remarked quietly, 'but, accordingly to my
sources, your husband is in remarkably good condition
both physically and mentally.'

Eden nodded, a little of her tension ebbing, and then
she heard a distant whirr. She jerked, throwing her head
back to search the sky with fraught eyes. She saw a
dark speck, watching it growing larger, her whole being
centering on the helicopter as it came in to land. She
still could not quite credit that Damiano was on that
craft, that Damiano was about to emerge and walk
across the Tarmac towards her.

In spite of everything she had been told, she was still
terrified that somehow all these people and even his
family had got it wrong and that the man who had
turned up in Brazil wasn't really who they thought he
was. An impostor—well, why not? Wasn't that at least
possible? Mightn't somebody have boned up on
Damiano's life and even had plastic surgery? Wouldn't
it be worth a try to step into the shoes of so very rich
a man? And wouldn't Nuncio, who had worshipped the
ground his elder brother had walked on and who had
been inconsolable when he'd gone missing, have been
an easy and credulous target?

Rigid, she watched the helicopter settle down about
a hundred feet away. A door thrust open. She trembled,
cold and clammy with fear. And then she saw a very
tall, very well-built male springing out, with long, powerful black-jean-clad legs, and also wearing a white

T-shirt and leather flying jacket. Black hair, far longer than she would have expected, blew back from his lean, hard-boned features. His skin was deeply bronzed. Her breath caught in her throat. She couldn't breathe. There was just this massive explosion of crazy joy inside her and she didn't notice herself moving forward at first hesitantly and then breaking into a run.

Damiano let her run to him. He just came to a halt about thirty feet from the helicopter. Later she would remember that, wonder about it. But at that instant she was all reaction and no thought. Every prayer answered, every fear for that moment forgotten, Eden just hurled herself at his big powerful frame, heart racing so fast she reeled dizzily against him as he closed his arms around her.

'You missed me, *cara*?' His rich, dark drawl wrapped round her, shutting out everything else as he bent his head down to her level.

Her face was squashed into his chest. He smelt so good, he smelt so familiar and she drank him in as if he were life-giving oxygen. 'Don't joke...*please* don't joke!' Eden sobbed into his shirt, clinging to him with both hands to stay upright.

CHAPTER TWO

For a couple of minutes, Damiano simply stood there holding Eden and she got the chance to get a partial grip on herself again and recall that they were in a public place.

'OK?' Damiano checked softly.

Eden breathed in shakily and lifted her head. 'I love you so much.'

She hadn't planned to say it, had not even thought of saying such a thing but the words came out in what felt like the most natural declaration in the world. She encountered eyes so dark and intent they were black. Unfathomable. A tiny spasm of fear tensed her muscles. Suddenly she became conscious of how rigid he was, how tight was the control he had over himself.

'And even after all this time, not a single doubt. I have to be the luckiest guy in the universe, *cara*,' Damiano responded with a roughened edge to his dark deep drawl, black eyes flashing gold as he scanned her anxious face, and then bent to sweep back up the travel bag he had set down. 'Come on, let's get rid of the welcome committee.'

He kept his arm round her narrow shoulders and walked her over to where the others hovered. Eden was still trembling, her mind in a tail-spin. She couldn't focus on what she had just said or his reaction. It was an effort to think far enough ahead to put one foot in front of the other and move. Yet on some subconscious level she sensed the difference in him but could not put a

21

label on what it was. Damiano had always been very controlled and very hard to read. He kept the volatile and expressive Italian side of his powerful personality under wraps. Except in bed.

That recollection made her cheeks burn and then slowly pale again. The luckiest guy in the universe? No, not in the bedroom with a wife he had once called the biggest prude in the western world! No, she had been a really dismal failure in that department, hampered by both her upbringing and her inhibitions, but most of all in the end by *his* dissatisfaction. For the more exasperated Damiano had become, the worse the problem had got. By then aware that everything she did and didn't do behind the bedroom door was under censorious appraisal, Eden had felt a shrinking reluctance she hadn't been able to hide from him. The pleasure he had given her had had a price tag attached and the cost had been too high for her pride to bear.

But when Damiano had gone missing, when she had had to face up to the appalling reality that he might be dead and might never come home to her again—oh, how she had beaten herself up for her failings then! In retrospect, her own hang-ups had begun to seem pathetic and selfish. Chewing at her lower lip, utterly dislocated from the dialogue which Damiano was coolly maintaining with what he had called the welcome committee, she focused on the long silver limousine pulling up with a surprised frown.

'The car's here. I don't want to hang around,' Damiano stated with a blunt lack of social pretence she had never heard him use before.

'Am I allowed to ask where you're heading, Mr Braganzi?' Rodney Russell enquired with the edged delivery of a male who, with the arrival of that chauffeur-

driven car, had just been made to feel even more superfluous to requirements.

'Home...where else?' Damiano responded.

Home? Dear heaven, was he planning on having them
driven straight back to London and yet another family
welcome? A joyous celebration at which she would
simply be the spectre at the feast?

'Where *is* home?' Damiano prompted with a rueful
laugh as he strode towards the limousine. 'You had better give the driver directions.'

Her level of panic momentarily subsided at that clar-
ification and she scolded herself for forgetting that, of
course, he was already aware that she was no longer
living in the vast Braganzi town house in London.
However, he seemed to have taken that development in
his stride. Having done as he requested, she climbed
into the luxurious rear passenger seat. But the sense of
panic swiftly returned to reclaim her. She had not
thought beyond the moment of seeing Damiano again,
indeed had barely attempted to even visualise what she
could not imagine after so long. But now she felt like
someone in a canoe without a paddle heading for the
rapids.

'This feels weird to me too. Don't worry about it,
cara,' Damiano breathed, reaching out without warning
and closing his big hand over her tautly clenched fingers. 'No long-winded explanations of anything today.
I'm back. You're here. That's all that matters at this
moment in time.'

Eden stared at him. It seemed to be entirely the wrong
time to be registering just how gorgeous he still was.
The classic features, the superb bone-structure, the sensual curve to his perfectly modelled mouth. Damiano
was stunningly good-looking but, unlike many such

men, intensely masculine. Senses starved of him were already reacting to that unfortunate reality. The old familiar shame flooded her as she recognised the coil of heat in her belly, the swelling heaviness of her breasts beneath her clothing. Inwardly she cringed at how inappropriate and humiliating those responses were in the presence of a male who had rejected her outright on the one occasion she had plucked up the courage to invite him back to the marital bed. No, he definitely wasn't going to need her *that* way, she reminded herself, mortified by her own foolish susceptibility.

Once she'd got a hold on her embarrassing thoughts and tamped them firmly down again, her anxious eyes roved over his strong dark features and now marked the changes. His hard cheekbones might have been chiselled out of bronze and carried not an ounce of superfluous flesh. He was pale beneath that bronzed tan, his brilliant deep-set dark eyes shadowed with exhaustion. He would have had so much news to catch up on with his family that he probably hadn't slept on the flight back to England. In fact, he looked as if he hadn't slept in a week.

But there was an edge there now in that lean strong face that hadn't been there before. A tough, hard edge stamped like an overlay of steel on him. The smooth, sophisticated coolness she recalled had been replaced by a colder, deadlier quality. She had seen it in action with the welcome committee. There had been no apologetic pretence about his impatience to be gone. His accent had altered too. Five years of speaking Spanish and nothing else, no doubt carefully modelling his speech pattern on those around him. He was a very clever guy. He had not become the chairman of the Braganzi Bank by birth and precedent as his late father had. He had been voted in at the age of twenty-eight because he was quite simply brilliant at what he did.

The silence had become charged with an intensity she didn't understand. A slight frown-line indented her brow as she connected with his eyes. Eyes that now burned like golden flames. In a sudden movement, he meshed his other hand into her hair and brought her startled mouth up under his.

It was a shockingly intimate and shockingly unexpected sensual assault. Indeed, Eden, accustomed to the belief that her husband found her about as physically appealing as an ice bath, could not have been more stunned. The plunging eroticism of his tongue searching out the tender interior of her mouth shook her to her very depths and then sent such a current of scorching excitement through her that a strangled gasp was wrenched from her.

Instantly, Damiano released her, feverish colour scoring his cheekbones as he took a swift look at her shaken face, lowered his thick black lashes and breathed in a hoarse undertone, '*Mi dispiace*...I'm sorry, I can't think what came over me.'

Neither could Eden but most ironically she hadn't been about to complain. Her heart was banging as if she had run a three-minute mile. Her wretched body was tense and expectant; it had been so long since she had been touched in an intimate way. And she was hugely embarrassed because it was so obvious that Damiano regretted having kissed her. Lowering her head in self-protection, she chose to study their still-linked hands instead. Just grabbing was a sort of guy thing, she decided, trying to work out what had motivated Damiano, which was a challenge. After all, he had always confounded her understanding.

His hand tightened its grip on hers. 'Did I hurt you?'

'No...' So great was her self-consciousness, her response was a mere thread. Just grab me any time you
like, she would have said to him had she had the nerve
to credit that such an invitation would be welcome. But
she didn't have the nerve and laboured under no such
confidence-boosting belief in her own powers of attraction. Five years earlier, in a desperate attempt to save
their marriage, she had tried to bridge the estrangement
between them and failed miserably. Shortly before that
disastrous trip to Montavia, Damiano had rejected her.
He had said no to the offer of her body. What was more,
he had said no with the kind of sarcasm which had cut
her to the bone.

In the taut silence she brought her other hand round
his and then, finally noticing the unfamiliar roughness
there, turned his hand over and looked at it, for want
of anything better to do. In complete bewilderment, she
ran a fingertip over his scarred knuckles, his broken
nails, and checked his palms. It was the hand of a man
accustomed to hard and unrelenting manual labour.

'Challenge for the manicurist,' Damiano commented
lazily.

'But...but how—?'

'I spent over three years working in a quarry six days
a week. There wasn't much in the way of machinery—'

'A q-quarry?' Eden stammered, cradling his hand between both of hers with the most giant surge of shocked
protectiveness surging up through her. A quarry?
Damiano labouring in a quarry?

'After the first year, the military government awarded
political status to all rebel prisoners. Good move. If
you've banged up about a quarter of the entire male
population and the country is so poor you can't afford

to feed them, you have to prepare the footwork for an amnesty to let them out again,' Damiano explained levelly. 'And put them to work in the short-term so that they can produce enough not to be a burden on the economy.'

'A quarry...' Eden framed in shaken disbelief, emotion overpowering her even in the face of that deadpan recitation. 'Your poor hands...you had s-such beautiful hands—'

'*Dio mio*...I was *glad* to work! Beautiful hands?' Damiano countered with very masculine mockery. 'What am I? A male model or something?'

Squeezing her eyes tightly shut against the stinging tears already blinding her, Eden lifted his hand to her face and kissed his fingers. She couldn't have spoken or explained why to save her life, but she could no more have prevented herself from doing it than she could have stopped breathing.

In the aftermath of that gesture, the silence was so charged it just about screamed out loud.

Damiano withdrew his hand. Eden raised her face and clashed with stunned dark eyes and her face began to burn up like a bonfire.

'What's got into you?' Damiano demanded raggedly, his disconcertion over her emotional behaviour unconcealed.

'I'm...I'm sorry...' she mumbled, wishing a big hole would open up and swallow her, suddenly feeling so absolutely foolish.

'No...don't apologise for possibly the only spontaneous affection you have ever shown me!' Damiano urged, studying her with bemused intensity.

'That's not true,' she whispered in dismay at that

charge, uttered with such assurance as if it were a fact too well-known to be questioned.

But Damiano forestalled any further protest on her part by suddenly leaning forward to frown out at the suburban street the limo was now traversing to ask in honest bewilderment, 'Where on earth are we going?'

Eden tensed, 'My flat. It's on the outskirts of town—'

'You left our home to move into a *town* flat?' Damiano demanded in astonishment. 'I assumed that you had moved to Norfolk so that you could live in a country house!'

'It wasn't as simple as that, Damiano. For a start I wouldn't have had the money to buy myself a house and what would I have lived on? Air?' Eden heard herself respond with helpless defensiveness. 'The bank may have continued trading after your disappearance but all your personal assets were frozen which meant that I couldn't touch any of your money—'

'Naturally I am aware of that fact,' Damiano cut in drily. 'But are you seriously trying to tell me that my brother was not prepared to support you?'

It was amazing just how swiftly they had contrived to arrive at the very nub of the problem. The hard reality that Eden had become estranged from his family during his absence, news that would never, ever have gone down well with a male as family orientated as Damiano. And news which would go down even less well should he be told the truth of *why* the bad feeling had reached such a climax that she had no longer felt able to remain under the same roof.

'No, I'm not trying to tell you that,' Eden countered tightly, unable to bring her eyes to meet his in any direct way, playing for time while she attempted to come up with a credible explanation. 'I just felt that it was time I moved out and stood on my own feet—'

'After only four months? It did not take you long to give up all hope of my return!' Damiano condemned grittily.

The sudden silence reverberated.

And then Damiano made an equally abrupt and dismissive movement with one lean brown hand. 'No, forget that I said that! It was cruelly unfair. Nuncio himself admitted that he had believed me to be dead the first month and you never grew as close to my family as I had once hoped. The crisis of my disappearance divided you all rather than bringing you closer together—'

'Damiano,' Eden interceded tautly on the defensive.

'No, say no more. I would accept no excuses from Nuncio and I will accept none from you. That my brother should have flown out to Brazil *without* bringing my wife with him struck me as beyond the bounds of belief!' Damiano admitted grimly, his firm mouth hardening. 'Only nothing could have more clearly illustrated how deep the divisions between you had become—'

'Yes...but—'

'My disappointment at that reality was considerable but it is not something which I wish to discuss right now,' Damiano interrupted with all the crushing dismissal he could bring to any subject which annoyed him and which she well recalled from the distant past.

Eden had gone from shrinking terror at what might be revealed if she dared to protest her own innocence to instinctive resentment of that innately superior assurance. Dear heaven, did he think they were all foolish children to be scolded and set to rights on how they ought to be behaving? And then just when she was on the very brink of parting her lips and disabusing him of that illusion, it occurred to her that it would be wiser to let him think as he did for the present. Let sleeping dogs lie...only for how long would they lie quiet? Stifling that ennervating thought, Eden swallowed hard.

However, she need not have worried about where the conversation was going for at that point the limo drew up outside the narrow building where she both lived and worked. Damiano gazed out at the very ordinary street of mixed housing and shops with raised ebony brows.

'It may not be what you're used to but it's not as bad as it looks.' Eden took advantage of his silence to hurriedly climb out and lead the way, only to find herself hovering when Damiano paused to instruct the chauffeur in Italian. The limo pulled away from the kerb again and drove off.

Well aware that Damiano would not associate her with the name James etched in small print below the sign, 'Garment Alterations,' on the barred door, Eden hastened on past and mounted the steep stairs. The shop was shut. On Wednesday, most of the local shops took a half-day.

With a taut hand, she unlocked the door of her flat. Damiano strode in. In one all-encompassing and astonished glance he took in the compact living area and the three doors leading off to bathroom, bedroom and kitchen. 'I can't believe you left our home to live like this!'

'I wish you'd stop referring to the town house as *our* home. It may have been yours but it never felt like mine,' Eden heard herself respond, surprising herself with her own vehemence as much as she could see she had surprised him, for he had come to an arrested halt.

Damiano frowned. 'What are you talking about?'

'Living in the town house was like living in a commune—'

'A *commune*?'

'The communal Italian way of living; no matter how big the house is, there is never one corner you can call your own,' Eden extended jerkily.

'I was not aware that you felt like that about living with my family.' Damiano's outrage purred along every syllable of his response.

Eden knotted her trembling hands together. She was shaken by the strength of her desire to shout back at him for his refusal to accept the obvious and understand. That lack of privacy had contributed to their problems.

'Although I consider it beneath me to make the reminder, you came from a home no bigger than a rabbit hutch where I am quite sure it was an even bigger challenge to find a corner you could call your own,' Damiano framed with sardonic bite.

It was so crazy to be arguing about such a thing now. Her brain acknowledged that reality but, hurt that he should refer to the vast difference between their backgrounds, she could not keep her tongue still. 'So because you viewed our marriage as being along the lines of King Cophetua and the beggar maid—'

'King...who?'

'I was supposed to be *grateful* to find myself in a house that belonged to not just one but *two* other women!'

'What other women?' Having given up on establishing who the fabled King was, Damiano was studying her now as if she were slow-witted.

Eden's hands parted and then knotted into fists.

'Nuncio's wife, Valentina, and your sister, Cosetta. It was their home long before I came along—'

'I cannot believe we are having this absurd argument.'

'I couldn't even redecorate my own bedroom without offending someone...and you think I should have *liked* living like that? Always guests with us at meal times, always having to be polite and on my best behavior, never being able to relax, never being alone anywhere with you but in a bedroom—'

'And there least of all if you could help it,' Damiano slotted in reflectively. 'You would fall asleep in company before you would go upstairs at night. I *did* get the message.'

At that unanswerable reminder and assurance, Eden turned pale. The pained resentment went out of her then as if he had punched a button. She was both taken aback and embarrassed that she should have dragged up something which was so outstandingly trivial and inappropriate in the light of what *he* had endured since. And so great was that sense of shamed self-exposure, she just turned round jerkily and hurried off into the kitchen, muttering feverishly, 'You must want a coffee.'

She left behind her a silence, a huge silence.

With a trembling hand, she put on the kettle. 'Do you want anything to eat?'

'No, thanks,' Damiano countered. 'With Nuncio fussing round me like a mother hen, I was practically force-fed all the way from Brazil!'

He had followed her as far as the doorway. Out of the corner of her eye, she snaked a nervous glance at his enervating stillness. So tall, so dark, so heartbreakingly handsome. He was here, he was home—well, in her home temporarily. She loved this guy, she really,

really loved this guy. And here she was raving at him about stuff that was five years out of date and of about as much relevance to him now as an old weather report!

Was she out of her mind? It wasn't fair to hold his shock at the way she was living against him. He had left her behind in a mansion with twenty-five bedrooms and a full quota of domestic staff. Evidently, he had assumed that she would be protected by his brother's wealth from the usual financial problems of a wife with a husband who had vanished. So it was understandable that he should be astonished, even annoyed to find her ensconced in a tiny flat, existing on a budget that wouldn't have covered what his sister spent on shoes in a week.

'I didn't realize that you disliked living with my family...I never thought about that possibility,' Damiano admitted flatly.

'It's all right...I don't know why I mentioned it,' Eden gabbled in an apologetic surge, desperate to placate. 'It's so unimportant now—'

'No, it's not. I'll stay here until this evening *but...*'

Oh, dear heaven, he was going to leave her again! In a short space of time, it seemed she had alienated him, driven him off. A chill so deep it pierced her like a knife spread through Eden.

'I just need more space around me right now...OK?'

'OK...' Eden whispered so low she was almost drowned out by the boiling kettle. Space? Personal space and freedom, the sort of psychological stuff the Foreign Office advisor had tried to give her a crash course in understanding, she presumed, feeling sick. He wanted space away from her, he wanted to *escape* from her after less than a hour. She felt as if the roof were coming down on her, crushing the breath from her body.

'I've got twenty-four hours of meetings mapped out ahead of me already,' Damiano said levelly. 'There are legal niceties to be dealt with, press announcements to be made, new arrangements to be set in motion at the bank. I can't stay here. I *have* to be in London.'

He had never intended to stay. This had just been a flying visit. Literally! While he'd spoken, she had started to make the coffee on automatic pilot but as he continued to speak, and her heart sank, automatic pilot failed her. She didn't even notice that the cup she was filling was overflowing.

'*Porca miseria!*' Suddenly Damiano was right there behind her, his hands closing urgently over her taut shoulders as he yanked her back out of reach of the pool of boiling water about to cascade off the edge of the worktop. 'You almost scalded yourself!'

Pale and trembling, Eden focused on the hot water pouring down on to the floor with dismayed eyes.

'Just go and sit down…I'll deal with the flood,' Damiano asserted, thrusting her towards the door with determination. 'I think you're still in shock.'

From the sitting room Eden paused to look back and watch Damiano mopping up. 'It just doesn't seem real…you doing something domesticated like that, you being here,' she mumbled unevenly.

She encountered brilliant dark eyes as intent on her as she was on him. 'You're as white as a sheet, *cara*. Sit down.'

She sat because she was honestly afraid that, if she didn't, she might fall down. It seemed just a minute later but of course it must have been longer than that by the time Damiano reappeared and placed a cup of coffee in front of her. Damiano, who had once pressed a bell to get a cup of coffee or anything else he fancied. Yes, she thought in the disorientated manner of someone too strung up to reason rationally: Annabel would have come running back had Damiano so much as snapped his fingers. Even *after* he'd married! Struggling to get her wandering mind back under control, Eden fought for some semblance of composure.

'You're just coming apart at the seams...' Damiano groaned, bending over her without warning and lifting her up, only to lay her down again full length on the sofa. He snatched up the throw from the arm of one of the chairs and carefully arranged it over her. He hunkered down on a level with her, smoothed her hair back from her drawn face and breathed in a ragged undertone of regret. 'I've always been such a selfish bastard.'

The rawness of his emotions was etched in every line of his lean strong face. In the whole of their marriage, Damiano had never behaved as he just had or indeed looked or spoken as he did then. Eden was transfixed. Guilt...was this guilt she was hearing, guilt that he had hurt her? For she had made a hash of things within the first minute of seeing him again. Telling him she *loved* him! Dear heaven, where had her wits and her pride been? Five years on from a marriage he had long known to be a mistake! It was a wonder that he had even been prepared to give her these few hours. He was trying to let her down gently but equally impatient to get back to his own life. Back to the bank, back to the family from hell...

'I have had a long time to think about our marriage,' Damiano stated almost harshly.

'I know...' She shut her eyes because she just wanted to shut him up before he said more than she could stand to hear. She did not want the full spotlight of his atten-

tion on her. She just might break down and start sobbing
and pleading.

'I was cruel…'

She jerked her chin in dumb acknowledgement and
then whipped over on to her side, turning her narrow
back to him, so much tormented emotion swilling about
inside her, she was afraid she would break apart under
the pressure. She crammed a fist against her wobbling
mouth, willing herself into silence.

'I tried to make you into something you couldn't
be…'

Sexy, adventurous, wanton, seductive. That was what
he had wanted. That was what he hadn't got. The sort
of female who pranced about in front of him in silk
underwear and was willing to have sex somewhere
other than in a bed with all the lights switched off. The
sort of female who played a more active part, who did
something more than simply *lie* there. The sort of female who was able to *show* him that she wanted him.

'I had unrealistic expectations,' Damiano breathed in
a driven admission.

Formed by a vast experience of other women to who
such outdated inhibitions had evidently been unknown,
she reflected with a bitter sense of squirming failure.

'I wasn't used to hearing that word, ''no''…'

Well, he had certainly heard it a lot both before *and*
after he'd married. Would it really have killed her to
take her clothes off in front of him or let him undress
her just once? Couldn't she have said, 'yes' that time
he had started kissing her in the car when he had come
back from a long business trip?

'What I'm trying to say is that I was wrong to make
the bedroom such an issue…do you think you could
say something?' Damiano murmured tautly.

'Nothing to say,' Eden whispered, keeping her back turned to him, tears running down her cheeks.

The silence fizzed like the shaken bottle of a soft drink, threatening explosion from pent-up pressure. She had done the wrong thing again. He wanted her to talk but what on earth did he expect her to say? Everything he had said meant just one thing to Eden: he wanted a divorce, a civilised one where blame was shared and platitudes were mouthed and nobody held spite. So he was smoothing over the past, trying to change it. What else could he be doing when he said he should not have made the bedroom such an issue?

For wasn't sexual satisfaction of major importance to most men? And, to a male of Damiano's ilk, a taken-for-granted expectation. After years of being pursued, flattered and treated to every feminine wile available, a rich and powerful man took it as his due that he would marry a sensual woman. But then she knew *why* Damiano had ended up asking someone as unsuitable as she had been to marry him, didn't she? Her tummy turned over. On the rebound from Annabel, he had been a male used to winning every time, and had been challenged by Eden's refusal to sleep with him.

'I've got some calls to make,' Damiano said flatly.

'I'm sorry, I—?'

'No!' Damiano countered with grim disapproval. 'I do not want to hear you always apologising. You weren't like that when I married you...I *made* you that way by acting like a bully!'

So taken aback was Eden by that declaration that she opened her eyes and lifted her head with a jerk, but the only reward she received was the decisive snap of the bedroom door closing. A bully? Was that how she had made him feel with her inability to talk or respond on the level he required? That idea pained her even more and sent her thoughts winging back into the distant past...

Her parents had married late in life and she had been an only child, her father the gamekeeper on a remote Scottish estate. One of her earliest memories was the hum of the sewing machine for her mother had been a gifted seamstress whose talents had brought in much-needed extra income. Hard work had been respected and idle chatter discouraged in a household in which emotions had been kept private and demonstrative affection had been rare.

By the time that Eden had gained her teaching qualification at college, her mother had died and her father had asked her to return home to live. When the sole teacher in the tiny local school had taken maternity leave, Eden had been engaged to fill the temporary vacancy. Over the years, the Falcarragh estate on which she had been born had changed hands many times. Having gone out of private ownership, it had been traded just like a business investment and had long been run by a London-based management team of executives, who had rarely visited but who had excelled at cutting costs.

Even though she had by then been twenty-one, love and its attendant excitements had played little part in Eden's life. The estate manager's son, Mark Anstey, her childhood playmate, had remained her closest friend. As a teenager, however, she had had a major crush on Mark. She had only outgrown it when she'd realised that although she'd been very fond of him, she just hadn't been able to imagine kissing him. Mark had felt more like the brother she had never had.

Damiano had stridden into Eden's life that same win-

ter when his car had gone off the road in the snow. Her
father had been away from home, staying with his
brother who had been ill. The adverse weather had
closed the school early the day before. The following
evening, Eden had been astonished when the dogs had
started barking to warn her of a visitor for, with blizzard
conditions, threatening outside, all sensible people had
been safe indoors.

Answering the door, she'd stared in initial dismay at
the very tall and powerfully intimidating figure which
Damiano had cut in a snow-encrusted black coat.

'*Mi dispiace,*' he stated hoarsely, frowning with the
effort concentration took. 'But I need...I need the
phone.'

Registering only that he was feverishly flushed,
swaying on his feet and showing the confusion brought
on by being frozen, Eden stopped being intimidated at
speed. If he collapsed, she knew she wouldn't be capable of lifting so big a man. With innate practicality,
she closed her hand over his sleeve and urged him over
the threshold. 'Come in at once...'

She guided him towards the warmth of the hearth but
not too close to the heat. 'Phone...*per favore,*' he said
again, his dark-timbred drawl accented, the words
slightly slurred, but it was still a remarkably attractive
voice.

Stretching up on tiptoe, Eden instead began to remove the very heavy and sodden coat he wore, forcing
him to release the travel bag he still clutched as if his
life depended on it. Finding the jacket of the business
suit he wore beneath damp, she scurried round him to
unbutton it and ease him out of that as well. Damiano,
silent for possibly the only time in their entire acquaintance, stood there registering complete bewilderment at

what she was doing and blinking lashes long as black silk fans. *'Signóra?'*

'You must have a death wish,' she groaned out loud. 'Such unsuitable clothing for this weather—'

She hauled a blanket out of the chest by the wall and tried to reach up high enough to drape it round his shoulders, finally surrendering and planting a hand to his broad chest in an effort to persuade him down into the armchair behind him.

'Small...angel?' he queried, gazing down at her with bemused fascination, dark as midnight eyes lingering on her delicate features as he clumsily pinned her hand in place with ice-cold fingers. 'No rings...single?'

'Sit down,' Eden told him, hurriedly pulling her hand free.

He sank down heavily into the chair but continued to stare at her.

Eden arranged the blanket round him and then crouched down at his feet to remove his wet shoes and socks as quickly as she could, continuing to talk for fear that he might still lapse into unconsciousness. 'What's your name?'

'Damiano...'

She looked up and focused properly on his features for the first time since his arrival. She stilled, her absorbed gaze roving slowly over that startlingly handsome lean, dark face, her breath tripping in her throat. Even wet, he was just so incredibly good-looking. Gorgeous bone-structure, incredible eyes.

'Damiano,' she repeated shakily.

He gave her a sleepy but charismatic smile that rocked her heart on its axis and said something else in his own language.

With extreme effort she dragged her attention from

him and unzipped his travel bag in search of warm dry clothing. She extracted a pair of khaki jeans and an oatmeal sweater, the quality of both attracting her notice but not to the extent they should have done for she had little knowledge of designer labels. Was he a tourist? He was hardly dressed for the winter sports season. The coat and the suit were of the type a city businessman would wear to a formal meeting.

'You get changed while I'm heating up some soup for you,' she instructed him in an authoritative voice, the one she used with the rebellious older boys in her classroom. 'Don't you dare go to sleep on me!'

But even as she walked into the small scullery her heart was hammering so hard, she had to snatch in a sustaining breath and she could not resist the urge to glance back over her shoulder at him and look again.

She collided with beautiful dark deep-set eyes that made her feel dizzy and brainless for the first time in her extremely sensible life. 'You *do* look an angel...' he told her stubbornly.

'That's enough,' she tried to say briskly.

'No, it's only a beginning.'

And so it was. But, unfortunately, a beginning for two people without the slightest thing in common. Damiano soon recovered from that rare vulnerability which she found so very appealing. Having already discovered to his cost at the roadside that the reception was too poor in the area for his mobile phone to work, he was amazed when she let drop that her father had only got the landline phone connected the previous year and that the same problem with bad reception had prevented them from ever owning a television.

He was even more astonished that she didn't own a car. Yet he himself had climbed the steep-rutted track which ran over a mile down to the road and only a four-wheel drive could traverse it in bad weather. With her father away and the estate vehicle he utilised only insured for his use, Eden had been without transport. To get to school that week, she had been walking down to the road and catching a lift with one of her pupil's parents.

After eating, Damiano again requested the use of the phone and, since she naturally gave him privacy to make that call, she didn't pick up any hint of *who* he actually was. Mightn't she have drawn back and protected herself that night had she known how wealthy and powerful a male she had brought in out of the storm?

Indeed, although he later carelessly dismissed her claim as utterly ridiculous, Eden remained convinced that Damiano had *deliberately* avoided telling her that he owned the Falcarragh estate. In addition, he had not mentioned the Braganzi Bank or, for that matter, any facet of his high-powered lifestyle which might have alerted her to his true status. He had been content to allow her to believe that he was merely one of the salaried London executives involved in the running of the estate. Why, she had never understood, unless it had simply amused him.

By the time she showed Damiano into her father's bedroom, for he had no option other than to spend the night, she had talked herself hoarse. He had dragged the unremarkable story of her life out of her with a determination that only an ill-mannered response could have forestalled. And she had been flattered and fascinated by the heady effect of his powerful personality, mega-watt charm and stunning good looks all focused exclusively on her.

The next morning, after the snowplough had been through, he insisted on making his own way down to the road to be picked up, but before he departed he asked her to have dinner with him that night and she agreed; of course she did. She suppressed the awareness that her father would disapprove of her dating a male he would regard as one of the 'bosses'. Rain came on that afternoon and Damiano arrived at the door in one of the estate four-wheel drives.

He had taken a room in the only local hotel and was critical of the meal they received in the cosy bar. Naturally. While she saw nothing wrong with anything they were served, the meal could hardly have been of the standard to which Damiano was accustomed. It was like a dream date for Eden to be seen out with a male whom other women couldn't take their eyes off. She adored his good manners, hung on his every witty word of conversation and marvelled at his ability to reach for her hand and hold it as if it was the most natural thing in the world.

And then, on the drive home, her dream bubble burst.

'I would have asked you to stay the night with me at the hotel but I imagine that the local teacher has to be careful of her reputation in a rural area like this,' Damiano remarked with incredible cool. 'It's fortunate that you don't have neighbours.'

He had known her for precisely twenty-nine hours and *already* he was expecting her to sleep with him! Eden was shocked out of her enchanted cloud of romance, embarrassed and then angry with him for wrecking everything and angry with herself for having foolishly expected more of him. With the exception of his singularly smooth and sophisticated approach, it seemed that, after all, Damiano was little different from the college students who had hassled her with crude pick-up lines and horribly blunt sexual invitations.

'I have no intention of letting you stay the night,' Eden breathed curtly.

'That was a negative,' Damiano mused with indolent, even amused unconcern. 'I'm gifted at changing negatives into positives.'

Tears burned the back of her eyes but rage gathered inside her. 'That kind of behaviour isn't part of my life and it never will be—'

'You're planning to become a nun?' Damiano incised with lashings of mockery, quite undaunted by her attitude. 'Let me tell you something about Italian men…we're extremely persistent when we want something—'

'I do not want to discuss this!' Eden interrupted in growing mortification. 'Just drop the subject—'

'I'm an upfront guy, *cara*. And, at my age, I cannot imagine having a relationship without sex—'

'Well, I'm not planning on having a physical relationship with anybody until I get married!' Eden shot back at him between gritted teeth.

Damiano was so shattered by that accidental admission which he had provoked her into making that he shot the car to a mud-churning halt outside her home and turned to scrutinise her with openly incredulous eyes. 'You're kidding me?'

Releasing her seat belt, as desperate now to escape him as she had been to *be* with him earlier in the evening, Eden scrambled out of the car. 'Goodnight!'

Damiano sprang out of the driver's seat and intercepted her before she could reach the door. 'You're still a virgin?'

Nobody had ever spoken that word to Eden's hot face

before and she could think of nobody she could have wanted to hear it from less. He said it in the same tone of disbelief which some people reserved for UFOs.

'Urgent re-think…possibly the concept of enjoying out mutual passion tonight was slightly premature,' Damiano groaned with unashamed regret.

Eden was hauling her keys out of her bag with a shaking and desperate hand. If she had had wings, she would have spread them and flown away. Sex had never been mentioned in her home, nothing so intimate ever discussed. Apart from frequent references to the social and moral consequences of casual intimacy, sex had been no more prevalent a subject in the city vicarage where she had boarded with her uncle's family while at college. 'Please shut up,' she gasped.

'I'm trying to understand what's going on here—'

'I made it quite clear—'

'But you're surely *not* expecting me to propose marriage to get you into bed?' Damiano persisted with sardonic cool.

And reacting to that wounding sarcasm, she slapped him. Without thinking about it, without meaning to do it, she just lifted her hand and slapped him across one high, hard cheekbone.

'You—'

'I'm sorry but—'

Damiano surveyed her with outraged eyes that turned gold in anger and pulled her to him with powerful hands to crush her startled mouth under his with an explosive passion that just blew her away.

Releasing her again, Damiano studied her shocked face and the hectic flush he had fired in her cheeks and suddenly, without the slightest warning, he laughed with genuine amusement. 'Some day soon, I swear you're going to be begging me for that, *cara mia*. I can wait for the day.'

CHAPTER THREE

EMERGING from that emotive trip back more than five years into the past, Eden listened to the distinct tones of Damiano's cultured drawl as he talked on the phone in her bedroom and slowly breathed in deeply.

Hadn't his own sardonic question come true in the end? He *had* married her to get her into his bed and, understandably, having gone to such lengths and practised such patience, Damiano had expected a wildly sensual wedding night and an orgy of a honeymoon. Only that hadn't come off either, Eden recalled, wretched tears gathering again as she stuck her face in a cushion.

'I'm going to try and catch a couple of hours of sleep before I fold. I'm so tired, I feel like I'm only half conscious,' Damiano admitted heavily from the bedroom doorway. 'Do you want me to use the sofa?'

It was the last straw. He'd come back after *five* years and was offering to sleep on a sofa that was only four-foot long, even though there was a double bed in her bedroom and he had to have noticed it!

'Please use the bed,' Eden squeezed out, will-power keeping a tremulous wail of self-pity from escaping.

'The limo will be here at seven to ferry me back out to the airfield. Wake me up in time,' he urged.

It's over, she tried to tell herself with accepting fatalism. It never worked. Just be grateful he's alive. But it wasn't enough—by no stretch of the imagination was it enough to compensate her for the devastating effect of Damiano walking back into her life like the ultimate fantasy and then walking back *out* again. Here she was curled up like a hedgehog hiding from him. More or less business as usual, then? Here she was demonstrating all over again the kind of lie-down-and-die passivity that drove Damiano clean up the walls!

Was this *all* she was capable of doing? Acting like a helpless victim who had no influence over her own misfortunes? How come she had just fallen straight back into that old bad pattern of behaviour when she had changed so much during his absence?

For she *had* changed, had had no choice but to become stronger and braver after what she had experienced. When Damiano had mentioned leaving again, shock had settled over her like a blinding, suffocating blanket. She had just shrunk in stature down to the level of a carpet fibre, all fight, all confidence, all strength leeched back out of her again as her worst fears came true.

So are you just planning to let go without an argument?

Eden unfurled herself and stood up. The bedroom door was slightly ajar. For how long had she been lost in her own thoughts? She pushed open the door an inch at a time, her heart thundering at the base of her dry throat. Damiano was fast asleep in her bed, his glossy black hair and his bronzed skin in stark contrast to the pale bed linen. He was lying on his stomach, the duvet tangled round his narrow hips, his powerful shoulders, muscular arms and the long, spectacular golden sweep of his back exposed. He was a riveting sight. Totally male, totally breathtaking.

How often had she sneaked a look at Damiano half naked? Her cheeks burned. Strange, wasn't it, that she should have personally taken advantage of what she had consistently denied him? But hadn't she always secretly enjoyed looking at him? Hadn't a single glimpse of Damiano just with his shirt off thrilled her to death? But she hadn't ever admitted that even to herself until now. The way she had been brought up such a sexual thought would have been considered shameless and not how a good and decent woman would think.

So she had been raised in a repressed and puritanical home with parents who had been heading for their sixties by the time she'd entered her teens. Why had she taken all that baggage with her into her marriage? Why hadn't she tried to shake free of her inhibitions just a little? Well, the truth was, she was very stubborn and very proud. And so was Damiano. Neither one of them had been prepared to compromise.

That time she had offered herself and he had rejected her, what had she said?

'I want a baby…'

Damiano had studied her with chilling dark eyes. 'You just put a double lock on your own chastity belt. That has to be the least tempting proposition any woman ever offered me. When you want *me* and when you can prove that on my terms, I might consider coming back to your bed.'

Was it too late now? For Damiano had had to go missing before she'd been able to understand *why* he had been so angry with her that day. Eden's hands curled into fists over her own past stupidity. The face-saving excuse of wanting a baby had been a huge mistake. Then he hadn't appreciated just how desperate she had been or how she had naively believed that getting pregnant might have kept him with her.

She walked back out of the bedroom and into the kitchen. There was a bottle of vodka in the cupboard.

Pam had given it to her for Christmas four years back, not then aware that Eden never touched alcohol. Yet another thing that had irritated Damiano: a bride who wouldn't even touch champagne at her own wedding! But she needed Dutch courage before she could do what she *had* to do, didn't she?

She poured herself a glass of vodka liberally combined with orange juice. Suppose he said no and fought her off? She would have to sort of creep up on him while he slept, not give him the chance to object. He had grabbed her and kissed her in the limo, hadn't he? For a split second, it had been as if he'd been unable to keep his hands of her! There surely hadn't been any women in that South American quarry and she had married a very highly sexed male. Turned him off it to the extent that she had actually started fearing that he might be obtaining what he no longer appeared to want at home *elsewhere*...

But, prior to his disappearance, Damiano had given her no cause to believe that he was being unfaithful, she reminded herself urgently. Now she had this one last chance. Maybe she had run out of chances. But he was worth the effort. She tiptoed back to the bedroom doorway and feasted her fraught eyes upon him. Oh, yes, he was still worth a major effort and in just a few hours he would be gone for ever!

Wrinkling her nose, she up-ended the glass and drank deep. Then she stripped off her clothes. She put on perfume, made careful use of her small stock of cosmetics and fussed endlessly with the blonde hair that tumbled round her shoulders in no particular style. As she usually wore her hair up, she had got lazy about getting it cut. She wondered if old vodka went off in strength and decided she had better drink some more. She was going to be everything Damiano had ever wanted just once. *Not* that prude he had left on the sofa. To prove that to herself, she walked naked out to the hall storage cupboard to dig out a box of keepsakes she had chosen not to leave behind in the town house.

Damiano had sent her a box of gorgeous silk lingerie the day before their wedding. The upfront guy spelling out his expectations, fantasies, hopes. No doubt, he had not appreciated just how outright intimidated she had been by that gesture or how deeply shocked her late father had been by the sight of such an intimate gift, for naturally the older man had demanded to know what had been in that wretched box and she had just cringed.

Eden slid into whisper-thin lilac panties and a matching low-cut bra. Better than being naked, she decided, bracing herself. She was beginning to feel a little strange…kind of skittish, enervated, gripped by the most ridiculous desire to dance. Damiano wasn't going to know what had hit him, she told herself, psyching herself up into her new and more adventurous persona.

Damiano was now lying on his back in a diagonal sprawl across the divan. Late afternoon sunshine was filtering through the thin cotton curtains at the window. From the foot of the bed, she eased up into the space left by the wall. She studied Damiano. The piratical dark stubble accentuating his strong jawline and beautifully moulded mouth, the riot of dark, curling hair hazing his powerful pectorals, the smooth golden skin wrapped round his sleek, strong muscles.

Just the thought of touching him made her tingle. Awkwardly, she edged further up the bed, ludicrously fearful of awakening him. She bent over him, mesmerised by the slow rise and fall of his chest, the soft rush of his breathing and finally by the vibrance of him even

asleep. She lifted her hand and rested her fingers very
lightly on his arm. He shifted, muscles flexing beneath
her hand. She tensed but the need to express how much
she loved him in the only way that seemed left was
more powerful.

Lowering her head, Eden pressed her lips to his taut,
flat stomach and ran the tip of her tongue over his skin.
The taste of him made her shiver. Heat flooded her own
trembling body, stirring her breasts, pinching her nipples into straining buds. The scent of him was an un-
believable aphrodisiac to senses starved for so long. Her
hand settled to a powerful male thigh to balance herself
and, breathing in deep, she began to ease back the sheet.

But with a slumbrous growl, Damiano shifted, startling her. He laced his fingers into her hair to draw her
up to him. Eden had barely grasped that he was wakening and that control was no longer hers before he had
claimed her mouth in a devouring and hungry kiss. Raw
need raced through every fibre of her shaken body in
response. Settling strong hands to her waist, he lifted
her over him, long fingers splaying to her slender hips
to urge her into potent contact with the virile force of
his arousal.

The heat he ignited fired an almost painful ache deep
in her pelvis. Eden quivered, a helpless moan of reaction escaping her. Almost instantaneously, Damiano
stilled. His hands whipping up to her forearms, he held
her back from him.

Stunned dark as night eyes clashed with hers. 'Eden?'
he faltered in apparent disbelief. *'Che cos' hai?'*

It was one of those ghastly moments when time hung
still and she would have done anything to move it on.
As she registered that Damiano had automatically responded to her caresses before he was even properly

awake, a burning tide of red skimmed up her throat to scorch her discomfited face. She watched in a state of stricken paralysis as his attention zeroed in on the scanty bra and brief set she wore. He blinked. Then he looked again with the kind of fixed attention which only accentuated his shock.

'*Per amor di Dio*...what on earth are you playing at?'

Prior to getting into the bed, Eden had nourished a comforting vision of Damiano waking up to snatch her to him with keen hands and mercifully silent enthusiasm. Instead, Damiano had pulled back from her to reassert control and was now asking what had to be the craziest question he had ever asked her.

'And why are you dressed like that?' Damiano enunciated with a level of incredulity which only seemed to be increasing with every second that passed. He now focused on the high-heeled shoes which she had put on and kept on.

'I...I don't know what you expect me to say...' Her admission emerged hopelessly slurred, the words tumbling together, provoking an even deeper frown between Damiano's winged ebony brows.

'Have you been drinking?' Damiano questioned rawly.

'Well, er...a bit—'

'*So*...' Damiano framed in a wrathful, low-pitched growl, black eyes blazing to gold as he scanned her guilt-stricken face. 'You had to hit the bottle to get back into bed with me?'

'Yes... I mean *no!*' she gasped, floundering in dismay and confusion at the anger he was revealing.

'*So* drunk you get into bed with your shoes on,' Damiano said thickly, fabulous bone-structure rigid as he swept her from him and dumped her back down on the mattress. 'I left behind a shy, uptight wife and now you're coming on to me tarted up like some high-class hooker!'

Aghast at that condemnation and utterly at a loss in the situation developing, Eden began to crawl backwards off the bed. 'No...no, it's not like that—'

'So *who* was it?' Damiano shot at her, his lean, dark features flushed with black fury, his dark drawl fracturing, long fingers snapping like handcuffs round her wrist before she could get out of reach. 'Who was it who worked this miraculous transformation while I was away? Don't you think I have the right to know who's been sleeping with my wife when I couldn't do anything about it?'

Her feverish colour had now ebbed to leave her pale. She stared back at him with shocked eyes. The savage tension churning up the atmosphere tore cruelly at her already frayed nerves. Damiano snatched in a starkly audible breath, lashes lowering on his smouldering gaze as he abruptly released her from his hold.

Eden scrambled off the bed and snatched up the dressing gown lying on the chair, pulling it on with shaking hands. 'Like some high-class hooker?' Was that how she had seemed to him? Mortification and shame churned up her stomach. He didn't want her...why had she imagined he would? Why had she got the crazy idea that five years on she might make good where she had failed before? Too little, too late. And now, thanks to her own foolishness, a nightmare seemed to be erupting around her: Damiano was already accusing her of having slept with some other man.

'Mark, I suppose...' Damiano gritted unevenly, his

hands curling into fierce fists. 'Sneaking, smooth little jerk just waiting his chance!'

For a split second Eden froze and then she backed out the door and fled into the bathroom. She thrust home the bolt on the door. So panicked by that final comment she could barely get air back into her lungs, she fought to get a hold of herself again. Did Damiano *know*, after all? Why else would he have mentioned Mark? Had someone already told him about those filthy lies printed about her by the tabloid press within months of his disappearance? What else was she supposed to think? Why else would he be thinking such a thing of her?

Damiano tried the handle. He rapped on the door. 'Open up, Eden. I've calmed down and we have to talk.'

But Eden retreated from the door and stared at the barrier, imagining herself growing old and grey behind it. Her brain felt like mush. She couldn't cope with this right now, couldn't cope with Damiano. Shedding the dressing gown, she tore off the scanty bra and briefs and thrust them into the waste bin with a shudder of chagrin. She kicked off the shoes and hauled on the dressing gown again, her face stiff with distress. Everything had gone horribly wrong; everything always seemed to go horribly wrong for her with Damiano.

'Eden...I'm going to break down this door if you don't come out.'

But she *knew* he wouldn't do anything like that. It wouldn't be cool. But then there had been nothing cool about the manner in which those accusations had come flying out of nowhere at her. 'You're leaving me anyway. Why am I letting you upset me? I'm not coming out!' she sobbed with sudden ferocious bitterness.

With a thunderous crash the door smashed open and banged off the wall behind it. Her compressed lips fell

open in shock. Pale as parchment, she surveyed
Damiano. He had pulled on his jeans but, bare-chested
and in need of a shave, his black hair tousled and his
brilliant eyes shimmering like starlight, he was an intimidating sight.

'Relax...' he urged in an evident attempt to soothe
her.

Eden was closer to collapse than relaxation. She
stared back at him with huge, shaken eyes. He had lost
his temper with her. He had smashed open the door
without hesitation. For that split second in her bewilderment at such unfamiliar behaviour, she was incapable of response.

Damiano strode forward and just reached for her. He
pulled her unresisting body close. His own heart was
hammering as fast as her own. He urged her back into
the sitting room. Her legs felt as weak as cotton wool
beneath her. She was shaking like a leaf.

'Why are you accusing me of leaving you?' Damiano
chided, evidently not having taken that accusation seriously. 'Why can't you just fly back to London *with*
me? It will only be for a couple of days. As soon as I
get these meetings over with, we're flying out to Italy.'

'Italy?' Finally, it dawned on Eden that she had misunderstood his intentions earlier. He might be leaving
her apartment but he was not planning to leave her behind as well. Sheer relief washed over her in such a
gigantic wave that she felt dizzy.

'One of the first things my brother told me was that
Nonna died over four years ago.'

Eden was appalled to appreciate that she had forgot-
ten that that news would greet Damiano on his return.
Old news to everybody else but *not* to him. When
Damiano had gone missing, his grandmother had been

devastated. Stress had undoubtedly contributed to the heart attack which had killed her and Damiano had to know that, Eden conceded painfully, for Damiano was no fool.

'I gather *Nonna* was in the midst of yet another grand restoration project at the time.' Repressed emotion roughened Damiano's vowel sounds and she swallowed hard on the thickness in her own throat. 'In her will, she specified that the Villa Pavone should be completed and maintained until I had been legally presumed dead. Since that fact is not generally known, I hope this Tuscan *palazzo* will supply us with a peaceful bolt-hole free from the attentions of the paparazzi.'

Finally daring to accept that Damiano intended them to stay together in the immediate future at least, Eden slowly released her pent-up breath, her worst fear now banished.

Damiano curved long, sure fingers below her chin and turned up her face, dark, deep-set eyes demanding that she stop evading his gaze. 'I shouldn't have pitched that stuff at you in the bedroom,' he asserted with cool clarity. 'You believed I was never coming back. You thought I was dead. I haven't got the right to interrogate you about the past five years. Rationally, I *know* that. But for a few minutes, waking up as I did, I over-reacted—'

'But I went on feeling married… I went on thinking about you even though you weren't there,' Eden protested with urgent tautness.

'*Sì*…I checked the dust pattern below the photograph of me by the bed,' Damiano said with a wry self-mockery that just tore at her heart. 'I know you didn't just drag it out of the closet for show today.'

Tears lashed the back of her eyes as she thought of

him checking in such a way. 'You mentioned Mark,' she reminded him tremulously, dropping her head again, still metaphorically waiting for the axe to fall.

'I'm afraid I never did warm to your childhood play-mate.' Damiano shrugged as if to stress how trivial he considered that former response on his own part. Yet Eden was surprised for she had never realised that he disliked the younger man. Indeed, at her request, more than five years earlier, Damiano had hired the younger man to help manage the Braganzi country estate outside Oxford. However, by the time a tabloid photographer had taken a covert picture of Mark passionately em-bracing a small slim blonde woman, Mark had actually been working out his notice for the Braganzi family. The estate had been joint-owned by the brothers. Nuncio, challenged by the prospect of maintaining the same high-rolling lifestyle without Damiano's assis-tance, had sold it.

But Damiano definitely didn't know about her sup-posed affair with Mark, Eden registered with heady re-lief. He couldn't *know* and still refer to Mark in that dismissive tone of disinterest. Furthermore, Damiano was taking her to Italy with him. This was not the time to start making awkward confessions and explanations, was it? Most particularly when she herself was innocent of any wrongdoing. Why dredge up all that nonsense now? Of course, she would raise the thorny subject some time with him, but at that moment all Eden wanted to concentrate on was holding onto her long-lost husband by any means within her power.

'Damiano...there hasn't been anybody else—'

'I don't need you to say that just for the sake of it. I'm not asking.' His sculpted cheekbones might have been carved from bronze as he made that assurance.

'But I'm telling you all the same.' Eden gazed up at him with clear eyes. 'Just for the record, there *hasn't* been.'

Damiano studied her with glittering intensity. 'If that's true, what was that astonishing seduction scene all about?'

Finally Eden grasped why he doubted her plea of innocence. Hot pink flooded her complexion. Her own unusually bold behaviour in the bedroom had roused his suspicions and brought on the very accusations which she had most feared!

'I know I made a mess of it,' she muttered in mortified discomfiture, studying the carpet, 'but I just wanted to…I just wanted to do something you would like for a change—'

'Something I would like,' Damiano repeated in a roughened undertone that sent a current of alarm down her spine. 'Like a sort of *big* reward for me coming home alive—'

Eden paled. 'It wasn't like that—'

'You had to jump off the teetotal wagon to do it too,' Damiano continued grittily as if she hadn't spoken. 'A sexual invitation in broad daylight, no less—'

The tension in the atmosphere gave her a panicky sensation in her tummy and once again she tried to intercede. 'Damiano—'

'I think I need to make one thing clear *before* we go to Italy,' Damiano murmured with a chilling bite that took her back five long years. 'I don't want you doing anything solely to please me.'

'Sorry…?'

Damiano studied her bewildered face with grim intensity. 'Do you think I want you pandering to me like some harem slave trying to gratify her owner?' he de-

manded with icy distaste. 'Do you really think I'm that
desperate?'

'I was just trying to show you how much you meant
to me,' Eden framed with desperate dignity, hurriedly
turning away from him before she broke down. Like
some harem slave? She cringed at that label.

His long, lean, powerful body tensing in receipt of
that patently sincere response, Damiano expelled his
breath in an abrupt hiss. 'I'm sorry—'

'No, I'm sorry that I'm *still* such a big let-down—'

From behind her, Damiano closed his arms around
her but Eden was rigid with the pain she was holding
in. 'That's not true, *cara*—'

'Yes, it is…you didn't want me,' she pointed out
chokily.

'*Per amor di Dio!* Is that what you think?' Damiano
groaned above her head, his strong arms wound round
her tightly. 'What do you think kept me going in that
bloody hell-hole of a prison? Inspiring recollections of
making deals at the bank?' His dark, deep drawl dismissed that idea with incredulous scorn. 'It was the
thought of you…and the prayer that you would still be
waiting for me when I got out of there!'

In astonishment, Eden stiffened, afraid to believe and
then desperately wanting to believe what he was telling
her. Tears of joy and relief shone in her eyes. 'Then
wh-why—?'

'Am I ranting and raving at you?' Damiano filled in
jaggedly and, unusually, he hesitated before continuing.
'I think possibly lack of sleep and feeling very claustrophobic in these surroundings.'

Claustrophobic? Eden was suddenly aghast at her
own stupidity. When he had mentioned needing space
around him, she had totally misunderstood. It was in-

deed a *very* small flat, the sitting room the only area where two people could move without one continually standing back to let the other pass. And why on earth had she woken Damiano up when he was so exhausted? What strange madness had possessed her?

'You go back to bed,' she urged protectively and she tugged free of his arms with regretful determination. 'If we're being picked up at seven, I have a lot of things to take care of—'

'*Sì...*' Damiano sank down on the bed with lithe grace. 'I suppose you'll need to inform the school that you're resigning—'

'The school?'

'Wherever you're teaching now.' Long lashes lowered over his eyes as he settled back against the pillows and slowly stretched. Still clad in his jeans, he was a devastatingly attractive vision of relaxed masculinity. So powerful was her own response to that awareness that she looked away from him in embarrassment. 'I'm sure you don't like leaving your pupils in the lurch but my need for you is greater, *cara.*'

She supposed it was natural that he should have assumed that she was teaching somewhere. But explaining that the shop below was in fact hers did not seem important just then when further dialogue would mean keeping him awake.

Before she had even finished dressing, Damiano was sound asleep again. She didn't want to leave him. Her heart was behaving as if it had wings attached. She just wanted to sit down at the foot of the bed and revel in the reality that he was physically there. Damiano had said he *needed* her. Damiano had confessed that it had been the memory of her and the thought of coming home to her which had sustained him through his ordeal in Montavia.

However, she had arrangements to make. Refusing to dwell on the intimidating prospect of returning to the Braganzi town house even for just a couple of nights, she packed a case. Fortunately her assistant, Pam Jenkinson, lived nearby and Eden was grateful to find the older woman at home when she called. The year before, Pam had looked after the shop for several weeks when Eden's father had been dying. A prosperous widow, Pam had enjoyed being left in charge and indeed had already stated her interest in taking over the business should Eden ever wish to sell up. However, now, the older woman also wanted every tiny detail ironed out and it was some time before Eden was able to leave her.

As Eden hurried back to her flat, her restive mind began taking her back into the past again, back to her earliest days with Damiano, and she could not help thinking how ironic it was that *neither* of their families had wanted them to be together...

Damiano's first kiss had frankly frightened the hell out of Eden. That sense of being out of control had spooked her. It had been like sin coming knocking on her door with a thunderous crash. So she'd told herself she wouldn't see him again. Then he'd turned up the next morning and her resistance had crumbled. Right from the start, no matter how hard she'd tried, she'd been unable to fight that powerful desperate need to be with him.

That same weekend, her father had met Damiano. The name Braganzi had meant nothing to the older man but Damiano hadn't been gone five minutes before her parent had voiced his dour disapproval. 'Not our sort, is he? And you're not his. He's one of the bosses, Eden—'

'I work for the education authority, not the Falcarragh estate—'

'Folk will talk if you start running about with him and I don't want to hear loose talk about my daughter,' her father asserted grimly.

Eden had to reach the age of twenty-one before she could rebel against a stern paternal dictum. Over Damiano, she rebelled but only within certain boundaries.

'What do you mean you have to be home by midnight?' Damiano enquired with considerable amusement at their next meeting. 'Even Cinderella only lost a shoe. Does your father think you're only at risk of seduction *after* midnight strikes?'

'Please don't make fun of my father—'

Damiano meshed long fingers into her silky hair to make her raise her head again, a rueful smile chasing the mockery from his darkly handsome features. 'You're so ridiculously old-fashioned—'

'By *your* standards, not my own.'

'Pious too,' he muttered, caressing her lips with his own, making her shiver and then tense. 'I've been patient for three days. You *want* me.'

Yes and no, she might have told him had she had the courage. The more she felt that overwhelming excitement threatening, the harder she fought it to stay in control. Already she was beginning to instinctively pull back and freeze him out when he reached for her again. Somehow she set a pattern that she couldn't free herself from even after they married.

The next time Damiano came up to Scotland, he rented a luxury hunting lodge in the hills behind the estate and invited her there for a dinner provided by a chef from a fancy restaurant. At the end of that wonderful meal, Damiano murmured with slumbrous cool, 'Are you staying the night?'

'No.'

Lounging back in his carved dining chair, Damiano fixed sardonic dark golden eyes on her hot face. 'So out of academic interest and the reality that I focus best on a time frame...how many times do I have to see you for you to stay the night?'

'For goodness' sake, there isn't some *stupid* time frame!'

'Then it's the bridal band of gold or nothing,' Damiano countered drily. 'Nothing very spontaneous about that, nothing generous either. In fact, one cannot avoid the obvious conclusion that you're putting a price on your body just like a hooker.'

Pale with rage, Eden rose abruptly from her seat. 'That's it...don't you ever *dare* come near me again!'

'I'm not apologising. I just want a reason that I can understand and I want a warm, giving adult woman—'

'Yes, I imagine you've been with plenty of that sort!' Eden declared in unhidden disgust. 'And where are they now? Do you even remember their names?'

'I can promise you that I'm going to remember you.' Damiano sighed.

'Don't phone me again!' Eden snapped, stalking to the door.

'I wouldn't dream of doing so,' Damiano purred like a jungle cat flexing his claws. 'But you're going to miss me...'

He drove her home without trying to change her mind. She walked in, told her father, 'It's over' and went to bed. That *soon*, she missed him but she would have stood torture rather than admit it. Over the following two weeks, she lost weight, tormented herself with visions of Damiano finding solace with a more sexually available woman and told herself a thousand times that that had really been all he'd been interested in.

At the end of the second week, Damiano landed a helicopter in the field below her home. She was feeding the dogs outside and watched in astonishment as he emerged from the bright yellow chopper. Like a schoolgirl, she climbed the fence and ran to greet him.

'Have you got that reason I can understand worked out for me yet?'

Colouring, she studied the rough grass at his feet and the long dragging silence stretched while he waited. 'I want getting married to feel really special,' she finally admitted jerkily.

'The whole fairy tale. I'm not trying to mock your aspirations but I hear that first-time experiences aren't always that great—'

'That doesn't matter—'

'You missed me?'

'Yes—'

'How much?'

'Too much,' she whispered shakily.

'Good...come fly with me the only place you'll let me fly you, *cara*,' Damiano drawled wryly, closing a possessive arm round her and urging her back towards the helicopter. From that moment on, he respected her boundaries.

He returned to London that same night. Home from agricultural college, Mark Anstey called in the next day. 'Dad tells me you're dating Damiano Braganzi...*wow*!'

And from Mark, she heard all that she should have heard first from Damiano. About the bank, the estate, the fabulous wealth, the top-drawer blue-blooded pedigree.

'Why didn't your father say anything?' she mumbled in shock. 'Even to my father?'

'Braganzi expressed a desire for what he termed "privacy". And as my father said, if a billionaire wants privacy and you like your job, you keep your mouth shut.'

'Why didn't you tell me?' Eden asked Damiano in bewilderment that night on the phone.

'I didn't *not* tell you anything. You simply didn't ask the right questions.'

And he had told no lies either but she had definitely picked up the feeling that Damiano would have preferred her to remain in the dark until he himself chose to disclose his true status in life.

'What are you doing with someone like me?' she muttered, although she tried hard not to ask that question.

'The guy who has everything needs a challenge? Do you think your father might now do something other than grunt antisocially in my direction?'

'No, he's more likely to lock the door and pretend we're out the next time you come calling!' Eden groaned.

But only one short month later, Damiano suggested that they get married. 'I haven't got the time to keep on flying up here—'

'You hardly know me—'

'You want me to do seven years and then another seven years like Jacob in the bible?'

'Marriage is a big step—'

'*Sì, tesoro mio*…but we get to share a bed, don't we?'

And she got nowhere when she tried to pin him down to saying anything more serious.

'It'll not work,' her father forecast dourly to Damiano's face. 'You'll both be sorry. Eden's got no more idea of your life than you have of ours. She won't fit and she'll be miserable.'

'Nothing like being greeted with open arms by the in-law-to-be,' Damiano quipped out of her parent's hearing in the aftermath of the longest, bluntest speech Eden had ever heard the older man make.

Damiano then applied for a special licence and persuaded her into agreeing to a quiet ceremony the very next week. In her heart, she had known it was all too quick and that he was too casual altogether in his attitude. He told her how much he *wanted* her but he never mentioned love. But loving him as she did, she suppressed her every misgiving. He was marrying her. It was her ultimate dream.

She did not meet Damiano's family until they came north for the wedding.

'You do realise that my brother is still in love with Annabel?' Cosetta remarked casually at the small reception which followed at the hunting lodge.

'Who's Annabel?' Eden whispered, never having heard that name before.

'A lady who wouldn't be seen dead in that home-made wedding shroud you're wearing! But then Annabel is one of *us*,' Cosetta asserted cuttingly. 'Privately educated and from a decent social background. Damiano hasn't even mentioned her, has he? What does that tell you?'

'That she wasn't as important to him as you seem to think,' Eden dared to suggest.

'The woman he was engaged to for two years? Think

again. He's on the rebound. They only broke up three months ago. He was crazy about her and then they had some stupid argument. Damiano's far too macho to admit himself at fault. He'll live to regret that when he starts comparing the two of you.'

The flight to their honeymoon in Sicily started with an argument, Eden making tearful accusations on the score of her not having been told about Annabel, Damiano telling her that getting married didn't mean she had the right to interrogate him about his past. Then she began feeling unwell.

'Wedding-night nerves add to the pressure,' Damiano informed her. 'I did warn you that the fairy tale might be hard to capture in reality.'

She fainted when they landed in Sicily. A doctor came out to their fabulous villa and diagnosed the flu.

'In sickness and in health...you do love to throw me in the deep end, *cara*.' Damiano teased, trying to calm her down and comfort her while she sobbed out repeated apologies and felt like a total bridal let-down.

It was well over a week before they finally shared the same bed and consummated their marriage. And that long-awaited experience *was*...disastrous! Damiano then rode roughshod over her every mortified, indeed hysterical protest and insisted on getting the doctor out again to examine her to ensure that she was essentially undamaged by his attentions.

'You've just been one of the unlucky ones,' the medical man said.

The barrier of her virginity had been more than usually resistant. Making love for the first time had hurt much more than she had expected. In the circumstances that had been unavoidable but Damiano had still shouldered guilt for having caused her pain. Eden had been utterly wretched after what she had considered absolute humiliation.

'I suppose I'm really, really lucky that I *didn't* make it into bed with you before we got to the altar, *cara*,' Damiano commented on a reflective footnote. 'You would never have agreed to see me again in this lifetime.'

And looking back from the vantage point of five years of greater maturity, Eden returned to the present with a stifled groan over her own behaviour. She had come back from their honeymoon full of self-pity and hurt pride. She had *leapt* at the idea of separate bedrooms.

Throwing off that memory, knowing that she was a lot wiser than she had once been, Eden hurried back upstairs to her flat. In the hall, she froze at the sight of the rumpled but empty bed she could see through the bedroom door. Then she heard Damiano talking in husky Italian in the sitting room and she just sagged, skin turning clammy with relief. The truth was that, right now, she really could not *bear* Damiano out of her sight. Leaving him even briefly had entailed overcoming the ridiculously childish terror that if she left him alone, he might vanish again!

As she appeared in the doorway Damiano tossed aside his mobile phone. His black hair still damp from the shower, he was fully dressed again but not in the casual jeans he had worn earlier. A superb charcoal-grey suit, worn with a white shirt and silk tie, now sheathed his tall, well-built frame. Smooth expensive cloth outlined his wide shoulders and long powerful thighs with the exquisite perfection of fit only obtainable from a master tailor.

For a split second, it was as if time had swept her

back five years. He was the very image of a rich and powerful banker again. He looked fantastic but at the same time as he stirred her senses he also intimidated her. 'I thought you would still be in bed,' she began uneasily. 'Where did you get that suit?'

'It was delivered to me at Heathrow. Nuncio had my measurements faxed to my tailor before we even left Brazil,' Damiano drawled, a wry curve to his expressive mouth. 'I think he thought shares might crash if I made a public appearance in denim. I've also moved up our departure from here by half an hour. Where have you been?'

She told him about her garment alterations business on the ground floor. Damiano listened in silence, stunning dark eyes flaring with sudden exasperation. 'You've been *sewing* to make a living? What necessity was there for you to sink to that level?'

Colour flew into Eden's cheeks. 'I—'

'I spoke to Nuncio while you were out,' Damiano informed her drily. 'I believe he repeatedly attempted to set up a financial support package for you before you left our home but you refused it.'

In the tense silence, the phone began ringing.

Eden ignored it, dismayed that Damiano was already making judgements about events which had taken place during his absence. 'Damiano—'

'Answer the phone,' Damiano interrupted with stark impatience. 'It's been ringing every ten minutes since you went out!'

No darned wonder he had got back out of bed and given up on getting any further rest! And, of course, he would not have answered her phone when he would not have wished to identify himself and risk having his whereabouts confirmed, thereby inviting the descent of the press on her doorstep. Her conscience twanging as if *she* had been that incessant caller, she answered the phone.

'Eden?'

It was Mark Anstey's voice. As it had been a couple of months since she had heard from him, she was a little surprised but she smiled. 'Mark?'

'Glad I've finally got hold of you!' Mark said urgently. 'I caught a news bulletin on the radio at lunchtime. Tell me, is there any truth in the wild rumour that your long-lost husband has turned up alive and kicking and is now back in England?'

Eden tensed at the apparent fact that word of Damiano's return had already moved into the public domain. 'Yes…yes, there is—'

'Incredible! Is Damiano there with you right now?'

'Yes—'

'Can he hear what you're saying?' Mark continued in a conspiratorial tone.

Discomfited by that question, Eden reddened. 'Well, yes but *why*—?'

'Have you got around yet to mentioning those dirty weekends we're supposed to have enjoyed together?'

Eden froze in dismay at that brutally blunt question and lost colour. 'No…'

'*Don't* mention that tabloid story! Take my advice and keep it quiet for now. Tina will *never* tell the truth,' Mark asserted with even stronger emphasis. 'In fact, I think we need to meet up to discuss this situation face to face as soon as possible—'

At that moment the very last thing Eden wanted to think about was the unpleasant consequences of Mark's affair with Nuncio's wife, Tina, four years earlier. 'I'm sorry but I really couldn't manage that right now—'

'Eden…this *isn't* something you can run away from.'
Something in Mark's voice roused the oddest sense of
foreboding inside Eden.

'Look, I'll be in touch with you very soon!' Eden
swore in a rush and she replaced the receiver in equal
haste before Mark could say anything else to upset her.

She turned back to Damiano, rigid with discomfiture.
Mark had just urged her to keep a secret from her husband. Her conscience could have done without that reminder of what she was already doing! But being so
short with Mark also left her feeling disloyal and un-
grateful for, in the aftermath of his disastrous affair with
Tina, Mark had promised that should the occasion ever
arise he would tell Damiano the truth and clear Eden's
name.

Damiano was very still, his strong bone-structure
fiercely taut. Scorching golden eyes connected with her
evasive gaze and held her fast before she could look
away again.

'So Mark, the love of your life, is still hanging around
five years on,' Damiano breathed chillingly. 'What are
you trying to hide from me?'

In the electric silence of her appalled paralysis, the
doorbell buzzed.

CHAPTER FOUR

THE chauffeur carted Eden's case down the steep stairs and out to the limousine.

What are you trying to hide from me? Deeply unsettled by Damiano's shrewd recognition of her unease during that phone call from Mark, Eden slid into the limousine. However, just as quickly, she reminded herself that she was innocent of being anything other than her sister-in-law Tina's dupe and she lifted her head high again.

Chagrined colour warmed her complexion for she was affronted by Damiano's derisive reference to Mark as 'the love of your life'. Ironically, Damiano had merely employed the same phrase *she* had once used in rueful self-mockery before they'd married! Since then, she had read magazine articles which urged women to keep a still tongue when men asked nosy questions about previous attachments. How *right* those articles were!

Damiano did not like Mark. That was still fresh news to Eden and she marvelled that she had not previously managed to work that out for herself. But then Damiano might well have liked Mark better had she not confided that, as a teenager, she had been infatuated with the younger man. Recalling that trusting confession of her own youthful immaturity now made her cringe. After all, more than five years earlier, Damiano had been anything but confiding on the infinitely more important sub-

73

ject of *why* he had broken off his engagement to Annabel Stavely!

'I asked you a question,' Damiano reminded her with icy cool. 'Why did you look as guilty as hell while you were speaking to Mark?'

'Probably embarrassment!' Eden threw her head back, golden hair rippling back over her shoulders, green eyes sparkling with sudden annoyance. 'So you can stop acting like some Victorian domestic tyrant questioning his flighty child-wife!'

Taken aback by that angry assurance, Damiano's lean dark features froze. 'I beg your pardon?'

'Mark is my friend and I don't feel that I should have to justify that.' Eden tilted her chin in defiance. 'After all, he was never an *intimate* friend...not like you and Annabel, who as an ex-fiancée was put under my nose practically every day of our marriage!'

'What an exaggeration!' Damiano's wide sensual mouth twisted. 'Annabel was my sister's closest friend. Did you expect me to tell Cosetta that Annabel was no longer welcome in our home?'

'No, indeed. Such a sensitive request would never have occurred to you on *my* account!' Eden slammed back at him helplessly as the humiliation of a hundred whispered giggling conversations and scornful glances surfaced in her memory like rocks on which she might still run aground. Annabel and Cosetta had worked together to undermine Eden's every attempt to feel secure in her position as Damiano's wife.

'*Accidenti*—'

'You made me put up with Annabel,' Eden recalled bitterly. 'I wasn't allowed to be possessive...in fact, you called me silly and petty and spiteful when I suggested that your sister could socialise with Annabel some place

other than our home, so you can just put up with my
fondness for Mark's company!'

'Is that a fact?' Damiano drawled smoothly.

'Yes, that is a fact.' Clashing unwarily with eyes as
broodingly dark as a stormy night, Eden then found
herself subsiding like a pricked balloon. Indeed, a sense
of panic once again gripped her for she was frightened
by the undeniable urge she seemed to have to hurl re-
criminations about the past. Right now their relationship
was too fragile to bear the strain.

'I knew you felt threatened by Annabel back then,'
Damiano asserted, taking her very much aback with that
admission. 'I liked the idea that you were jealous. In
those days, I liked punishments of that variety. It was
my version of the whip and the chair.'

Focusing on him with truly shocked intensity, Eden
parted her lips and then slowly closed them again.

'Manipulative wheels within wheels, a war of attrition which you were in no way equipped to fight, *cara*,'
Damiano conceded with wry regret, reaching out to
close his hand over her tensely curled fingers where
they rested on the seat. 'You really didn't have a clue
what was going on beneath the surface of our marriage,
did you?'

'No,' she conceded unevenly, colliding with his stunning dark eyes, rational thought suspended, for in the
back of her mind she knew that if she actually thought
through what he had just smoothly admitted, it would
scare the life out of her to accept that he had once
played such dangerous and hurtful games with her.

'Never again,' Damiano swore softly, unfurling her
taut fingers within his and drawing her closer.

Her heartbeat speeded up. Suddenly she was very
short of breath. Gazing into those spectacular eyes

smouldering with golden highlights, she felt a little burst of heat ignite deep within her and her colour heightened. He was taking his time but she was just desperate for him to touch her, so desperate that she trembled with anticipation.

'Nothing has to be rushed,' Damiano murmured with slumbrous cool.

Her free hand clenched into his shoulder to steady herself. She could not have agreed with him. Even that dark, deep, sexy drawl of his did something extraordinary to her senses and, brought that close to his lithe, powerful frame, it was as if her body were being whirled into the eye of the storm and out of her control. The straining peaks of her breasts tingled and tightened within her clothing. Lacing his fingers into her silky hair, Damiano let the tip of his tongue delve in a provocative flicker between her soft lips. She jerked as if he had burnt her, a flood of such hunger released, she closed her eyes in quivering aftershock.

'I'm not about to fall on you like a sex-starved animal,' Damiano asserted a shade raggedly, his husky sexy vowel sounds running together. 'Try to relax.'

Not while she was the victim of her own most secret memories. Her mind filled with erotic recollections of Damiano pinning her to the bed with dominant male sexual power and driving her out of her mind with pleasure, she felt utterly wanton.

'Try to stop shaking,.' Damiano urged, sounding more than a little pained. 'I promise not to do anything you don't want to do—'

Eden tore her other hand free of his hold and curved it to the back of his well-shaped head in near desperation. 'Kiss me...*please*.'

Long fingers cupped her cheekbone. 'Eden—?'

'Shut up!' she gasped and pushed her mouth in a blind seeking gesture against his.

For a split second, Damiano was absolutely motionless. Then he tugged her head back to make access easier and crushed her eager mouth to his with a raw, deep urgency that her body recognised with surging joyous response. White-hot excitement engulfed her in a scorching wave. A formless little sound broke low in her throat as sensual reaction slivered through her every skin cell, leaving her weak as water but as attached to Damiano's hard, muscular physique as a vine.

However, he set her back from him. Eden opened passion-glazed eyes and attempted to breathe again. She was maddeningly conscious of the dampness between her thighs and of the extraordinary ache of craving he could awake in her so easily, but she was trying not to be ashamed of that reality in the way she had once been.

Damiano surveyed her from beneath semi-lowered long ebony lashes, feverish colour lying along his taut cheekbones in a scoring line. The thick silence smouldered. 'We're at the airfield,' he stated not quite evenly, scanning her hot face and the sudden downward dip of her eyes.

Wasn't a little enthusiasm what he had always wanted from her? Did he find it unfeminine? Or was he pleased? Unable to bring herself to look at him in case she discovered that once again she had done the wrong thing, Eden said nothing. Still all of a quiver, she climbed out of the limo on wobbly legs. What sort of a welcome would she receive from the rest of the Braganzi family? Her tummy lurched at the prospect. For Eden, it would be a very distasteful meeting.

When they landed at Heathrow, bodyguards met Eden and Damiano, ready to protect them from harass-

ment should the paparazzi appear. Eden was relieved
when they were able to leave the airport without incident. But tomorrow a press announcement would be
made. Damiano's return from the dead was a major
news scoop. The paparazzi would be desperate to track
Damiano down to gain that all-important first picture of
him.

Inside the unremarkable saloon car, chosen in place
of a more noticeable limousine, Eden's hands trembled
as she nervously smoothed down her dress. As the press
turned the media spotlights back on to Damiano, would
one of the newspapers choose to resurrect the allegations made against her three months after her husband
had gone missing? Her blood ran cold inside her veins.
That photograph which had been printed had looked so
utterly damning. While the face of the woman in Mark's
arms had been concealed, the registration of the car beside which they had stood had been distinct and that
car had, at that time, been Eden's.

The sheer emotional surge of a most extraordinary
day was now catching up on Eden fast and she felt
incredibly tired. They entered the town house from the
mews garages at the rear. Struggling just to keep her
eyes open, Eden was past caring about the reception she
was likely to receive.

In the grand hall, Damiano paused to rest dark, deep-
set eyes levelly on her. 'I'm not expecting you to mend
fences with my family tonight. Everybody is under too
much strain at present.'

But even that concessionary assurance filled Eden
with dismay for, without realising that he was asking
for a virtual miracle, Damiano was warning her that he
did expect her to heal those divisions some time soon.
Before she could comment, however, her attention was

distracted by the sight of a large photograph of Annabel Stavely prominently displayed on a side table. The undeniably gorgeous redhead, who had once had the power to drive Eden mad with jealousy, had one arm curved round a cute little boy with dark hair, presumably her son.

As Damiano thrust open the drawing-room door and stood back for Eden to precede him, Eden was assuring herself that she couldn't care less about the Braganzi clan's partiality for an ex-fiancée who should have been ancient history. Her eyes cloaked, Eden then scanned the three occupants of the elegant room with its coldly impressive blue decor. Nuncio was already moving towards them. Although he was four years younger than Damiano, he actually looked older. Stocky and portly, he had a weak jawline and brown spaniel eyes.

'Back home where you belong, Damiano!' Nuncio exclaimed in an emotional burst, coming between them to grasp Damiano by the arms and hug him again.

Damiano had probably been hugged all the way back from Brazil. Eden reckoned that Nuncio's slavish attachment to his elder brother was probably the only thing that she could now like about him. Cosetta, Damiano's sister, eight years his junior, remained by the fireplace, her dark eyes challenging Eden with derisive distaste.

Tina, Nuncio's wife, approached with an uncertain smile, like someone shyly testing the water but eager to please. But then Tina had always kept well in with Damiano, Eden recalled painfully, and, over five years back, getting friendly with Damiano's naive wife had just been part of that same self-serving strategy.

The Italian woman was small and blonde just like Eden but there the resemblance ended. Tina had had an oval face with delft-blue eyes and a Cupid's bow mouth. 'How are you, Eden?'

'Eden's exhausted by all the excitement and I'm sure you'll excuse her,' Damiano intervened to answer for his wife. 'Why don't you take her upstairs, Tina?'

Eden left the room in Tina's company, grudgingly amused by what Damiano no doubt saw as a smooth move. Knowing that she had once been close to Tina, he probably thought he was doing her a favour in giving them the privacy to talk.

'Well...you being here with Damiano is quite a surprise, isn't it?' Tina remarked.

That almost childlike little voice sent an absolute shiver down Eden's spine. But then Nuncio's wife had perfected her non-threatening camouflage long before Eden had entered the family. Nuncio had been a student when he'd met Tina, who was seven years older. Tina had fallen pregnant at supersonic speed and had persuaded Nuncio into a quick marriage behind his big brother's back.

Ignoring the other woman's leading comment, Eden said proposally, 'How is my niece, Allegra, doing?'

Tina frowned at that reference to her six-year-old daughter and could not hide her irritation. 'Fine. She's in a boarding-school now.'

It was little comfort that she could now see so clearly through the other woman, Eden conceded. Over five years back, as an insecure new bride, Eden had been eager to believe that she had found a close friend in Tina and shocked to realise too late that she had fallen for the act of a woman who would do whatever it took to protect herself, regardless of how low she had to sink.

Reaching the imposing landing, Eden turned towards the bedroom that had always been hers.

'I'm sorry but Annabel and little Peter use those rooms when they're staying now.' Tina's apologetic intervention was saccharine-sweet. 'I'm afraid I just haven't had time to rearrange things yet.'

Staggered by that explanation, Eden suppressed a surge of pure raging disbelief. Annabel Stavely and her son had been allowed to take over the principal bedrooms in the house when they came visiting? What kind of a nonsensical arrangement was that?

Tina showed Eden into a guest room some distance down a corridor.

'You haven't forgiven me yet, have you?' Tina sighed.

Eden tensed. 'I don't think we should talk about the past—'

'But you can't ignore what's going on right now. Nuncio is just *dying* to tell Damiano about Mark and he won't keep quiet on your behalf for ever!'

'On *my* behalf?' Eden queried gently. 'You're the one who had the affair, Tina.'

'No comment.' Open ridicule gleamed in Tina's bright blue eyes.

'Five years ago, the tabloid press assumed that the woman in that photograph with Mark was me. I covered for you,' Eden reminded the other woman, provoked by her mockery. 'I didn't *want* to do it! But you persuaded me that it would be horribly selfish to tell the truth and cause trouble between you and Nuncio—'

'Well, so it would have been! After all, I was a mother as well as a wife. I had Allegra to consider and I didn't think that Damiano would *ever* be coming back!' Tina cut in defensively. 'Naturally I was grateful for what you did for me—'

'So *grateful* that as soon as you felt safe from exposure you joined Nuncio and Cosetta in calling me a slut and attacking me at every turn!' Eden interrupted with pained recollection of what she had had to endure. 'I was forced out of this house and you were just as keen as the others to see me gone!'

'Can't you understand that I was afraid that Nuncio might start suspecting *me* if I didn't play along?'

'All I understand is that while I was grieving for my husband, I took a heavy punishment for something I didn't do,' Eden framed ruefully. 'And you have to accept that if talk of that affair should surface again, I'll be telling Damiano the truth—'

'And I'll say you're lying! Who's going to believe your version this long after the event? Don't forget how much *you* were seen to lean on Mark after Damiano went missing.' Tina stressed with scorn. 'That's all anybody will remember.'

Eden paled. She saw what a fool she had been to allow herself to be bullied into protecting the other woman almost five years earlier. Tina had talked of her shame, her regret and of how much she had still loved Nuncio. Eden had been made to feel so guilty about her desire to defend her own reputation. Tina had been her friend. And all Eden had had to do was allow the assumption that *she* was the woman in that photograph to stand unchallenged. Unfortunately the consequences of shielding Tina had been far greater than Eden had foolishly foreseen.

'I honestly don't believe that Damiano would go tattling to Nuncio…oh, for goodness' sake, Tina,' Eden muttered in weary and distressed appeal. 'I told you that if Damiano ever came home to me, he would have to be told the real story and you agreed—'

'Of course I did.' Tina gave her a catlike smile of

acknowledgement on that point. 'I married a useless lump of lard but he's a very rich lump and there is *nothing* that I wouldn't do to fight my own corner!'

Eden studied the older woman with shaken recoil from that description of Nuncio.

Tina dealt her an even more disconcerting look of malicious amusement. 'Nobody will ever believe that I was the unfaithful wife, so you're in no position to threaten me—'

'I'm *not* threatening you—'

'You've got one *huge* shock coming your way in any case,' Tina murmured with venomous softness. 'But being sworn to secrecy by all parties concerned, I dare not let that particular cat out of the bag. Wait and see whether or not *your* marriage has a future before you waste your time *trying* to wreck mine!'

As the door closed on the blonde's triumphant exit, Eden was genuinely bewildered. 'One huge shock'? What on earth was Tina trying to suggest? Tired as she was, Eden took a quick shower in the *en suite* to freshen up. She only wished she could as easily wash away the memory of Tina's spite. Pure and pointless, spite, that's all it was, she told herself. At least Mark had no personal axe to grind over his affair with Tina, she reflected with relief. Damiano might not particularly like Mark but, if she needed Mark to clear her own name, he would surely accept the younger man's word.

Her suitcase still sat just inside the bedroom door. In spite of the fact that no Braganzi expected or indeed usually received anything less than twenty-four-hour domestic service, nobody had come to unpack for her. Eden smiled at the fact that she was feeling slighted and tugged out a nightdress. Clambering into the big comfortable bed, she wondered how long it would take Damiano to come upstairs and join her.

Eden had actually drifted off to sleep when a loud noise interspersed with raw male invective woke her up with a start. She sat up and switched on the light. Damiano, lean strong face grim with anger, had evidently tripped over her case in the dark.

'Are there no maids in this house? And why have you chosen to sleep so far away from me that I have to go on a major search to find you in my own home?' Damiano demanded with eloquent outrage, striding over to the bed, trailing back the duvet and scooping her off the divan without a second of hesitation.

'What on—?' she gasped.

Heading out into the corridor again with her still gripped in his powerful arms, Damiano breathed flatly, 'We share the same room, the same bed.'

Settled down on to a bed in a much more impressive room situated off the main landing, Eden flushed. 'Sleeping elsewhere wasn't my idea—'

'*Per meraviglia!* Do I look dumb enough to believe that?' Damiano was crushingly unimpressed by her plea of innocence.

Slinging his jacket on a chair, he swept up the internal phone to communicate terse instructions to some member of staff. As he spoke, he unknotted his tie and tossed it aside and began unbuttoning his shirt. Drymouthed, heartbeat accelerating, aware of the thunderous tension he was now exuding in primal waves but unable to concentrate on it, Eden watched him as he completed the call.

Languor was spreading through her body like a flood of warm honey. Even furious, he was breathtakingly beautiful to her mesmerised eyes. Her breathing frac-

tured as he let the shirt drop where he stood. Six feet
four inches of vibrant bronzed masculinity, wide,
smooth shoulders, broad chest, taut, flat stomach, all
rippling whipcord muscles.

Without warning, Damiano flashed a glance at her
and stilled, aggressive jawline squaring. *'What?'*

Eden jerked. 'Sorry?'

Damiano spread two not quite steady hands wide,
dark eyes blazing gold. 'I'm damned if I'm going into
the bathroom to undress. Just close your eyes!'

'But, Damiano, I *wasn't.*'

'I've gone nearly forty-eight hours without sleep,'
Damiano grated in a savage undertone. 'Just get under
the sheet, turn your back and pretend you're on your
own!'

Her teeth clenched. She hauled up the sheet and
flipped over on to her side. Why was he so set on misunderstanding her? She tautened. He was interpreting
her behaviour against a five-year-old yardstick and what
else could he do?

'I'm not as prudish as I used to be!'' Eden whispered
in a defensive hiss. 'I've grown up a lot!'

The mattress gave, the lights snapped off and
Damiano reached for her with both hands, hauling her
up against him and shocking her into silence. 'Grown
women don't need to fill up on vodka first, *cara,*' he
muttered thickly into her hair, dark, deep drawl steadily
lowering in pitch and clarity as his big powerful frame
relaxed. 'If I had an ego problem, you'd have made me
impotent. I spent seven months of marriage listening to
every excuse not to have sex that has ever been in-
vented. I spent most of the next five years between a
prison cell and a quarry. I'm sure I was the only guy

there who fantasised about a wife in a nightdress because he had never ever seen her naked!'

Trembling with mortification, tears stinging her eyes, Eden gulped and swallowed hard.

Damiano released a sleepy sigh. 'But you love me. On your terms, the shoes you wore to bed this afternoon were a massive statement of devotion. Right now, I'll settle for that.'

Right now? She opened her eyes, wildly conscious of his proximity, the sexy masculine scent of him, the heat he emanated. But he was now holding her at a slight distance from him. She swallowed again, wanting him so much she was burning all over. Finally, she moistened her lips and parted them. 'I don't need the vodka...'

Only silence greeted that announcement. She listened to the deep, even tenor of his breathing and rubbed her cheek helplessly against his hand where it rested loosely on the pillow. She had him back. It was enough. Whatever he wanted, he could have...she just wouldn't make her efforts to please so obvious the next time. She loved him *so* much. Even the family from hell wasn't going to part them!

At what felt like the crack of dawn the next morning, Damiano woke her up. Exuding cool self-command, Damiano was already fully dressed in a dark business suit, burgundy silk tie and a pearl-grey silk shirt. His stunning dark eyes rested on her with a slumbrous quality that drove her mind blank and sent her heartbeat racing.

'I have a press conference set up for ten,' Damiano drawled.

'Oh...' Her tummy flipping at the mere thought of attending a press conference, Eden paled.

'It'll be a circus and not your style. There's no need for you to come, *cara*.' Damiano sank fluidly down on the edge of the bed, brilliant eyes shimmering over her. 'I'm spending the afternoon with a whole collection of bankers and lawyers. I think it would be wisest if we fly out to Italy separately—'

'Separately?'

'I'm determined to keep our destination a secret from the paparazzi. One of my bodyguards will accompany you on a private flight this afternoon. I'll meet you at the villa…it could well be tomorrow before I make it.'

A sharp rap sounded on the door.

Exasperation flashing across his darkly handsome features, Damiano vaulted upright and strode over to answer it. Eden recognised Nuncio's anxious voice.

Before he departed, Damiano glanced back at her with a wry smile. 'The villa is, I believe, larger than a rabbit hutch and it is *not* communal,' he assured her with admirable cool.

Just a few more hours and she would be on her way to Italy. A sunny smile curved Eden's lips. A maid arrived with a breakfast tray laden with all Eden's favourite dishes. She had just finished eating when the phone by the bed buzzed.

The caller was Mark.

'How on earth did you work out where I was?' Eden asked in confusion.

'It hardly took genius. I was once a regular visitor to the town house,' Mark reminded her impatiently. 'Look, I've come up to London specially and I'd like to see you as soon as possible.'

And why shouldn't she see Mark before she left for Italy? Eden suddenly asked herself. He was a good friend and, although he had his flaws, she had never forgotten his sympathetic support in the aftermath of Damiano's disappearance. No doubt, Mark would also enjoy hearing the inside story on Damiano's return home. And shouldn't she tell Mark that, exactly as he had forecast, Tina was determined to lie about their affair?

Mark suggested that she meet him at his hotel. Eden called a cab to pick her up and she slipped out of the house by the rear entrance. A slimly built young man with dark blond hair and pale blue eyes, Mark, as elegantly dressed as always, was waiting for her in the lobby.

Eden accompanied him into the almost empty residents' lounge. 'It's so good to see you again,' she said warmly.

'Tell me what's been happening on the home front,' Mark invited, having ordered tea for Eden and a drink for himself.

'I was going to ask you how you've been doing first,' Eden told him ruefully. 'I haven't heard much from you lately.'

'I think your situation is rather more important right now.'

Eden grimaced. 'Well, what you said over four years ago has been borne out. You said I was a real fool to take the heat for Tina and you were right. It *has* come back to haunt me. Tina is still treating me like her worst enemy and Nuncio is eagerly waiting for me to make a full confession to Damiano. The sooner the whole wretched business is cleared up, the better.'

'So you *will* be wanting me to support your story?'

Eden flushed. 'I hope it won't come to that. That would be embarrassing for you—'

'I'll tell Damiano anything you like.' Mark shrugged. '*But*...I'm afraid there'll be a price.'

Her brow furrowed. 'A price?'

'Let me tell you a story.' Mark's mouth took on a sullen twist as he studied her. 'My longest-standing friend marries a fabulously wealthy bloke and what does she do to help me?'

Eden went rigid. 'What are you getting at?'

'You got me a lousy first job working for peanuts on the Braganzi country estate!' Mark derided. 'And when I asked for the cash to set up my own business, you said you were sorry but Damiano thought I was too young to be trusted with that size of an investment.'

Mark was delving way back to events which had occurred in the first months of Eden's marriage. At the time, those events had made Eden feel very uncomfortable with both her husband and Mark. 'I didn't realize you still felt like that about—'

'No, of course you didn't. Damiano went missing soon afterwards and I decided the rich Mrs Braganzi was a long-term investment to be nursed along.' Beneath her stricken gaze, Mark vented a sour laugh. 'Just two more years and Damiano would have been legally presumed dead. No matter how hard his relatives fought, you would still have copped most of the loot as Damiano's wife! Would you have been generous then, Eden? That *was* what I was waiting for—'

'I can't believe you really mean what you're saying...' A queasy sensation of mounting fear was engulfing Eden. 'You were so kind to me after Damiano disappeared.'

'But you'll have to pay me to get service like that again. I won't admit that I had that affair with Tina

unless you make it well worth my while…if you don't,
I'll take Tina's side and drop you in it with Damiano—'

'That's sick!' Eden gasped and then, realising that
she had attracted the attention of the elderly woman
seated at the far end of the room, she reddened fiercely.

'Think *very* hard before you tell me to go ahead and
do my worst,' Mark advised thinly.

'But to try to blackmail me…' Eden condemned
shakily.

Only now was she recalling Mark's bitter resentment
when Damiano had refused to invest in him until he had
more business experience. She had chosen to forget that
unpleasant episode but Mark had just made it brutally
clear that he had only continued their friendship beyond
that point because he had expected to profit from it.
Damiano's survival must have come as a very unwelcome surprise to Mark, she conceded painfully.

'So now I'll tell you what I want…' With complete
calm, Mark went on to mention a sum of money that
made Eden pale.

'Not all up front at once of course; he conceded
grudgingly. 'But I expect a down payment as a guar-
antee of your good faith. Since you've always been so
frank with me, I know exactly what you've got in your
bank account. You won't be needing that money for
your own use any more so I'll take a cheque now—'

'Mark, *please*—'

'Make your choice. Tina will not hesitate for a second if I approach her with a similar offer,' Mark warned
her smugly. 'Then it'll be goodbye to Damiano, Eden.'

Picturing both Tina and Mark conspiring together to
destroy her marriage made Eden feel trapped and physically ill. What would her word be worth to Damiano
if everybody else swore that she was guilty as hell?

With a trembling hand that seemed to have developed a will of its own, Eden dug into her handbag for her cheque-book. Without looking back at Mark again, she scrawled out the cheque and left it sitting on the table. Then she stood up and walked out of the hotel lounge.

CHAPTER FIVE

IN THE shattered emotional state she was in, Eden wandered round the shops for a while until she got a grip on herself again. She asked herself what sort of a fool she was that she had not seen through Mark to the greed and resentment beneath the surface. She had trusted him absolutely and now he was blackmailing her!

How on earth was she to get out of the dreadful nightmare she had brought down on herself? She was bitterly ashamed of having simply surrendered to Mark's threats. But most of all she now loathed her own blind, trusting stupidity. When the press had exposed that affair and wrongly identified the woman involved, she should not have kept silent to protect Tina. How could she have been that foolish? But she knew how and why. Distraught over losing Damiano, she had been an easy mark for Tina's guile.

As she walked by the electrical section of a big store, Eden's attention was caught by the shock value of seeing Damiano on several television screens at once. The press conference was being televised and a bunch of shoppers was glued to the screens. Having come to a dead halt, Eden moved slowly closer to watch.

The cameras loved Damiano. As he fielded questions with assurance and humour, his natural charisma made him a class act. Every so often a different camera angle would take in the people standing near him. Nuncio, proudly intent on his big brother. A couple of directors of the Braganzi Bank, glowing at Damiano's every witty response, no doubt highly relieved that the male once dubbed a genius in the money markets should have returned with all his faculties intact.

A powerful surge of guilt engulfed Eden then and she turned away. In retrospect, she was ashamed that she had snatched at the excuse Damiano had given her and avoided the press conference. From the moment that tabloid story had been printed nearly five years earlier, she had been terrified of the media. Instead of giving way to that cowardice, she should have fought it and, even though Damiano had not appeared to be in much need of wifely support, she would have been prouder of herself had she at least *offered* it.

Eden was really running quite late by the time she got back to the town house. As she crossed the hall, Tina emerged from the drawing room, looking extremely smug. 'You have about ten minutes to freshen up before you leave for your second honeymoon in Italy.'

Ignoring the blond's honeyed scorn, Eden asked, 'Is Damiano back yet?'

'No, but he did try to call you. He wasn't very pleased when I told him that I hadn't a clue where you were.' A malicious smile curved the older woman's voluptuous mouth. 'Then I took the trouble to call him back and mention that just before you went out, dear old Mark had phoned, given his name and asked to speak to you. Mark was never discreet, was he?'

Paling at Tina's venom but determined not to respond in kind, Eden raced upstairs to change. Over an hour later, she entered the airport, accompanied by a single bodyguard. She was totally unprepared for what happened next. A man with a camera appeared about ten feet away and blinded her by taking a flash photo.

Within the space of sixty seconds, she was the centre
of a heaving crowd of reporters shouting questions.

'Why weren't you with your husband at the press
conference?'

'Is your marriage in trouble, Mrs Braganzi?'

'Why did the Braganzi family fly out to Brazil without you?'

'Why have you been in hiding all these years?'

If the airport security men hadn't come to their rescue, they would never have managed to escape. White
and trembling, Eden only began breathing evenly again
when the small private plane took off for Italy.
Somebody must have tipped the press off that she would
be arriving at the airport. Who? Tina? Or was she so
strung up now that she was imagining things?

Whatever, her every worst fear seemed to be coming
true. Damiano was big news and, by the same defini-
tion, so was the state of his marriage. Her absence from
the press conference had evidently created comment.
How *long* did she have before that old scandal about
her was dug up again?

Late that afternoon, the car which had whisked Eden
out of Pisa turned off a twisting mountain road into an
avenue hedged and shadowed by tall cypresses.
Through a break in the trees, Eden saw a lake with a
surface like a silver mirror and then she caught her first
glimpse of the Villa Pavone.

The magnificent building was sited on the hilltop.
Ornate stucco decorations and a grand run of Ionic columns embellished the villa's impressive frontage. As
she got out of the car, the glorious warmth of early
summer enfolded her. Citrus trees in giant metal urns
dispelled an aromatic scent which hung heavy in the

still air. As she moved towards the entrance, an eerie plaintive shriek made her glance nervously over her shoulder. She was just in time to see a glimmer of ghostly white disappear behind a topiary tree. An instant later, a glorious white peacock strutted into view, his fantastic plumage spread like filigree lace. The bird regarded her with expectant beady eyes, seemingly awaiting a burst of appreciative applause.

Eden grinned, the last of her anxiety falling away. She strolled towards the huge front doors which stood wide. The paparazzi were behind her in London along with Damiano's dreadful relatives *and* Mark, she reminded herself cheerfully. In a few hours surely at most, Damiano would be with her again.

She walked into a breathtaking foyer, so big it echoed loudly with her footsteps. The walls were adorned with fabulous classical frescos. Far above her hung a superb gilded and painted ceiling.

'Where the hell were you this morning?'

Eden almost jumped right out of her skin. She spun round, green eyes very wide and startled. Damiano had magically appeared in a doorway which she had not previously noted in her awed scrutiny of her surroundings. 'You're here already?' she gasped in delighted surprise.

He looked incredibly attractive in well-cut beige chinos and a short-sleeved cream cotton shirt that accentuated his bronzed skin and black hair. But Damiano was surveying her with glittering dark eyes, his lean, strong face hard as granite, megawatt tension emanating from the stillness of his long, lithe, powerful frame.

'You were with Mark—'

Eden blinked, tautening. 'Yes,' she conceded jerkily, determined to stick as close to the truth as was possible.

'For *hours*?' Damiano derided harshly. 'You almost missed your flight!'

'No, I didn't cut it that fine,' she countered tightly and curled her tense fingers into her damp palms, the happy sensation draining away, leaving only stress in its wake. 'And I wasn't with him *all* that time. I walked round the shops for a while—'

'You're not telling me the truth.'

The silence started feeling like a giant black hole spreading to within inches of her feet, ready to suck her in at any moment. The confidence with which Damiano made that charge was pure intimidation. It wasn't a question. It wasn't a sneaky carrot designed to draw her into speech and trip her up. No, what she was hearing was the challenge of a very shrewd male, who had not the slightest shred of doubt that she was concealing something from him.

'Why…why do you think that?' Eden prompted dry-mouthed.

His spectacular golden eyes struck sparks off hers. 'Tell me the truth,' he demanded with ice-cool clarity. 'You're squirming like a fish on a hook.'

Eden worried at her lower lip with her teeth and stared back at him, horribly impressed by his power of perception. 'I…'

'Yes?' Damiano grated in the explosive silence.

'I only trailed round the shops because I was upset and that's why I was so late getting back to the house,' Eden volunteered in a driven rush. 'No big mystery.' She shrugged awkwardly. 'I just saw Mark as I hadn't managed to see him before…and I didn't like what I saw. So for that reason, I *won't* be seeing him again.'

A faint frown-line had appeared between Damiano's winged ebony brows. She registered that she had disconcerted him, had roved wildly off whatever script he had expected her to pursue. 'What—?'

Eden folded her arms in a defensive movement and straightened her slim shoulders. 'Look, it was unpleasant enough finding out that Mark wasn't the wonderful friend I thought he was. I don't need you demanding to hear it all, so that I can feel a right idiot all over again!'

'You've decided to end the friendship?' Damiano seemed to be having a problem grasping that reality. 'When did you decide that? Right there this minute when it dawned on you that I'm angry?'

Her shoulders sagged. 'Oh, boy, are you paranoid...'

Damiano went rigid, faint colour arching across the hard slant of his high cheekbones. 'I merely requested that you explain yourself—'

'And I politely refused to go into any greater detail. Mark's just not important enough for us to be arguing over him.' Eden meant that assurance with every proud fibre of her being.

'*Santa cielo*...I am *not* arguing...where the blazes are you going?' Damiano raked at her in a lion's roar as she began walking back in the direction of the front doors.

'I thought maybe if I went out and then came back in again, you might give me a nicer welcome.'

A dropped feather could have sounded like a thundering avalanche in the rushing silence which followed.

Eden heard Damiano move behind her but she was still quite unprepared to find herself being suddenly snatched right off her feet and up into his powerful arms. For a moment, the world tilted crazily. Then she met the mesmeric lure of his burnished golden eyes. Simultaneously she ran out of breath and rational thought. An instant burst of wanton heat ignited inside her, sending her heartbeat crashing, her pulses pounding.

A scorching smile slashed Damiano's lean, powerful face. 'This is the kind of welcome I should l have given you, *tesoro mio.*'

He pressed his mouth to the tiny pulse flickering like crazy below her delicate collar-bone. Her throat extended, her entire body jerked. She lifted a shaking hand to curve it to his dark head and then his mouth found hers. A huge brilliant fireworks display blazed up in the darkness behind her lowered eyelids. She was so hot, so excited, she clutched wildly at him. He lowered her down onto a hard, cold surface, closed his hands over her knees and parted them so that he could haul her back into even closer contact.

A hoarse little cry of response was wrenched from her as he let his long fingers glide up her slender thighs beneath her dress. She was shivering, shaking, alight with a hunger that burned. Damiano rested his hands on her slim hips and lifted his head to gaze down at her, dark, deep-set eyes shimmering gold, strong face hard with raw male need, beautiful mouth almost ruthless in its line.

'So now you show me that you don't need the vodka,' Damiano murmured in thickened invitation.

For a split second, her veil of desire was pierced by an inner screech of shock. What? *Here? Now? On a marble table?* And then Eden collided with those dark golden eyes that had haunted her dreams from the very hour of their first meeting. She literally felt her body melt. Awareness slid away again. The world could have ended right there and then and she wouldn't have cared.

'I don't mean *here*,' Damiano husked, laughter roughening his rich, deep, sexy drawl.

He tugged her off the table and wound her fingers calmly into his to urge her through the doorway which he had appeared in earlier. Her legs felt weak and wobbly supports. Yet her every skin cell felt almost painfully alive. Sexual tension was twisting her into a deliciously tight knot. Their footsteps echoed as they passed through yet another vast room, full of marble columns, glittering crystal chandeliers and huge oil paintings. As Damiano led her beneath an ornate portal which opened onto the fantastic double flight of stairs which wound gracefully up to the first floor, she was gazing in astonishment at their palatial surroundings.

Upstairs, Damiano walked her into a room that at first glance struck her as the size of an aircraft hangar. A hangar with a bed, that was. And what a bed, overhung by a giant gold coronet from which glorious brocade hangings descended into extravagant folds down onto an exquisite rug. 'You can live the fairy tale like the little princess.'

'You being here with me...' Eden muttered unevenly. 'That's enough of a fairy tale.'

Damiano dealt her a slumbrous sexy look from beneath black spiky lashes. He settled his hands to her slim shoulders and turned her slowly and carefully round. As he ran the zip down on her dress, her breath feathered in her throat. Light was flooding through the tall windows, light so bright she could see dust motes dancing in the air. And she felt terribly shy and self-conscious but she didn't feel like rushing across the room to close the shutters and plunge them into darkness.

Once she had tormented herself with secret humiliating comparisons between Annabel's long-legged voluptuous shape and her own infinitely slighter and

smaller attractions. The urge to keep her seeming deficiencies covered from view had risen to obsessive proportions. But in allowing herself to think in that way,
she had forgotten the only thing that really mattered.
Damiano had married *her*; Damiano had chosen her, *not*
Annabel Stavely.

He eased her dress from one slight, taut shoulder,
making a production out of the process. She shut her
eyes tight. '*Santo Cielo...*' Damiano swore huskily
above her head. 'I'm burning for you, *cara.*'

He lifted her hair and bent her head forward and let
his expert mouth trail across the exposed nape of her
neck. She quivered, every sense leaping. 'Oh...'

'This will be so good,' Damiano promised with husky
sensuality.

The very sound of his voice could turn her boneless.
A muted little gasp escaped her as her dress drifted
down to her ankles. She fought the instinct to cross
shielding arms over herself. She could feel the tips of
her breasts hardening into straining little points within
her bra. She could feel the wave of heat travelling over
her and her knees started to wobble.

'You are doing *so* well,' Damiano purred appreciatively. 'You're quivering like a racehorse ready to bolt
but you're still in the same room.'

'No vodka,' she mumbled, trying to match him in
humour but her voice came out all shaky.

'Open your eyes, *cara,*' Damiano urged as he lifted
her clear of the tangle of cloth round her feet and spun
her back to him. 'Enjoy me admiring you.'

He was pushing too far too fast. She knew she had
small breasts and hips that were just a little too full for
the rest of her and legs that were just legs, not especially

long or especially anything, sturdy enough to be useful, not flashy enough to attract attention. 'I *can't*!'

'Would you prefer to sleep alone in that bed tonight?'

Her lashes lifted high on stricken green eyes. *'No!'* she gasped with even greater force.

'Gotcha...' Damiano drawled with smouldering satisfaction, brilliant dark golden eyes scanning her blushing face. 'I cheated. You have no chance of sleeping alone.'

Her brow indented. 'No...?'

Bending down, he swept her up again into his arms and strode over to the bed to settle her there. She kicked off her shoes and began scrabbling at the bed linen to get under it.

'Ah...ah...' Damiano allowed her to get under cover and then, hooking long brown fingers round the fine linen sheet, he flipped the bedding deftly back into a fold at the footboard. 'It's a sort of knee-jerk reaction, isn't it? But a little modesty goes a long way with me, *cara.*'

Rather than remain splayed out in only her bra and pants, she sat up again and hugged her knees, hands tightly clasped. She was striving desperately to think of something witty or cool to say. 'I...I, well—'

'Shut up,' Damiano broke in with tender amusement. 'You may not like your body but I *love* it!'

She studied his stunningly attractive features and felt that melting sensation down deep inside that just overwhelmed her. She didn't place much credence in what he said but she knew he wanted her. She had felt the hard urgency of him against her, could not doubt the physical reality of his desire. She watched him peel off his shirt. Her lashes lowered, carefully screening the directness of her gaze, but she was as hopelessly mesmerised by his potent male beauty as she had always been. He had no inhibitions and she adored that blatant, blazing self-assurance he emanated, so very different from her own.

As he unzipped his chinos, exposing the taut, hard flatness of his stomach bisected by a silky dark furrow of hair, a tight little stab of sexual awareness twisted low in her tummy. He was all male, full of dynamic energy and hot-blooded intensity. Shimmying her hips back deeper into the shadows cast by the drapes festooning the bed, Eden watched the chinos being cast aside with keen interest. She studied the long flow of his smooth brown back, the lean masculine hips in pale boxer shorts, the long hair-roughened thighs. She did not look away as she had once done. Indeed she was hot with curiosity to see him totally stripped but terrified that he might notice.

Damiano disposed of the boxer shorts. Her face flamed. Aroused he was distinctly intimidating but it was of the variety of intimidation that filled her with hot, quivery sensations. Suddenly ashamed of what she recognised as pure lust within herself, she dropped her head, no longer able to see anything but Damiano's beautifully shaped brown feet approaching the bed.

The mattress gave slightly under his weight. The silence hummed. She sat there, head lowered over knees.

'You're such a little cheat,' Damiano condemned with a throaty chuckle as he reached for her and tumbled her down against the comfortable pillows.

'Sorry?' Eden spluttered, disconcerted by the swiftness of that move.

Rolling over, Damiano slid a long hard masculine thigh between hers and held her captive beneath his superior weight. He trailed a mocking forefinger along the curve of her soft lower lip and made it impossible for her to avoid his intent scrutiny. 'I saw you watching me.'

He was just inches away. She reddened fiercely. Her mouth ran dry.

'And...' Damiano dragged out the word '...I also think you *like* what you saw—'

'No—?'

'*No?*' Damiano questioned, raising a sardonic dark brow.

'I m-mean yes, but—'

'Don't want to hear the "but".' With a husky growl of very male gratification, Damiano teased at her mouth with his own, lighting a trail of fire to run through her shivering body. Those light, frustrating kisses merely stoked her growing tension. She squirmed under him seeking greater force, her own hunger demanding more.

'So tell me you want me,' Damiano invited thickly.

'What?' she framed blankly, fingers curling into his broad shoulders with a frustration she could not suppress.

'I want to hear the words...' Damiano confided, sliding down the bed and, by so doing, revealing to her for the first time that he had already somehow contrived to remove her bra without her noticing.

Dismay flashed through her. '*Damiano!*'

'No, *cara*...' His hands clamped down over her wrists before she could attempt to cover her bare breasts. 'You're beautiful...you are really beautiful and I need to look at you just as much as you like to look at me,' he spelt out in a devastatingly effective demand for equal rights.

She trembled, feeling so horrendously vulnerable, staring down at her pale breasts with their shamelessly swollen pink nipples. And then she saw Damiano surveying the same view like a hungry tiger, hot golden eyes pinned to her with a visual intensity that shook her. He had already released her wrists but she had little difficulty in resisting her once compulsive need to conceal herself from him. She was now watching him in total fascination. She arched her back slightly, shifted her hips, feeling like a madly seductive stranger beneath such erotic male appreciation.

He was just looking and she was already starting to burn again. He lifted a hand that was noticeably unsteady and curved it to her super-sensitive flesh. He lowered his proud dark head and let the tip of his tongue flick a pouting peak and her whole body just surged up in response. 'I want you!' she moaned, helpless in the grip of that devastating wave of sexual hunger.

Damiano rewarded her with a wolfish smile that made her heart flip over and filled her with such a flood of love that she felt as fluid as water. 'You're all mine,' he breathed raggedly. 'You're the only woman I have ever been with who has only ever been mine. I really get a high out of that.'

He brought his mouth down on hers with an explosive passion that she needed as much as he did. Heartbeat thundering in her eardrums, she gasped as he stroked her breasts and she dug her fingers into the dark silk luxuriance of his hair. She couldn't get enough of that hard, demanding mouth. She strained against him, controlled by the heat and the strength of her own craving, every defence finally abandoned.

'Please...' She gasped, struggling to get breath back into her lungs but desperate to get his hot urgent mouth back on hers again.

'You've changed so much,' Damiano ground out, his

breathing even more fractured than her own as he skimmed an impatient hand down over her quivering length and deftly rearranged her so that he could remove her briefs.

She had never been so conscious of being naked but the daylight had nothing to do with it. Erotic anticipation now fired her. She was reaching for him even before he was reaching for her again. Tiny broken sounds were wrenched from her as he pushed her back against the pillows and employed his lips and his tongue on her tingling breasts with a hard, sensual expertise that was entirely new to her. And, new as that more forceful approach was, it drove her crazy with excitement.

'I never thought I would see you like this…out of your mind with desire for me!' Damiano extended with raw appreciation, black hair tousled, tough cheekbones scored with feverish colour. 'Eden…Eden…'

And even the way he raggedly groaned her name made her react. She was all heat and constant movement. The burning fever that had taken control of her was way beyond anything she had ever experienced. With a sure hand, he found the damp, pulsing heart of her and she cried out loud on the incredible surge of excitement he unleashed.

Glittering golden eyes invaded hers. He was watching her every reaction. Disconcertion tried to penetrate the blinding, all-pervasive sway of passion and for a split second she attempted to regain some measure of control. But she was way beyond that ability and dimly registering that shocked her too, only his dominant control over her was too great by then.

'I…I can't help it…' She tried to say, not really knowing whether she was trying to apologise or not and, if she was, what she might be attempting to say sorry for.

'I *know*…'

She was enslaved, enthralled by the passion, her writhing body entirely ruled by his knowing touch. And in no time at all that oh, so skilled touch became near agonising torment for she wanted…she wanted *so* much. And the hunger was so powerful it was eating her alive and her hands were clinging to him, her hips rising, the ache of emptiness a torment.

'Please…' she begged.

In one lithe movement, Damiano came over her, tipped her back, a devouring need more than equal to her own blazing in his smouldering golden gaze. As he entered her yielding flesh, she uttered a high-pitched moan and jerked in sensual shock from that invasion. Her excitement was at such a pitch by then that she thought she might pass out from the sheer overload of pleasure. The powerful response of her own body gripped her now. Heart crashing, he drove her to the heights she had never known existed. Stunned by the wild ecstatic intensity that shattered her into a million pieces, she sobbed with joyful release and slowly went back into free fall.

Eden's eyes were awash with tears but wide with shock at the same time. Never ever had she imagined she might experience such glorious pleasure.

Damiano released her from his weight and hauled her back into intimate connection with his damp, hot frame. He kissed her breathless and held her back from him, scanning her still shaken face with questioning intensity. 'You truly *didn't* realise that you were missing anything five years ago,' he breathed on the back of a rueful laugh.

'You mean...it's *always* supposed to be like that?' she gasped, too taken aback by the idea to be self-conscious.

'I used to think of spiking your pure orange to make you let go in bed but I knew you would never forgive me.' Damiano splayed long brown fingers round her cheekbones, gazing deep into her incredulous green eyes. 'You just would not relax. You had so many hang-ups. You hit my male ego right where it hurts. The only woman I couldn't satisfy was my wife...'

'I was quite happy with what...well...you know,' she mumbled, thinking in a positive daze at what she had just learned. How could she have known there was more when she had never experienced anything more until now? She remembered pleasure but a pleasure that was frankly mild in comparison with what she had just enjoyed. She remembered liking the start better than the finish and vague feelings of dissatisfaction but nothing she hadn't accepted as normal and natural. From that first painful initiation, she had stubbornly decided that making love would always be something he received more pleasure from than she did.

But there was more to it than that, Eden recognised in sudden shame. She had had resentments of her own from very early in their marriage. The marital home in which she felt like an intruder, the family who had regarded her as a social inferior, Annabel, the ex-fiancée, who wouldn't quit flaunting her own preferential status. She had blamed Damiano for her unhappiness and had made no attempt to overcome her inhibitions. Damiano, she registered with shaken new self-awareness, had not been the *only* one set on a war of attrition...

Damiano curved her to him so that she was plastered to every powerful angle of his indolent length. 'Sex was a taboo subject. You once said that it was bad enough having to do that sort of thing without being expected to talk about it as well,' he groaned.

Eden stifled a groan of her own. 'The only woman I couldn't satisfy was my wife.' One very revealing statement from a male of Damiano's sophistication and experience, she reflected in strong dismay.

'It didn't matter to me enough…I didn't understand,' she muttered in a tone of feverish regret, kissing a damp brown muscular shoulder in belated apology. She loved him so much. She had almost lost him. She was so hugely grateful that he had chosen to come back to her and give their marriage another chance.

'Past and forgotten,' Damiano assured her.

Suddenly she had a driving need to ask him if, as his family had insisted, he *had* considered divorcing her before he'd gone missing. But she hesitated and questioned whether she could handle a confirmation that would devastate her and add to her anxieties in the present. For if Damiano admitted that he had been on the brink of ditching her, wouldn't she now feel as though she was still on probation? No, some questions were better left unspoken.

Damiano snatched her from such thoughts by tugging her up out of concealment. Lustrous eyes smouldering like topaz in sunlight, he shifted fluidly beneath her, urging her into stirring contact with his renewed arousal. 'You know when I said that I wasn't going to fall on you like a sex-starved animal, I was being a wolf in sheep's clothing…I was lying my head off, *tesoro mio*,' Damiano confided thickly. 'I had been deprived for so long that not ripping off your clothes in the limo the first day was an act of remarkable restraint!'

'R-really?' Eden stammered hot-cheeked, helpless excitement gripping her as he crushed her parted lips hungrily under his, sending her senses reeling again with almost terrifying ease.

'I didn't want to risk scaring you into a fit... I intended to play a waiting game—'

'No more waiting,' she broke in urgently. 'No need for any games.'

All hot-blooded Italian male at that moment, Damiano surveyed her, patently revelling in the response she could neither conceal nor control and the dark flood of sensual pleasure already taking hold of her as he touched her.

About an hour later, having satiated them both on high-voltage sex, Damiano announced with admirable energy that he was hungry and rang for some food to be brought up.

'Service just like home...I take it,' Eden teased, catching the oversized towelling robe he tossed onto the bed for her use.

Damiano frowned. 'Obviously you didn't appreciate that kind of service...'

She stiffened at that note of censure. 'What do you mean?'

'Oh, come on...' Damiano said drily. 'You dump my name, walk out on my family and keep yourself by bloody sewing! You're a qualified teacher. If you had to work, why didn't you look for a teaching job more appropriate to your status?'

Eden had gone rigid. Tightening the robe into a waist-strangling knot, she scrambled off the bed, an angry flush mantling her face. 'You are such a snob!'

'Like hell I am!' Damiano launched at her. 'When you refused Nuncio's support, you were *also* rejecting everything that *I* ever gave you—'

'Your snobby name?' Rage had come out of nowhere to engulf Eden. She was so furious, she was shaking. 'Your ghastly family? What did you give me? A lot of jewellery and a flashy car and loads of credit cards and I was *miserable*!'

'Were you really?' Damiano purred between gritted white teeth.

'Yes, I was... I only stuck it out because I loved you!' Eden raged with clenched fists. 'Once you were gone, I could happily have lived in a hedge and worked as a tramp—'

'Tramps don't work,' Damiano inserted with cool, cutting logic.

'If I had gone for a teaching job, I would have had to explain who I was and there's something *you* don't understand. I doubt if I would have got the job. People treat you like a leper when your husband has gone missing—'

'Cut the melodrama,' Damiano advised witheringly.

'No, because you don't know what it was like for me. People haven't a clue what to say to a woman who was in my situation. They're also terrified that you're going to break down and embarrass them...although that type are preferable to the *other* sort who revel in every gruesome detail of your misery!' she flung at him. 'I wanted privacy and the only way I could have it was to set up a small business guaranteed not to attract attention.'

'So that you could star as the all-singing, all-dancing sewing version of the Little Match Girl?' Damiano drawled with silken scorn.

'I'll have you know that I'm making a darned good living!' Eden countered furiously. 'And I'll happily go back to it any time. Just you say the word!'

In the explosive silence that followed that threat a soft knock sounded on the door. Eden whipped round and stalked out through the French windows spread wide on the balcony outside. With trembling hands, she gripped the worn stone balustrade and stared out into the starry night. The lake far below reflected the pale crescent moon. She breathed in and shivered at the temper which had ripped up through her without warning. It was stress, she finally acknowledged. How could any woman be blissfully happy when she was being blackmailed and living in mortal terror of an exposure that might cost her the man she loved? She *had* to tell Damiano about Mark and Tina's affair within the next few days.

'At the press conference, there were a lot of cracks about how you chose to support yourself in my absence,' Damiano admitted from behind her.

Recalled from her frantic and fearful thoughts, Eden paled in dismay. 'The press already know where I was living...about the shop?'

'Evidently...come and get something to eat.' Damiano detached her death grip on the balustrade and stepped back again. 'Listen to me. Snobbery has nothing to do with this issue—'

'No?'

'No. What disturbs me is the fact that you so quickly rejected our whole life and everybody and everything connected with me. In my mind those are exactly the things to which I should have held fast in the same position.'

As he made that honest admission, tears of shame at

the truth she was refusing to tell him swam in her eyes. Had her position not become untenable with his hostile family, she would have chosen to stay in the town house. She whirled round into his strong arms like a homing pigeon. She drank in the warm, wonderfully familiar scent of him like an addict without hope of reclaim and muttered hoarsely, 'I'm sorry that you got embarrassed like that at the press conference—'

'*Dio mio, cara...* I'm not so sensitive. I have skin like a rhino after Montavia.' Damiano gazed down at her with sardonic amusement. 'Nothing short of the news that you had been working the streets to survive would have fazed me!'

Or that she had been blamed for having a torrid affair mere months after he had disappeared? Stifling that enervating thought, Eden let him usher her back indoors.

CHAPTER SIX

'I REALLY *do* want to know everything that happened to you in Montavia,' Eden murmured seriously.

His lean, strong face taut, Damiano studied her where she sat on the edge of a padded lounger by the side of the superb swimming pool. He hauled himself up out of the water with easy strength, wet and bronzed and stark naked. She blushed furiously, struggled to rescue her concentration, but his sheer magnificence challenged her hard.

It was mid-afternoon the next day and after a late and leisurely lunch they had finally dragged themselves out of the bedroom. She ached all over from the wildness of their lovemaking but there had been something even more precious about just *being* together even though they hadn't talked about anything in particular. And she knew that Damiano had felt that too for neither one of them had made the slightest effort to go to sleep in spite of their exhaustion.

Snatching up a fleecy towel, Damiano gave her a wry look of comprehension. 'The kidnapping is a long way back in the past for me, *cara*.'

'I'd still like to know...I *need* to know,' Eden persisted.

The quiet broken only by the background buzz of the crickets lingered.

'OK. In the first minute, my driver was killed in front of me,' Damiano delivered with grim abruptness, his hard bone-structure clenching, his eyes shadowing. 'I was bundled into the back of a covered truck and beaten up. Standard stuff.'

Her tummy lurched with nausea and she lost colour. 'But why did these soldiers go after you in the first place? What did they hope to achieve?'

'Some total idiot decided that by holding me hostage they might magically get the previous government's loans written off.' Damiano's hard mouth twisted with derision at that fanciful belief. 'Then once I was taken, someone rather brighter realised that kidnapping an international banker would hardly impress the world with the new regime's credentials...or attract any further investment.'

She nodded jerkily, fighting not to think of him being beaten up but tears were burning the back of her eyes.

'Suddenly I was a liability, surplus to requirements. The only way I managed to stay alive until the camp was attacked was by persuading the commanding officer that I was so filthy rich, he could ransom me back to my family for his own personal profit,' Damiano revealed flatly.

She shuddered. 'And then you were hurt again—'

'When the rebel forces attacked, a grenade was thrown into the hut where I was being held. When I came round, I was being carted through the jungle on a pallet. Both my legs were broken...I was totally helpless and temporarily blinded by the explosion,' Damiano recalled with a grimace. 'I also had a fractured skull. But I acted a lot more confused than I was until I had come up with a credible identity with which to satisfy my rescuers that I was on their side. Then just when I had got mobile enough to make a covert break for the nearest border, the field hospital was overrun by government troops.'

'And then you dared not admit who you really were,' she completed heavily for him, recognising what a bitter source of frustration that must have been after he had gone through so much.

'The months after that were the toughest,' Damiano confided grimly. 'I spent a lot of time isolated in a punishment cell because I was always getting into fights.'

Eden gaped at him. 'Always getting into fights? *You?*'

Damiano dealt her an impatient look. 'Two of the guys I went in with were murdered by other inmates,' he told her flatly. 'I'd be dead if I hadn't learned to defend myself. By that stage, I was convinced I was going to spend the rest of my natural life locked up. For a while, I didn't much care *what* happened to me! It was months before we were sentenced for our supposed crimes against the state. Only then did I realise that I'd be released in a couple of years.'

Eden coiled her hands tightly together, feeling the full guilty weight of her own naivety about what it was like to live in such tough conditions. 'It must have been hell for you,' she mumbled, and the minute she'd said that she wished that she could have come up with something less inane.

But a long dark shadow fell over her. Damiano reached down and separated her trembling hands to tug her upright. His spectacular dark, deep-set eyes glittered with hard self-assurance. 'Montavia taught me to value what I have. *Not* to live in the past when I was damned lucky just to survive! I lost my freedom but I didn't lose anything that really mattered. And now that I am home, I will be ruthless in discarding anything I don't want from my life!'

Her eyes slid fearfully from his, tummy somersaulting at that blunt declaration of intent. What would he do when she told him about Mark and Tina? Whose story was Damiano most likely to believe? Hadn't Damiano always shown more faith in his family than he had shown in her? She had a horrendous vision of being ruthlessly discarded from Damiano's life in the way he had just mentioned. Damiano might not waste much time agonising over whether or not she might be guilty.

Nor could she easily forget all that the man from the Foreign Office had warned her about. What if Damiano's present desire for her *was* just a temporary thing? A transitional phase? He had never said that he loved her. Yet he cared about her and he still found her physically attractive. That latter combination wasn't a lot though, was it? How would she bear it if Damiano chose to walk away from her in a few weeks' time? And how much more likely was that development when he learnt about that wretched affair and his faith in her was tested?

'What's wrong?' Damiano asked, terrifyingly attuned it now seemed to her every change of mood.

'Nothing!' Thinking at frantic speed, she tilted her head to one side. 'I was actually wondering how you contrived to arrive here *ahead* of me last night. You never did explain that.'

'I walked out early on the board meeting at the bank.'

In considerable disconcertion, Eden stared at him.

'In five years the bank has had three different acting chairmen. With that many changes of policy, not to mention lax management, profits have dropped. They want me back in spite of the fact that I'm out of touch.' Damiano's expressive mouth curled. 'In fact they want me back like yesterday.'

'So...er, why did you leave the meeting early?'

His strong jawline squared. 'I saw no reason why I should allow myself to be put under pressure the instant I arrive home. The Braganzi Bank must wait.'

Eden swallowed hard on a statement which he would have once considered heresy. Once Damiano had *lived* for the Braganzi Bank, the cut and thrust of the money markets, the latest exciting and all-important deal. He had been a thriving workaholic who had taken twelve- to eighteen-hour working days in his stride. Damiano had sandwiched their marriage into the tiny spaces left over between appointments, trips abroad, late-night business powwows and a social life that had occupied several evenings a week.

'In about three weeks' time, I'll be attending another meeting in Rome. My Italian colleagues are possibly just a fraction more aware of what a man wants and needs after a long time away from his woman...' Damiano gazed down at her with a sudden outrageously wolfish grin, white teeth flashing, brilliant eyes full of self-mockery.

'Are they?' Her mouth ran dry and her heartbeat quickened. Beneath the onslaught of that teasing appraisal, that sexy assessing look he never made the slightest attempt to downplay, she felt as dizzy as a teenager. Damiano could shamelessly telegraph hot desire across a crowded room with a single lingering glance.

'Especially when the guy concerned is aware that his wife was once one of the most neglected wives in London—'

'But you used to notice me around bedtime—'

That charismatic grin merely slanted in easy acknowledgement of that direct hit. 'It didn't get me far, did it? You had me climbing walls in frustration—'

'But not any more,' she inserted in haste, struck afresh by the dangerous mistakes she had made during those early months of marriage. Such a gorgeous guy denied sex, made to feel unwelcome the one place he had had a right to feel welcome. Some men would have given up on her and strayed.

'You just made me want you more and more...' Damiano laughed throatily and grabbed her up into his arms, smouldering eyes raking over her heart-shaped face. 'In fact I don't mind admitting that, in the dark, you and your inseparable nightie gave me some incredibly exciting climaxes. There was always that aura of the forbidden to revel in. Not to mention the wonderful night I discovered that you were biting the pillow because you were so scared of making a noise. I suppose you didn't want to encourage me with the idea that you could be enjoying yourself that much—'

Cheeks aflame, she exclaimed, 'No...it was the knowledge that your sister, Cosetta, was in the room next door!'

In the very act of stepping down into the pool and lowering her into the shimmering turquoise water, Damiano stilled, sudden comprehension flaring in his spectacular dark golden eyes. '*Per amor di Dio*...you were *that* self-conscious?' he groaned, all amusement vanquished as he caught her close to him. 'That never occurred to me. What a baby you still were...and you do choose your moments, don't you? Just when I was about persuade you out of your bikini and into rampant sex outdoors...'

Damiano's provocative drawl broke off at that precise moment, brows pleating at the clackety-clack noise of an approaching helicopter in the skies above. 'What the hell?' he began indignantly as if he owned the airspace as well as most of the land in sight.

A huge grin crept up to curve Eden's trembling mouth. 'And here you are stuck in the water naked as a jaybird. Suppose it's the paparazzi?' she whispered wickedly. 'I know you love risk, Damiano...but if Nuncio thought the shares might crash if you appeared in denim, what will happen if you appear in nothing but your skin?'

Even so, it was a shock to them both when the helicopter flew directly overhead and then began a descent on the far side of the villa. 'Visitors?' Eden yelped aghast.

Meshing one lean powerful hand into her hair, Damiano tipped her face up. 'You little witch,' he husked in a sexy growl, scanning her with hot, dark appreciative eyes and claiming her startled mouth in a devastatingly hungry kiss that wiped helicopters, visitors and even the fact she was standing in water right out of her mind.

Damiano lifted his head again, splaying his hands possessively over her bottom to urge her against his hotly aroused length. Then with an impatient curse in Italian, he set her back from him with pronounced reluctance. 'Who outside the family knows that we are here?'

It was some time before Eden discovered the answer to that salient question. While Damiano was able to dress at speed in the changing area by the pool and head straight off to greet their visitors, she had only a wrap to pull on over her wet bikini and had to rush upstairs to find clothes.

When she came down again, she walked straight into

the main salon, a grandiose state room furnished on a princely scale with Brussels tapestries and magnificent gilded furniture. Even Damiano had been thrown by the sheer size of it when they had done a casual mini-tour of the principal rooms on the ground floor the night before. Immediately recognising the slim redhead seated all by herself on a sofa, Eden hurried to greet the other woman.

'Darcy? Why on earth are you sitting here on your own?'

Rising to her feet, coolly elegant in a flowing turquoise dress, Darcy looked amused. 'Well, in the first fine flush of male bonding, your husband and my husband just totally forgot about me. I've just seen them walking along the terrace out there with drinks in their hands!'

'Oh, dear...' Eden glanced in the direction of the windows but the two men were no longer within view.

Darcy reached for Eden's hands with quiet but sincere warmth. 'I'm so happy for you and Damiano, Eden. I cried my eyes out when I heard the news.' Her eyes took on an apologetic light. 'And I'm afraid that Luca just couldn't *wait* to see Damiano again.'

'I can understand that,' Eden said without hesitation for the Italian banker, Luca Raffacani, was Damiano's oldest friend. 'Did you bring the children with you?'

'Good heavens, no! I thought the two of us was quite sufficient,' Darcy said ruefully. 'Five would have been an invasion force!'

'Five...*five*?' Eden was doing basic sums and finally appreciating just how long it had been since she had seen the other couple. 'You've had another child? For goodness' sake, of course, I'm really out of touch. Zia must be eight now and we were at Pietro's christening shortly before Damiano disappeared,' she recalled slowly.

'I had another little girl two years ago...look, Eden, that's not important,' Darcy countered, her delicate but vivid face looking troubled and serious. 'Do you remember the last time Luca called with you in London?'

'Yes, of course I do.' After Damiano had gone missing, Luca had visited her regularly when he'd been in London on business. However, Nuncio and Cosetta had always insisted on being present when anyone of Luca's importance had called and Eden had never got the chance to talk to Luca alone.

'Well, Luca was very disturbed by the way Damiano's brother and sister were treating you. He described the atmosphere as "poisonous",' Darcy confided with characteristic bluntness. 'We were going to ask you to come and stay with us but before we were able to *do* anything—'

'I'd left London and vanished without even mentioning what I was planning to do.' Eden's smile was strained as she attempted both to conceal her discomfiture at the direction in which the conversation was heading and stall it. Just how much *had* the formidably shrewd Luca Raffacani understood about what had been happening in the Braganzi family during that period? And was Darcy hinting that Luca might well bring Damiano up to speed on the same events?

'Luca made strenuous efforts to trace you.'

'That was very kind of him but I honestly managed fine, Darcy. I'm afraid I needed to come to terms with Damiano's disappearance on my own and I really wouldn't have wanted to inflict my misery on other people.' Eden used the distraction of lifting the phone to

order refreshments. Her hand was trembling as she replaced the receiver.

'I've got this awful feeling that I've given you the
wrong impression,' Darcy admitted anxiously. 'Luca
and I just wish we had made a move sooner and done
more to help before the situation got out of hand.'

'You did everything you possibly could and it was
very much appreciated, believe me.' What situation?
What was Darcy referring to? But, ironically, Eden was
much too scared to ask. She suppressed her fears by
telling herself that Luca Raffacani was far too clever
and worldly wise to even consider making revelations
which would cause trouble in a friend's marriage. 'But
let's not look back. Right now, I can't help just wanting
to revel in the fact that Damiano *has* come home to
me.'

'Which is exactly as it should be,' Darcy agreed immediately, but her fine skin was flushed, her eyes now
veiled. 'And in the normal way, I really would agree
that family matters should stay strictly private *but*... Oh,
dear, there I go again and Luca did warn me not to
mention it!'

Eden took strength from that rueful admission and
decided that it was highly unlikely that news of her
supposed torrid affair nearly five years earlier had travelled as far afield as Italy. She really was getting paranoid! A single story by one British tabloid newspaper
would scarcely have made news round the world, she
scolded herself. She gave her outspoken companion a
sympathetic smile. 'Have you ever noticed that the minute you're warned not to say something, it's the one
thing that you can't get out of your mind?'

'Isn't it *just*?' Pushing back her springy auburn curls
from her brow, Darcy relaxed at that rejoinder and

laughed. 'I'm no good at keeping things in but Luca is wonderfully discreet!'

Receiving that as a reassuring declaration, Eden recalled how envious she had once been of the strength of Luca and Darcy's happy marriage. Such different personalities yet they complemented each other: Darcy so guileless and down-to-earth, Luca, infinitely more complex and reserved. The two women walked along the terrace, taking in the wonderful views of the Tuscan countryside drowsing in the afternoon heat and eventually found Luca and Damiano.

Both men interrupted their keen conversation to glance at their wives with the slightly wary expressions of males belatedly recalling their existence. Eden was tense until Luca Raffacani greeted her with a lazy smile, his legendary reserve nowhere in evidence with friends. Damiano dropped his arm round Eden and drew her possessively close, the heat and proximity of his sun-warmed body soothing the last of her concerns and firing a glow of happiness in her eyes. In times gone by, Damiano would not have been so demonstrative in front of other people.

Eden watched Luca tug at a strand of Darcy's tumbling pre-Raphaelite curls, his wife's answering smile up into her husband's eyes. And then she found Damiano looking down at her, his burnished golden gaze pinned to her tense face, a slight frown-line drawing his expressive dark brows together. The memory of that rather questioning look stayed with her.

The conversation roved on to the theatrical grandeur of the Villa Pavone which had been restored right down to the smallest detail. Damiano explained that his late grandmother, Livia Braganzi, had left architectural historians in charge of the project. 'They had four years in which to complete their work—'

'And the only power showers are in the pool complex,' Eden chipped in with amusement, recalling Damiano's comical horror in the early hours when he had gone into the massive *en suite* bathroom to take a shower and found only a giant bath in the shape of a clam shell.

'So there's still a few improvements to be made because I have no intention of living *in* the eighteenth century,' Damiano commented feelingly. 'We have a pool only because *Nonna* was a keen swimmer.'

'Your grandmother brought you and your siblings up after your parents died, didn't she?' Darcy prompted Damiano with interest. 'To manage that *and* devote her life to restoring historic buildings, she must have been a very active woman.'

Only a great deal less active in the parenting stakes, Eden reflected inwardly. Livia Braganzi had been an extremely rich intellectual. Widowed with only one child while she was still a young woman, she had been obsessed by her restoration projects and not remotely maternal. Damiano's parents had died in a car crash when he was thirteen. His grandmother had idolised him, he had once admitted to Eden, purely because he was so clever. His brother and sister had fared less well against that demanding yardstick of approval. Damiano's protective attitude towards his siblings had been fostered from an early age.

Pressed to do so, Darcy and Luca stayed to dinner before taking their leave.

'Why were you uncomfortable with Luca?' Damiano enquired within minutes of the departure of their guests.

They were sitting over fresh coffee in the picturesque

vine-covered loggia watching the sun sink down behind the hills. Eden flushed and tried not to stiffen. 'Was I?'

'Initially noticeably ill at ease, then you seemed to relax.' His lean, strong face taut, Damiano studied her with cool condemnation. 'It bothers me that I should have to hear from someone else what I should have been told by you.'

To mask her growing nervous tension, Eden had begun stirring her coffee, and, so stricken was she by what Damiano was saying, she kept on stirring as though her life depended on it. The *affair*…it had to be that he was talking about! She could feel the blood draining from her features, the sudden clamminess of her skin, the sick sensation of foreboding turning her tummy queasy.

'*Dio mio*…I am genuinely grateful that Luca chose to be so frank with me,' Damiano continued, his hard mouth ruthlessly cast. 'Why couldn't *you* tell me that, virtually from the moment of my disappearance, my family began treating you like dirt?'

At that revealing question which told her that her guilty conscience had provoked near panic far in advance of any true threat, Eden's head jerked up. 'Well…er, I—'

Anger now clearly evident in his splintering dark gaze, Damiano rammed back his chair and rose to his full commanding height. 'Luca said he noticed their hostility towards you the very first time he visited. He said my sister embarrassed you in front of the staff by countermanding your instructions and indeed went out of her way to stress that *she* was the hostess in what was *your* home!'

'It was always like that when you weren't around,' Eden admitted grudgingly.

Damiano stared at her in complete shock. She saw

that he had listened to what Luca had said but had undoubtedly hoped that Luca had somehow misinterpreted
what he had seen during his visits to the town house.
'Even *before* I went missing?' he emphasised rawly.

Eden sighed and then nodded.

'Yet you never uttered a single word of complaint!'
Damiano surveyed her with thunderous incredulity.

'You told me that your family was the most important
thing in your life. Furthermore, the last thing a new wife
wants to do is to start criticising her husband's relatives
when she *has* to live with them,' Eden responded flatly.
'I'm afraid they had got used to the idea of you marrying Annabel and I was a very unwelcome surprise.'

'But Tina, at least, was your friend…'

'*Not* if it was likely to bring her into conflict with
Nuncio or Cosetta. Tina would never cross Cosetta.
That's how she keeps the peace.'

Deprived of even the comfort of believing that his
sister-in-law had been supportive, Damiano expelled his
breath in a stark kiss. 'I understand that Nuncio implied
within Luca's hearing that it was somehow your fault
that I had gone to Montavia.'

Eden gave a second reluctant nod of affirmation.

'*Porca miseria!*' Damiano exclaimed in outrage.
'How the hell could my own brother make such a ridiculous charge against you?'

Eden paled. 'Your brother and your sister were aware
that our marriage was under strain before you left. They
believed that if you had been more happily married you
would have let one of the bank executives make that
trip.'

Damiano was now white with rage below his bronzed
complexion. '*Accidenti!* To say such a thing to my wife
when she was grieving for me was unforgivable!'

'Damiano…when you went missing, everybody went haywire,' Eden tried to explain gently. 'But, let's face it, I should have stood up for myself long before that happened. Instead I let your family walk all over me and sat feeling sorry for myself, rather than *doing* something about the situation.'

'Do not attempt to excuse them for their appalling behaviour!' Damiano grated. 'You were my *wife*—'

'Yes, but—'

'My wife, who stood to inherit everything I possessed once I was officially declared dead. No doubt that in itself made you a target for their resentment,' Damiano interposed, settling on mercenary motives for his family's attitude with a cynical speed that shook Eden. 'Forgive me for *ever* questioning your refusal to accept my brother's financial support!'

'Don't go over the top about this.' Dismayed by his attitude, Eden got up from her chair. 'Your brother and sister were devastated by your disappearance and their distress *was* genuine—'

'*Santo Cielo*…how could I have been so blind?' Damiano demanded abruptly, his brilliant dark eyes bleak. 'How much did my *own* thoughtless behaviour contribute to what you suffered at their hands?'

'Don't make such a big deal of it now,' Eden urged, seeing no benefit to anyone in his fury so long after the event. 'As long as you never ask me to live with them again, I can let bygones be bygones.'

'You are much too forgiving and generous, *tersoro mio*. There will, nevertheless, be a calling to account,' Damiano delivered with grim assurance. 'I will not let this matter die. Indeed, I cannot. I trusted my family to look after you when I could not be there for you.'

'But I didn't need looking after,' Eden protested.

Damiano pulled her into his arms, crushing her into the heat and solidity of his big powerful frame with strong hands. 'I'd have gone mad in Montavia if I had known that you were being victimised and hurt by those closest to me!' he bit out in a still wrathful undertone above her head.

'I *still* would prefer you to let all this stay buried. Everybody's been upset enough and I do wish Luca Raffacani had minded his own business!'

'Since it's obvious you weren't going to tell me, I'm glad *he* had the sense to do so,' Damiano countered without hesitation. '*Dio mio*...one needs to know who one can trust.'

That phrase sent a stabbing little chill down Eden's spine. Would Damiano still trust her if he knew what she was keeping to herself? And then her eyes flashed angrily as she registered the astonishing level of her own guilt. What had she done? *Nothing!* It was time she reminded herself of that fact. Why shouldn't she protect their wonderful togetherness from all malign influences? Why should *she* have to make an awkward explanation about the sordid scandal which Tina and Mark had selfishly created? Well, she would tell Damiano when she was good and ready and in the meantime? In the meantime, she was determined not to allow that business to hang over her like an executioner's axe, filling her with fear and unease as it had this afternoon when Darcy had spoken rather too frankly.

Damiano anchored his hands round her and lifted her high. A wry smile chased the remnants of anger from his lean, strong face. 'You look *really* cross with me—'

'Not with *you*.' Her heart in her eyes, Eden gazed

down at him with helpless tenderness. 'With Luca for
laying all that on you now.'

Damiano strode indoors with his arms still firmly
wrapped round her. 'I was surprised but evidently what
he witnessed left a deep impression on him. I dare say
he was shocked. However, I'm tough, *cara mia*. Why
do we have to trek a mile to get to our bedroom in this
house?' he lamented, lowering her slowly down the
length of his taut, muscular physique, catching her up
again halfway through that manoeuvre to take her lips
with passionate hunger.

She clung to him with feverish force, stretching up
on tiptoe to let her fingers plunge into his springy black
hair and hold him close. Her body was coming alive all
on its own. He was kissing her with the same deep,
driving sensuality with which he made love. He fired a
tide of hot, quivering longing that made her breasts ache
and her thighs tremble. He sank down on a gilded chair
that creaked in alarming complaint beneath their combined weight.

Dragging his mouth from hers, he got up again in
haste and vented a rueful laugh. 'Right, you can put the
twee dainty chairs into storage for starters. I'll choose
comfort over authenticity any day!'

'One, power shower,' she whispered, utterly dazzled
by his glorious smile, heart racing to such an extent she
could hardly catch her breath. 'Two, chairs to do *more*
than sit in—'

'Did I say that?' Damiano asked mockingly as he
headed for the stairs.

'For once, I'm ahead of you.'

'And without the vodka too—'

Eden reddened and mock-punched a broad shoulder.
'That was low—'

'No, low would be discussing the episode in depth and telling you that I really do wish that I had kept my mouth shut five minutes longer...' Damiano regarded her with smouldering eyes and a thoroughly wicked grin '...just to see what you had planned for me—'

'Damiano—'

'Instead of which I blew a gasket but you can blame Ramon Alcoverro for that development,' Damiano informed her without warning. 'Do you know what Ramon said very quietly to me one minute before I left Brazil?'

Eden frowned in bewilderment as Damiano lowered her down onto their bed. 'No...what?'

'"Your wife's been playing away...thought I should mention it since your little brother didn't have the guts!" Bastard!' Damiano ground out feelingly, adding something in Italian that sounded extremely derogatory, mercifully not looking at her as he slipped off her shoes. 'So I had the entire flight back to London to wonder about what I was coming home to and work out this trite little speech about how I understood if there had been other guys...like *hell* would I have understood!'

Eden closed her shattered eyes and now remembered how incredibly tense Damiano had been with her those first few minutes at the airfield. 'I—'

'*Sì*...I agree. That is a totally unreasonable attitude considering that you spent a good four and a half years of your life thinking you were a widow,' Damiano conceded, into full, unstoppable flow now on a subject which had patently disturbed him a great deal. 'But a guy who's been caged like an animal for the same length of time is *not* reasonable, I assure you. I put you on a pedestal like a little saint. I couldn't bear even to consider the idea that you might have slept with another man—'

Eden sidled back into the shadows cast by the bed curtains. She was pale as death.

Damiano breathed in deep, shimmering dark eyes full of raw emotion as he came down on the edge of the bed. 'If I had lost you, I would have felt as if I had lost *everything*,' he confessed with roughened urgency. 'I had so much faith in you...but I was very scared that Ramon might be telling me the truth!'

It was the moment when she should have spoken up, explained why Ramon had said such a thing. Evidently that nasty little tabloid story had travelled as far as Brazil in terms of gossip at the least. But she lay there like a stone on a riverbed resisting the force of the current and said unevenly, 'Would you have divorced me?'

'Shush...' Damiano scolded with a wince at the sound of that word and he lifted her hand, spread her fingers and pressed his lips almost reverently to her palm. Then he raised his handsome dark head and surveyed her with immense appreciation. 'I may not have respected your moral scruples before we got married, *cara mia*...but I clung to my memory of them every day I was in prison.'

'Hmm...' Eden's voice was so small it was practically inaudible. 'Would you have divorced me?'

'What is this preoccupation with that subject?'

'I'm...I'm just curious,' she mumbled half under her breath.

Sì...probably,' Damiano groaned in frustration at her persistence. 'Out of pride and jealousy and pain. Now you're annoyed with me, aren't you?'

Eden had flipped away from him onto her side. 'No!'

With a throaty chuckle, Damiano tugged her relentlessly back into his arms. 'Don't you know how much I need you?' he husked, stringing out a teasing line of kisses across her sealed lips. 'Now, I've never told any woman that before—'

Involuntarily, a smile crept up on her tense mouth. '*So* macho—'

In the midst of that sentence, he brought his mouth down with sexy provocative heat on hers and she knew she hadn't spoken when she should have spoken but, once he had said that about divorce, she knew she just couldn't take that big a risk. She would tell him before they left Italy and returned to London, she promised herself. Chain him to a wall first, lock every exit, she told herself fancifully.

Over three weeks later, Eden strolled through the wild woodland at the lower end of the Villa Pavone's terraced gardens. Damiano had been away for thirty-six hours in Rome. He had asked her to accompany him but she had said no. Saying no had cost her but they had spent endless days and nights solely together and intelligence had warned her that it was time to stand back and not cling like a neurotic.

This time, Damiano was going to come home. In her head she knew that but she hadn't slept a wink the night before because there was no common sense to be found in her heart. She missed him so much, she was counting the hours and minutes still to be got through. He was due home in the evening. He had phoned her several times. Once in the middle of the night to complain that he kept on waking up because she wasn't there. She had oozed sympathy but she had liked that—oh, yes, she had liked that, wouldn't have been at all happy if he had slept like a log without her.

Damiano was more hers than he had ever been. Damiano was treating her like the most precious and wonderful woman in the world. It seemed that losing each other had taught them to value each other more and value pride a great deal less. And, of course, loving him to bits helped. Not to mention the mutually insatiable passion which she no longer felt threatened by. Indeed, she thought, feeling a slight flush warm her face, she was pretty shameless in that department now. Well, in *her* estimation, she was. Almost every problem resolved…just the one left.

However, it did take courage to face up to the nasty necessity of finally telling Damiano about Mark and Tina's affair and the consequences she had foolishly brought down on herself. But, Eden reflected anxiously, it had to be done. Tiring of the shaded walk, she wandered off it into the sunlit maze between towering dark hedges as impenetrable as walls. Would she be able to find her way to the centre without Damiano's superior sense of direction as guidance?

'Ed-en!'

A huge smile of surprise flashed across her face as she recognised that distant call. Evidently, Damiano had returned from Rome sooner than he had expected. She yelled back and cursed the fact that she had gone into the maze. Excitement had caused her to lose her bearings and, absurdly, she had to keep on shouting.

It was ironic that while she was attempting to find the fastest way out again, she instead found herself on a one-way path and ended up at the centre of the maze instead. The fabulous fountain there shot sprays of glittering water high into the hot still air. 'I'm at the fountain!' she called with a grin and the knowledge that she would never let on that she had arrived there accidentally.

'*Per amor di Dio*...I am not in the mood for some stupid game!'

That comeback made Eden flush in disconcertion. But then possibly he was tired and had been searching the extensive gardens for longer than patience could bear. About thirty seconds later, she heard his footsteps crunch on the gravel surface within the maze. 'I'm not playing a game...it's just I thought you could come in quicker than I would find my way out!' she announced on a note of apology.

Just ten feet away from her, Damiano strode suddenly into view. He stopped dead then as though a repelling forcefield surrounded her. And he looked at her as he had never in his life looked at her. With seething anger and derision and hatred. And *that* quickly, Eden knew, long before he spoke, even before he flung the newspaper cutting in his hand, that she had waited far *too* long to tell him that story...

CHAPTER SEVEN

THE newspaper cutting fluttered down onto the sunlit gravel. Eden gave the crumpled snap of Tina and Mark's torrid embrace only a brief and pained glance.

'It is your deliberate deception that disgusts me most!' Damiano breathed in a stupendously quiet assurance that nonetheless cut through the surging silence like a whiplash. 'At every opportunity when you might have spoken up, you chose to lie.'

'No, I haven't told you any lies,' Eden murmured tautly, snatching in a breath of the hot, still air, perspiration dampening her upper lip. 'It was Tina who had the affair with Mark. That is Tina, *not me*, in that photograph, Damiano—'

'*Accidenti!* I'm not listening to nonsense like that—'

Eden's pale face tightened. 'Well, while you're not listening, would you please tell me where you got that cutting from?'

His aggressive jawline clenched. 'Yet another one of the well-wishers who appear to surround me but, on this occasion, an anonymous one. That tabloid trash was delivered to me by special courier this morning. It was sent from London.'

Eden was fighting to keep calm, fighting to stay in control and not give way to the reality that she was weak with shock. 'Probably by Tina. Now that she views me as a threat, she's keen to see me drummed out of the family. If you think about this awful business calmly—'

'Calmly?' Damiano derided thickly as if he was having difficulty even getting that word out, but volume-wise he was doing very well.

'I swear that I have never been intimate with Mark. We haven't ever even kissed. It was always a platonic friendship…'

Ashen below his bronzed skin, Damiano continued to stare at her with unreadable fixity, eyes black as obsidian, stunningly handsome features as inflexible as a stone carving.

Knowing as surely as if he had told her that he was recalling that she had once admitted to having had a teenage crush on Mark, Eden trembled and set off hurriedly on another track. It was dreadful that her mind should let her down in the midst of such a confrontation. But panic had such a grip on her, she couldn't get her teeming thoughts in order or even work out quite where to begin to tell her side of what had happened almost five years earlier.

'I didn't *know* Mark and Tina were having an affair until the story broke in that newspaper,' she told him tautly. 'Mark visited the town house a great deal those first weeks after you were missing. He and Tina got on well but I never thought anything of that…I mean, why would I? I was too wrapped up in my own misery to be that observant. Tina began to suggest that we went down to the country house at Oxford at weekends. Mark was still working there then—'

'You're wasting your time with this,' Damiano drawled lethally. 'I lost my freedom, not my brain, in South America.'

Eden just kept on talking for, now that she had begun, she could not stop the words spilling out. 'We would drive down in my car. Tina said it was good for me to have to do something that I had to think about and she was probably right...I was like a zombie then. She left me alone a lot those weekends but it never occurred to me that she was with Mark. I wasn't much company, so I wasn't surprised when she would say she was off to visit friends and she took my car...where are you going?' she gasped as Damiano simply swung on his heel and started to walk back into the maze.

'You're telling me lies a child could tear apart. Mark was *your* friend. Mark was *your* constant visitor. Mark was living down on our country estate purely because *you* insisted that I employ him. But then you always had to keep Mark within reach. Why the hell did you marry *me*?'

Eden unfroze from her stupor and raced after him. 'How on earth can you ask me that?'

Damiano stilled without turning back to her, broad shoulders taut with savage tension beneath the fine cloth of his charcoal-grey jacket. 'I don't trust my temper...I don't want to continue this pointless dialogue—'

'You owe it to me to hear me out!' Eden broke in incredulously.

'I don't owe you anything now...' Damiano vented a sudden raw and bitter laugh that made her shiver. 'But thanks for a few memorable lays.'

'Just you turn round and say that to my face!' Eden launched at him shakily.

Unexpectedly, Damiano did swing back. 'Do you know what I really thought was wrong with our marriage before I went to Montavia?'

Eden folded her arms jerkily, her legs trembling beneath her. 'No.'

'Mark...every which way I turned, I came on Mark! You seemed much closer to him that you were to me,'

Damiano delivered grittily, black eyes beginning to take on a stormy glitter of gold, the determinedly level drawl now harshening. 'Naturally I resented him; naturally I was jealous of him—'

'J-jealous?' Eden stammered with a sinking sensation in the pit of her stomach for that was something, and a very dangerous something, which she had never once suspected.

'Remarkable that, isn't it? That *I* should have been jealous of a weak, unscrupulous little jerk, who was openly out for everything he could get? Do you think Mark would have been such an attentive friend if you had married a poor man? He played you like a violin, Eden. I had to stand back and watch it!'

Every syllable of that contemptuous and humiliatingly accurate assessment of Mark's character bit deep into Eden's shrinking flesh. Damiano had seen what she had not. Just a few weeks ago, she would have loyally defended Mark. Now the knowledge that she had allowed Mark to blackmail her weighed her down with a numbing sense of her own inadequacy.

Damiano studied her with hard, biting derision, dark, deep-set eyes frighteningly bleak. 'When my family turned against you after I went missing, Mark must have seemed like your only refuge. Presumably that's how you ended up in bed with him,' he breathed in a chilling assumption that shook her rigid. 'Did you then tell yourself that you were in love with him?'

Eden was aghast at that question and even more by the reasoning he had employed, explaining to his own apparent satisfaction how she might have succumbed to such an affair. Registering that her efforts to defend herself had so far made no impression whatsoever on

Damiano, she exclaimed, 'I didn't end up in bed with Mark! I swear I didn't!'

His lean, powerful face grim, Damiano appraised her with embittered contempt. Swinging on his heel, he strode off, feet crunching on the gravel. The sun beating down on her, Eden stayed where she was, in so much shock she could not immediately react.

Damiano had sent her reeling with revelations of his own. She saw now that she was in much deeper trouble than she could ever have imagined. Damiano had *always* been jealous of her attachment to Mark! Jealous to the level of having once believed that her fondness for the younger man was threatening their marriage. For a split second she could have screamed her frustration to the skies for Damiano had carefully concealed that jealousy from her. And now circumstances had combined horribly to construct a scenario which Damiano appeared to find disturbingly credible. He was quite prepared to believe that, in the fraught aftermath of his own disappearance, she had turned to Mark for more than the comfort of friendship.

So hot that her dress was now sticking to her damp skin, Eden found her way out of the maze. Now she couldn't believe she had been so stupid as to allow Damiano to walk away from her. In panic she raced through the beautiful gardens, heart thumping like a crazed drumbeat driving her on. She had to climb two long flights of stone steps to reach the terrace at the rear of the villa. She sped indoors, dizzy from exertion and frantic with fear that Damiano might already have swung back into his limo and departed.

When she found Damiano in the library which he had begun using as an office soon after their arrival, she fell still in the doorway, breasts rising and falling as she struggled just to catch her breath again. Relief filled her to overflowing in those first taut seconds.

His lean, strong-boned features savagely taut, Damiano sent her a dark look of scorching aggression. 'Get out,' he said softly, a slight tremor marring his usual even diction.

'Not until you give me the chance to defend myself.'

Damiano gave a great shout of sardonic laughter. 'Defend yourself? Who are you trying to kid? Do you think I don't appreciate what's been going on around me since I came home? Everybody *but* me knew that you had had an affair!'

'But I didn't have an affair!' Eden flung back at him wildly.

'Now I understand why Nuncio did not bring you to Brazil. Now I know why you ditched my name and went into hiding. You were embarrassed and ashamed—'

'No, I was just fed up with your family and the whole stupid mess I'd landed myself in! I only made *one* mistake, Damiano. When the press erroneously identified the woman in that photograph as me, I was faced with a very difficult choice,' Eden insisted in growing desperation as she moved deeper into the room, her whole concentration bent on him. 'If I spoke up and pointed out that that woman was Tina, I was going to wreck her marriage and she begged me to keep quiet—'

'Tell me, how long did it take you to come up with this melodramatic tale in which you were the only victim and *every* member of my family was rotten to the core?' Damiano slashed back at her in unconcealed disgust.

'Tina said it was my fault that her affair with Mark

was exposed and, in a twisted way, she was right,' Eden conceded shakily.

'What are you trying to say?'

'That there wouldn't have *been* a story if that paparazzo photographer hadn't assumed that that woman kissing Mark was me! And my only claim to fame was being the wife of a well-known banker who had gone missing in a huge shower of publicity. That was what made me a target and that was what made that story of my supposed infidelity worth printing!'

'I am never going to believe that someone as prim and proper as you used to be agreed to be labelled an adulteress for Tina's benefit!' With that seething proclamation of disbelief, Damiano strode past her, long, powerful strides carrying him towards the stairs at a far faster rate than she could emulate.

'All right, what I did was downright stupid but you should know me better!' Eden protested as she hurried breathlessly up the stairs in his stormy wake. 'I thought you were dead. I was trying to cope with my own grief. I really didn't *want* to feel responsible for Tina losing Nuncio as well!'

With a ground-out exclamation in Italian, Damiano fell still on the landing, his lean hands clenching into powerful fists. 'Stop this *now*! Where is your dignity?'

'When have I *ever* lied to you?' Eden demanded rawly.

She looked up at him. He looked back down at her. The atmosphere was thick with sizzling undertones. She collided with his stunning dark golden eyes and finally saw the tremendous pain he was attempting to hide from her, the savage restraint he was exerting over his emotions.

Eden trembled, tummy churning. She sensed that she

had finally said something that penetrated, something he was finally prepared to consider.

The silence hung like a giant weight ready to fall.

Damiano's black spiky lashes lowered, eyes narrowing to glittering pinpoints of ferocious intensity. 'You have never had cause to lie to me before.'

Eden flinched as if he had struck her, the feverish colour in her cheeks draining away, 'And you have *never* trusted me,' she muttered in a stricken tone of discovery. 'Evidently you didn't even trust me when we were first married. What did I ever do to deserve that?'

Dark blood scored the high cheekbones which stood out with such chiselled prominence below Damiano's bronzed skin. He said nothing.

Eden mounted the remaining stairs until they were level, the shock and hurt in her eyes unconcealed. 'You hid so much from me five years ago...I had no idea that you resented Mark. I really didn't understand what I was dealing with until now.' Her throat aching with unshed tears, Eden turned away. 'That's, it, then, isn't it? Because I don't have any proof of my innocence to offer you!'

As she headed down the corridor to their bedroom, a lean hand suddenly snapped round her wrist, staying her. Damiano scanned her strained, tear-wet face with savage dark golden eyes. 'What do you mean, ''That's it''?'

Eden pulled free of him in an equally abrupt movement. Even though she was shaking like a leaf and starting to feel rather dizzy, she thrust up her chin in challenge. 'Well, what do you think I mean?'

Eyes a scorching, aggressive gold, Damiano growled, 'No way are you leaving me!'

Thoroughly confused by that assurance when she had

assumed *he* was set on walking out and leaving *her*, Eden blinked. 'B-but—'

'You tell me the truth and I'll attempt to put this matter behind us.' Damiano gritted out each word of that promise as if it physically hurt.

Eden was so taken aback she simply gaped at him.

'The *truth*,' Damiano emphasised.

'But you won't believe me.'

'Maybe you never actually went as far as *sleep* with him...maybe I could believe that,' Damiano ground out thinly between clenched teeth, misinterpreting what she had said.

Eden tilted her pounding head to one side, wishing that annoying dizziness afflicting her would recede, and looked at him in increasing bewilderment. 'You really don't know *what* to believe, do you?' A great weariness engulfed her then. 'And I can do nothing but tell you the rest of the story. Tina and I discussed this in London. She has already said that she will lie to protect herself...and Mark is only willing to tell the truth for a price.'

Damiano frowned down at her without comprehension. 'A price?'

'He said he'd throw his lot in with Tina and lie if I didn't give him money,' Eden mumbled sickly. 'Mark is blackmailing me, Damiano.'

Wrenching open the door, Eden fled into the bedroom. One glimpse of Damiano's transfixed expression was sufficient to make her slam the door. With her emotional turmoil at a level beyond what she could handle, making that final confession had made her feel marginally better. She had finally told him the entire truth.

Only a full two minutes *after* making that admission did her intelligence kick back in and shriek that she should have kept quiet about the blackmail. Now Damiano would be absolutely convinced of her guilt!

CHAPTER EIGHT

EDEN listened to the silence. Damiano did not follow her into the bedroom.

Still feeling dizzy and absently wondering whether stress could make one feel *that* light-headed, she flung herself on the bed and cried until there were no tears left. By then her eyes were sore and puffy and she was hot and exhausted. Pulling off her crumpled clothing, she crawled into the bed. Then she lay there dully wondering what to do next.

Was she supposed to be pleased that Damiano evidently cared enough about their marriage to declare that he would try to put her apparent infidelity behind him? What she did appreciate was how little she had once been able to read the volatile male whom she had married. Damiano jealous of Mark? It was as if Damiano had never ever quite been able to bring himself to believe that she loved him...why?

Somewhere in the midst of trying to work out that mystery while trying not to succumb to an urge to go and search the villa to see if Damiano was still in residence, Eden fell asleep. When she opened her eyes again, the room was dimly lit. She moved her head experimentally and was relieved that that strange dizziness had receded. She turned over then and got a shock.

Damiano was sprawled in an armchair only about a foot away. Jacket and tie discarded, black hair tousled, he had not followed his usual habit of shaving a second time in the evening. A definable blue-black shadow of stubble outlining his formidable jawline, he was nursing a brandy goblet between his lean hands while he studied her from below lush ebony lashes with keen intensity.

'Wh-what?' she stammered unsteadily, unnerved by that scrutiny.

Damiano loosed a heavy sigh and stretched his big shoulders back. 'I want to hear about Mark trying to blackmail you,' he admitted.

Tensing up even more, Eden paled and stared at him in bewilderment. 'I...I gave him the money—'

All apparent relaxation abandoned, Damiano leapt up like a lion about to spring, an expression of unholy disbelief etched on his tough features. 'You did...*what*?'

Eden gulped and sat up, clutching the sheet to her quaking frame. 'He threatened to support Tina's story instead. What was I supposed to do? How do you think you would have reacted to all this coming out within days of you getting home? I wanted time with you...I didn't want everything ruined—'

'You do realise that you are damning yourself more with every word you say?' Damiano cut in flatly.

'But it *is* the truth I'm telling you,' Eden insisted. 'I was scared of the damage Mark might do if he got together with Tina, so I gave Mark all the money I had in my bank account when he asked for it—'

An expression of shaken fascination stamping his lean, strong face, Damiano sank down heavily on the edge of the bed. 'You just *gave* him it...how much?' he practically whispered.

After chewing at her lower lip for a second or two, she surrendered and told him. 'I thought our marriage was worth it,' she muttered heavily.

'That is a highly original excuse for paying a blackmailer,' Damiano conceded grittily, his broad chest

swelling as he breathed in very deep as if he was having
a hard time controlling his temper. 'Anstey demanded
the money the day you flew out here, didn't he?'

She gave a jerky nod and swallowed hard.

'That creepy little bastard!' Damiano condemned
with a sudden vicious force that made her flinch.

'I'm sorry...I'm so sorry about *all* of this!' Eden
sobbed, flopping down to push her face wretchedly into
the pillows.

'Console yourself with the thought that by the time
I'm finished some people are going to be a great deal
sorrier,' Damiano imparted darkly, and he went on to
ask further detailed questions concerning Mark. But
Eden had few concrete answers to offer. She knew
Mark's mobile phone number but not his current address and was unsure of the exact location of the organic
farm company at which she understood he worked.

She heard Damiano stand up again and she lifted her
head. 'I never would have slept with Mark,' she swore
in a vehement rush. 'I couldn't imagine doing that with
anybody but you.'

'That does have a certain ring of veracity, *cara mia*.
Sadly, however, the vodka incident you treated me to
the first day doesn't do much to support your case,'
Damiano admitted bluntly. 'To me that now looks very
much like you overcompensating out of a massive guilt
complex.'

Eden looked at him with reddened eyes now finally
beginning to spark with angry resentment. 'Right...just
you go on thinking that. Just you go right on rational-
ising your conviction that I'm guilty. Frankly, I think
I've had enough grief over something I didn't do!'

In the rushing silence which followed, Damiano shed
his shirt.

Eden bounced up against the pillows, no longer limp and weepy. 'What do you think you're doing?'

Unzipping his tailored trousers, Damiano gave her a level glance. 'I'm coming to bed—'

'You're not coming to bed with me!' Eden declared in angry astonishment. 'You don't believe me about Mark... So you can go and sleep somewhere else!'

At a leisurely pace, Damiano removed the remainder of his clothing. Naked and unconcerned, he strolled back across the room.

'OK...you can sleep here if you must.' Eden withdrew her objections just as suddenly as she had made them for she recalled with a shiver of foreboding just how much of a distance separate bedrooms had imposed between them in the distant past.

'*Grazie,*' Damiano purred in liquid Italian.

'You're not thinking of a divorce, then?' As the lights went out, that demand just erupted from her and she cringed, embarrassed by her lack of control over her own tongue.

'Not just at the moment, no,' Damiano drawled flatly. 'But I'm probably going to make your life hell while I try to come to terms with this.'

'Is that a threat?'

'A warning.'

In the darkness tears welled up again and stung her eyes. He didn't believe her; he was *never* going to believe that she hadn't betrayed him with Mark.

In an abrupt movement, Damiano closed lean hands to her waist and tugged her across the great divide between them into his arms. Nervous as a cat, Eden vented a startled gasp.

'I still want you, *cara,*' he breathed rawly.

Now in intimate contact with his lean, muscular physique, Eden was in no doubt of the truth of that claim, but she was taken aback. 'But you—'

'I'm not so sensitive,' Damiano growled. 'And you can't afford to be.'

Flung into disarray by that uncompromising approach, Eden quivered against him, the heat and hunger of him striking her at every treacherous pulse-point.

'Damiano—?'

'You want me too. The love might be fake but the sex is *real*,' Damiano spelt out raggedly. 'And I'm quite happy to settle for a great time in bed right now.'

Those words hurt her so much but she was painfully aware that he was hurting too and she blamed herself entirely for that. But so strained and unhappy did she feel that she genuinely believed she would not be able to respond. And then Damiano crushed her mouth under his with demanding hunger. It was a considerable shock for Eden to find herself not only responding but clinging with a kind of desperate fervour way beyond anything she had expected to feel.

'You're *my* wife...' Damiano spelt out, releasing her swollen lips and then delving them apart with the invasive eroticism of his tongue before she could reply.

He sent such a jolt of sensual excitement leaping through her, she gasped beneath that onslaught. And so it went on. The stroke of his hand across her breast followed by the urgency of his mouth on the aching peak, arching her spine off the bed, making her cry out. By the time he discovered the moist readiness at the heart of her, she was way beyond control, possessed by a frantic intensity of need and excitement combined.

And then, without any warning at all, Damiano was suddenly thrusting her back from him, gritting out something savage in Italian. A split second later, Eden was sitting up in shock. In the shadowy path of the moonlight filtering into the room, she watched Damiano vault off the bed and stride into the bathroom. With an unsteady hand, she switched on the lights. She listened to the power shower he had had installed running at full force.

Shattered by his last-minute rejection of her, she got up, pulled on a light robe and sank down in the chair he had vacated earlier. Her body ached and she hated it for aching for she knew that what had just transpired was infinitely more important than any transitory pleasure. He had intended to make love to her. His body had been as eager as her own. But at the very last minute some mental barrier had triumphed and he had drawn back.

Damiano reappeared, a towel knotted round lean hips. 'I'm sorry,' he breathed starkly. 'I thought I could be cool about it…but I can't be. I can't make love to you with this much anger in me. I might have hurt you.'

He said all that without looking at her once as if the very sight of her was suddenly an offence to him. His bronzed profile fiercely taut, he went through to the connecting dressing room where she heard him slamming through units and drawers and then talking on the phone in Italian. She just sat there white-faced and sick inside. Damiano might as well have hung out a placard printed with the words. 'The end'. It was eleven at night. He had got out of bed, he was getting dressed.

She stood up, walked over to the open door and eavesdropped as he spoke tersely on the phone. Then she went into retreat again because she knew she was out of her depth and currently at a stand. She had told the truth and he could not accept it. He had contrived, however, to put on the act of the century. He had kept his rage under wraps. He was, she registered on a flood of desperate love, in infinitely more turmoil than she was.

He emerged from the dressing room, sheathed in a formal dark suit, hard, dark face as remote as the Andes. 'I'm going back to London—'

'Let me come with you...*please.*'

'I need some time,' Damiano breathed harshly, lifting a lean hand that wasn't quite steady in an expressive motion that he did not complete. 'You don't want to be around me right now. I need to be on my own.'

'Like Greta Garbo...' she muttered helplessly.

'*Accidenti!* You think I'm running away from this?' Damiano roared at her, his control splintering into black fury right in front of her. She fell back a step in sheer fright. 'I'm leaving for *your* sake. If I stay, I will very probably destroy what we have and I don't want to do that, so give me some space.'

Dully she nodded and turned her pained eyes away. 'I love you—'

'It doesn't feel like it,' Damiano ground out, his accent very thick.

The most dreadful silence set in.

'I've bought another country house in England...it was supposed to be a surprise,' Damiano admitted bleakly. 'You can go there as soon as you like. I'll make the arrangements.'

'You're going back to the town house to live,' she assumed, feeling as if she had been kicked. It was a separation, whatever he chose to call it.

'No. The bank has an apartment I can use.'

Long after Damiano had gone, Eden sat on in the empty bedroom. She felt gutted. Was this the end of the transition period that she had been warned about?

Stop avoiding the real issue here, her conscience urged her. Almost five years ago, she had created the current situation by being weak, sentimental and foolish. Damiano had come through hell to come home. No matter what the risk, it would have been wiser to tell him the whole story immediately. Secrecy and evasion did not instil trust. She, who had once prided herself on her honesty and her scruples, was ashamed of her own behaviour in retrospect. In *his* position, she too would have been angry, bitter and suspicious.

Forty-eight hours after Damiano's departure, Eden flew back to London and was driven out to Greyscott Hall.

It was a charming Elizabethan manor house set in wooded parkland. Damiano had phoned her twice since his return to London but the smooth impersonality of those dialogues had done little to raise her spirits. Indeed as she walked into the beautiful hall scented with the sweet perfume of a gorgeous arrangement of roses she was anxiously thinking that Damiano had cunningly contrived to rehouse her. Should he decide not to return to their marriage, he would not have the inconvenience of either moving himself or asking her to move.

'The instant I saw the video tape the agent sent, I knew you'd fall in love with Greyscott,' Damiano had informed her expressionlessly on the phone. 'It's full of character. It's big but it's not pretentious. It has a homely aspect.'

To Eden's knowledge, no Braganzi, raised from birth to consider magnificence their natural milieu, had ever aspired to live in any building which might be described by that word, 'homely.' Was it any wonder that she should feel nervous when Damiano had emphasised that Greyscott Hall was to be the home of *her* dreams?

The housekeeper took Eden on a guided tour. Even in the troubled mood she was in, Eden was entranced by her surroundings. Knole sofas covered with tapestry and a delightful window-seat adorned the sunlit room which overlooked the rose garden. Damiano had bought some of the contents of the house. He had also hired a design company to furnish the empty spaces in the main reception rooms and the master bedroom, so that the hall was ready for immediate occupation. So far, Eden had not been able to tell what was original and what was not and she was impressed by the care that had been taken. That timeless air of welcoming warmth and ever so slightly faded charm which was the hallmark of an old country house had been maintained.

'I believe you're a keen needlewoman,' the housekeeper remarked with a warm smile, spreading wide the door on a wonderful sewing room kitted out with every possible aid for such a purpose.

'Yes, I am.' But tears of disconcertion pricked Eden's eyes as she studied the array of equipment which included an elegant antique tapestry frame. Obviously Damiano remembered her stitching away all those years ago in the drawing room at the town house. In those days, she had used sewing as a distraction. With her hands busy and her head bent, it had been easier to ignore the snide comments and scornful looks which had come her way when Damiano had not been present.

Eden walked over to the window and kept her eyes very wide until she had herself under control again. The male who had gone to so much trouble on her behalf had really thought about what would make her happy. It was ironic that the evidence of Damiano's desire to surprise and please her should now inspire only a distressed awareness of what she had so recently lost.

Everything at Greyscott Hall had been planned and executed *before* Damiano had received that newspaper cutting.

Would she ever see Damiano again? She could not prove that she had remained faithful to their marriage. Nor in the circumstances did she feel that she could fault his distrust. As she wandered round the upper floor of her new home, it seemed perfectly credible to her that Damiano might not physically meet with her again. It would be so much easier for him to write their marriage off and call in the lawyers. After all, he had managed to live without her for a very long time. Surely he would remind himself of that unfortunate reality?

How much had those ecstatically happy weeks at the Villa Pavone actually *meant* to Damiano? Wasn't she inclined to place far too much importance on what they had shared? In fact, wasn't she guilty of being hopelessly naive? Damiano had spent four and a half years in prison. Then he had flown to Italy to embark on sun-filled weeks of sexual intimacy with a very willing and available partner and all the freedom, relaxation and comfort he could handle. Just about *any* man, fresh from a similar ordeal, would have thoroughly revelled in all that was on offer!

Hurriedly suppressing thoughts which threatened to drag her down into despair, Eden stilled the doorway of a room whose former purpose was still evident in the built-in corner cupboard. The worn hand-painted panels depicted children's toys. The nursery, she reflected gloomily—the nursery destined *never* to be filled.

But mere seconds in the wake of that thought, an extraordinary realisation struck Eden. Naturally, she was no longer taking the contraceptive pill which she has used when they had first been married. Well, whoopee, Eden, why has it taken until now for you to recall that fact? Dumbstruck by the belated awareness that she and Damiano had been making love without the slightest consideration of consequences for several weeks, Eden walked very slowly downstairs to be served with morning tea.

Damiano's miraculous return from the dead had simply blasted all such practicalities from her mind, Eden acknowledged in a daze. It had been almost five years since either of them had been required to consider precautions against pregnancy. Well...Damiano had not been any quicker off the mark than she had been on that count. Indeed, babies might well have come via the stork story the way the two of them had been behaving!

Eden almost knocked her cup and saucer over as she made a sudden lunge at her bag to dig out her diary. Another wave of that irritating dizziness washed over her, forcing her to lift her head again and breathe in deep before she felt able to check dates in her diary. She thought about the light-headed sensations which had been annoying her for almost a week and discovered that her period was a few days late. Her cycle was normally regular.

A beatific glow slowly enveloped Eden. She might be pregnant right now, she thought in shock; right this very minute, she might be pregnant! And how would Damiano feel about that? Well, the guy who had said he was tough would just have to *be* tough. What she really needed was confirmation one way or the other from a doctor and she wasted no time in reaching for the phone.

After Damiano had gone missing, Eden had just about broken her heart over that reality that there had not been the slightest chance of her being pregnant.

Although she had chosen to stop taking the contraceptive pill, Damiano had not shared her bed again in those final weeks. She had believed then that in her situation a child would have been an enormous comfort.

As soon as she had had lunch, Eden was driven back to London to keep an immediate appointment with the Harley Street medical practitioner whom the Braganzi family patronised. She prayed while the pregnancy test was being done. Twenty minutes later, she settled back into the limo shaken, smug and over the moon.

Indeed, Eden did not begin descending to planet earth again until she went to bed that night in solitary state at Greyscott Hall. With increasing anxiety, she was by then wondering how Damiano would react to the news that she was carrying his child. The insane desire to rush straight to the phone and tell him in the hope of bringing him home had receded fast. Five years ago, admitting to Damiano that she wanted a baby had gone down like a lead balloon. And how could Damiano possibly want her to have his baby now when they were estranged?

Everything always seemed to condense down to one humiliating fact: Damiano did not love her. If he had ever loved her, he would have told her. She had never forgotten Annabel Stavely, egged on by Cosetta, showing off her necklace etched with a loving inscription from Damiano. Even so, back then, she had often wondered what Damiano had found *to* love in Annabel. The redhead's undeniable physical perfection? Her endless joy in shopping? Her enthusiastic description of each designer garment purchased? Her apparent inability to utter a single intelligent sentence? While prepared to admit that she had scarcely been an unprejudiced judge, Eden had been stumped.

At noon the next day, having entertained herself with a trip to the nearest design and interiors shop and returned with a couple of wallpaper books, Eden was down on her knees in the nursery. To cheer herself up, she was comparing the merits of fluffy bunny rabbits on a border as opposed to dancing teddy bears, and when she heard footsteps behind her she simply assumed it was the housekeeper.

'What do you think?' she asked.

'Love those drunk-looking teddy bears...' Damiano breathed without warning above her head. 'But why are the rabbits jumping over gates like sheep?'

Eden froze.

'Artistic licence, I expect,' Damiano answered for himself, his dark, deep drawl so constrained it screamed his tension louder than any tannoy. 'Not very sophisticated but certainly novel.'

CHAPTER NINE

IN DISCOMFITED haste, Eden flipped shut both the wall-paper books. 'I wasn't expecting you,' she admitted before she could think better of it.

'Do I need to make an appointment now?' Damiano enquired tautly.

'Of course not.' Eden did not notice the hand he extended to help her up off her knees. She was flustered and waiting for him to ask why she had been studying nursery wallpapers. She smoothed down her fitted short-sleeved apricot blouse and the toning cotton skirt she wore with nervous hands. 'When did you arrive?'

Damiano flashed her a narrowed glance from spectacular dark, deep-set eyes, high cheekbones taut. 'Almost an hour ago. I expected to stumble upon you faster.'

He had been in no hurry to find her, Eden translated, heart sinking at that amount of reluctance after a separation which had lasted three days. Not that three days was that long a space of time, she tried to tell herself. She focused on him with helpless intensity, greedily absorbing every detail of his appearance. The sophisticated pale grey suit cut to enhance every hard line of his wide shoulders, narrow hips and long, powerful thighs. The black silk luxuriance of hair, the strong masculine profile, the authority and intrinsic sensuality of a breathtakingly attractive and powerful male.

'To be frank, I was thinking…thinking in depth,' Damiano extended flatly, snapping her out of the abstracted thoughts that were already beginning to make her face burn. 'Trying to work out what to say to you and, I'm afraid, not getting anywhere fast.'

That honest admission struck Eden with force and filled her with fear. Nobody with any finer feeling found it easy to find the right words with which to break news that would hurt. 'Let's go downstairs,' she urged, swiftly stepping past him.

No, he wasn't the type to bring in the lawyers without telling her first face to face that he wanted a divorce. There was nothing cowardly about Damiano and nothing underhand. His cool reserve might once have defied her comprehension but he had returned to her, considerably more willing to express what he felt and what he thought. Her fingers fluttered across her tummy in a fleeting protective gesture that she hurriedly cut short. Telling Damiano that she was expecting their first child promised to be a most humiliating challenge. From his point of view, that could hardly be good news, but she had no doubt that he would politely strive to hide that reality for her sake. Her throat thickened with tears.

Damiano followed Eden into the sitting room. Eden left him again to order coffee but she was ashamed of that weak prompting to play for time. The arrival of coffee was hardly likely to deflect Damiano from his purpose.

When she reappeared, Damiano was lodged by the stone fireplace. The angles of his lean, strong face were tense. 'It's ironic to think that this is really our first home. I don't think the town house counts.'

Eden was at the stage of reading threatening vibrations into everything that now passed his lips. She was convinced that the irony he saw in his purchase of Greyscott Hall as their first supposed home was that he now knew he would never *share* it with her. 'No, I suppose it doesn't,' she agreed tightly. 'Are you planning to sell the Villa Pavone?'

Dark golden eyes veiled, Damiano shot her a sudden frowning glance. 'That idea hadn't occurred to me. But I believe that the villa should be opened to the public for some part of the year in honour of my grandmother's work.'

A light knock on the door heralded the arrival of coffee. Eden busied herself over the cups but her hands were all fingers and thumbs and she had to do everything very slowly. The atmosphere was so full of charged undertones that her tummy was in knots and her palms damp.

'*Grazie…*' Damiano breathed flatly, retreating back to the fireplace with his cup and saucer as if there were a dividing line down the centre of the room and he could only briefly visit the zone designated as hers. 'Do you like the house?'

'It's really beautiful. I was delighted with the sewing room too. That was a lovely idea,' Eden completed in a voice that just trailed away on the reflection that that reminder of his warmer intentions towards her might now be unwelcome.

Across the room, a shaft of sunlight playing over his dark, well-shaped head, Damiano stared down fixedly into his black coffee.

Eden feasted her attention on him, noting the taut line of his beautifully shaped mouth, and then watched his cup rattle on the saucer for a split second before she realised that he couldn't hold his hand quite steady. Almost as quickly, Damiano set his coffee down with a low-pitched exclamation in Italian.

Strained dark eyes claimed hers before she could

evade that contact. 'I very much regret what happened in Italy—'

Eden went rigid, registering that the main issue could no longer be avoided. 'Fine, absolutely fine,' she slotted in with a mindless desire to stop him speaking before he could say anything that might hurt her.

The silence smouldered.

'No, it *wasn't* fine,' Damiano contradicted. 'I should never have reacted as I did. I owe you an explanation.'

Eden tore her pained gaze from his. She rose from her seat because sitting still had suddenly become impossible for her and she walked over to the windows. She did not want any long-winded explanations. She *knew* how he felt; she wasn't stupid. He had been willing to give their marriage another chance but the belief that she had had an affair had blown that ambition out of the water.

'When I saw that newspaper cutting, I was confronted by my biggest fear,' Damiano admitted in a driven undertone. 'And I am very conscious that I did not shine like a star in dealing with it.'

'But I understood how you felt,' Eden conceded heavily.

That tabloid story furnished with a convincing photograph and backed by her own suspicious silence on the subject would not have impressed any man with a belief in her innocence.

'I doubt it...'

Eden looked up uncertainly.

Damiano studied her with bleak dark eyes. 'I thought the worst because I felt that I *deserved* the worst. I was too upset to be rational,' he confessed with a ragged edge to his dark, deep drawl. 'But even when I was being a lousy husband five years ago, even when I was

being unreasonably jealous, I always knew in my heart
that you were the most honest and sincere woman I had
ever met.'

'You...you did?' Eden pressed in surprise.

'*Of course*, I did,' Damiano asserted forcefully. 'No
matter how damning the evidence appeared, I should
have accepted your word that you had not had an affair
with Mark Anstey.'

Eden continued to stare at him, utterly disconcerted
by that final statement. Meeting the level look of regret
in his spectacular dark golden eyes, she realised that he
meant what he was saying. No longer did he suspect
that she had been unfaithful! The most enormous tide
of relief rolled over Eden and left her feeling weak. She
sank heavily down on the window-seat and slowly
breathed in deep to steady herself.

'I wish I could tell you that I reached that conclusion
without hesitation,' Damiano continued with a pronounced air of discomfiture. 'But I'm afraid I can't—'

'You can't?' Eden cut in anxiously, wondering if she
had misunderstood his declaration of faith in her mere
seconds earlier.

'I was able to purchase the entire roll of film that was
taken of Anstey and his female companion that day.'
Damiano withdrew several photographs from the inside
pocket of his jacket. Colour scored his hard cheekbones
as Eden frowned in bewilderment and then stared
fixedly down at the snaps he was laying out on the
window-seat for her inspection.

'I didn't realise that there was more than that one
photograph taken!' Eden snatched up the first. She was
astonished to find herself studying a photo of Tina in
the act of climbing out of the car, a photo which nobody

who knew both women could possibly have mistaken as being of Eden.

'I had begun negotiations to buy that film before I even landed back in London,' Damiano informed her wryly. 'I wanted to ensure that neither the original nor any further photos that might have been taken that day could appear in print again.'

Eden slowly shook her head over the spread. Distaste filled her as she thought of the hidden photographer out simply for profit but ultimately responsible for causing so much heartache. Leaving the photos where they lay, she got up and walked away from them in growing disgust and bitterness. 'Naturally, the newspaper was only interested in printing that one picture that showed the big kiss but not the woman's face! So it was just a case of mistaken identity, was it? Some creep who didn't know either Tina or me well enough to tell us apart?'

'I have put the matter in the hands of my lawyers. My opinion is that the mistake was deliberate because it provided a tacky little story but I may be proved wrong. Can you forgive me for doubting you?' Damiano demanded tautly.

'Oh, don't be stupid!' Eden exclaimed, still outraged by what she had learnt from seeing those photographs. 'I'm just so annoyed that I didn't have the wit to get in touch with the family legal firm and order my own investigation years ago!'

Crossing the room, Damiano reached for her tightly clenched hands. He closed his fingers over hers. 'Eden...?' he prompted grittily. 'I'll beg if you want me to.'

Her hands relaxed in the grip of his. She forgot all about the photographs as finally she allowed herself to fully appreciate that the nightmare was over. Happiness began to surge up where once there had only been fear and anxiety. She looked up at him and collided with shimmering eyes that made her heart sing. 'Would you beg?' she could not resist asking with considerable curiosity.

'*Per amour di Dio...*' Damiano murmured with ragged stress, almost crushing the life from her smaller hands. 'Could you doubt it after what we were to each other in Italy, *tesora mio*? Don't you know that even if it *had* been you in that photo, I would have come back to you?'

'Really?' Eden gazed up at him with shaken eyes.

'Now you're being stupid...' Damiano muttered with roughened tenderness, gathering her into his arms and releasing his breath in a pent-up hiss. 'I only came back to London because I was afraid of wrecking what we had found together.'

'An excess of tact doesn't become you...or suit me. I would have preferred you to stay and talk,' Eden confided, her mouth running dry and the breath shortening in her throat.

Being pressed into intimate connection with his lithe, powerful physique awakened little quivers of responsive heat in what felt like every inch of her body. A very feminine smile curved her lips as he shivered against her, his heated male arousal something he could not conceal from her.

'*Sì...*' Turning up her face, Damiano appraised her with scorching golden eyes and then, linking his hands with hers again, he groaned unevenly. 'I have missed being with you so much. Could we complete this conversation upstairs, *cara mia*?'

Eden pretended to consider his request and tilted her head to one side. Her eyes danced with provocation.

With a censorious growl, Damiano responded by
sealing his hot demanding mouth to hers. Soaring excitement laced her haze of joyous happiness. He released her long enough for them to reach the hall and
start up the stairs, but a couple of minutes were lost on
the landing when the temptation to kiss again proved
too much for both of them.

Damiano deposited her on the bed in the dark oak-
panelled master bedroom. Eden kicked off her shoes.
'Can't you just imagine this room lit by fire-light in
winter?' she whispered, studying him with dreamy eyes,
clasping her hands over her still flat tummy and deciding that she would tell him about the baby after they
had made love.

Damiano gave her a slanting grin. 'I like you in all
kinds of light. I'm not at all particular in that direction.'

Her heart just jumped at the innate charm of that
smile.

'Daylight, moonlight, lamplight, total blackout...'
Damiano enumerated in mocking addition, tugging
loose his silk tie and removing his jacket with a decided
look of intent that made her tense with anticipation. 'I
can't believe you're not throwing me out—'

Eden lifted a slim shoulder in an attempt to emulate
one of his slight fluid shrugs. 'I could still be considering it—'

Still half dressed, Damiano came down on the bed
and cupped her cheekbones with his spread fingers.
'Don't tease,' he urged feelingly, lustrous dark eyes
pinned to her tender smile in raw approach. 'I have no
sense of humour whatsoever when it comes to the idea
of losing you.'

She turned her lips into his hand and kissed his palm.
'That cuts both ways,' she said a little shakily.

Their eyes met, hot gold into anxious green, and suddenly they were kissing each other breathless with the kind of electrifying mutual hunger which brooked no denial. Eden wrenched at his shirt buttons at the same time as he attempted to deprive her of her blouse. With a groan of frustration at their colliding manoeuvres, Damiano pulled back and ripped off his shirt, sending a couple of buttons flying in his eagerness to discard it.

'Not very cool, Mr Braganzi—'

'Not feeling cool at all,' Damiano confided without hesitation, extracting her from her blouse and disposing of her bra.

He pressed his mouth hotly to the exposed slope of one small breast, succumbed to the lure of a pouting pink nipple and lingered there to tease her sensitive flesh with erotic mastery. She writhed under his attentions, possessed by a frantic craving that drove her on like a fever. He ran his hand up the extended length of one slender thigh, driving her wild with anticipation. She closed her hand into his hair, dragging his mouth back to hers again, straining up to him as his tongue delved hungrily into the tender interior of her mouth, leaving her quivering helplessly in reaction.

'I can't wait to be inside you, *cara*,' Damiano swore raggedly as he pushed up her skirt and deftly removed her panties.

'Don't wait...' Her every nerve-ending felt tightly stretched. She was so hot, so excited, she couldn't keep still. Her own impatience was unbearable. She wanted him; she wanted him *now*.

Damiano studied her with smouldering eyes of desire. She rocked up against him and his brilliant eyes suddenly flared stormy gold. He pulled her under him and sank into her with one bold, hungry thrust. For an instant she was shocked by the sheer surge of wanton pleasure. And then her hunger for him took her over again, wild and uncontrollable and torturously sweet as the lithe male dominance of his body over, and in, hers. Her heart was racing as he drove her higher and higher, her whole being centred on reaching that ultimate plateau. The explosion of ecstatic pleasure splintered through her with unforgettable strength and then dropped her slowly again back into the hold of her body.

In the aftermath, she held him close, awash with wonder and a little shock and loving tenderness. Damiano smoothed her hair, dropped a kiss on her brow, rolled back, but he kept her securely pinned to him with a possessiveness more than equal to her own.

'It's so special with you...' Damiano murmured with slumbrous satisfaction.

Her lips curved. 'And yet you said that what happened in the bedroom wasn't important enough to make a major issue,' she reminded him.

Damiano lifted her up to look at her. His brilliant eyes were full of devilment. 'Step one in my seduction plan was to defuse the tension—'

'Seduction plan?'

'I thought it would take weeks and weeks for us to make it this far,' Damiano confided with rueful amusement.

They lay in a relaxed sprawl. Damiano hugged her close and drawled. 'I've dealt with Anstey, by the way—'

'Mark?'

Damiano smiled like a sleepy tiger, eyes gleaming below dark lashes. 'He won't be bothering you again—'

'What happened?' she pressed anxiously.

Damiano shifted a noncommittal shoulder. 'He's re-paid the money and he'll think twice before he tries blackmail a second time.'

Eden sat up. *'Damiano…'*

'I hit him. OK?' Damiano gave her a level look of challenge. 'He frightened you. He caused you a lot of distress. He's lucky I didn't damage him permanently!'

Eden never approved of violence. Her principles fought with her lack of sympathy for Mark, whose callous behaviour had hurt her a great deal. While she was struggling with those opposing feelings, the phone by the bed rang.

Damiano reached for the receiver. His lean, strong face tensed, expressive mouth tightening. 'We'll be down in ten minutes.'

'Who is it?'

'Nuncio and Cosetta are here,' Damiano breathed, springing off the bed and a grim look in his eyes. 'I should never have given Nuncio the name of this place and I should have made time for him this morning when he phoned asking to see me, but I'm afraid I wasn't in the mood for my little brother.'

'You can't tell Nuncio about Tina's affair,' Eden warned him flatly.

'That's not your decision to make,' Damiano retorted with crisp clarity. 'You might have been prepared to let yourself be hung out to dry on Tina's behalf, but I'm not. In any case, my family was abusing you *long* before that tabloid story appeared!'

'But you don't repay spite with spite—'

'No, you repay wrong with right,' Damiano countered, unmoved by that line or argument. 'I won't listen to a single word spoken against you, so, for his own sake, I hope Nuncio has not come here with the intent of causing trouble.'

They went downstairs together. Eden was dismayed when she walked into the sitting room and registered that Damiano's entire family had chosen to descend on them. Nuncio, Cosetta and Tina were seated round the fireplace. But she almost laughed when she heard Damiano stifle a groan of exasperation at the same sight.

CHAPTER TEN

NUNCIO looked deeply uncomfortable, like a man who had been dragged somewhere he didn't want to be by the women in his life. His sister, Cosetta, gave him a charged look of expectancy and, when he failed to react, she rose to her feet with a pronounced air of self-importance.

'We need to talk to you in private, Damiano.'

Damiano dealt the sharp-faced brunette a withering appraisal. 'Eden's my wife and she stays, Cosetta.'

'I think Eden and I should go for a walk.' Tina stood up with one of her little deprecating smiles. 'What do you say, Eden? Shall we leave the Braganzis to it?'

'Not just right now, thanks,' Eden said quietly.

China-blue eyes hardening, Tina sat down again.

Nuncio began to say something in Italian to his brother.

'Let's stick to English,' Damiano cut in.

'I'll find this matter very difficult to broach with Eden present,' Nuncio protested.

'Then you have a problem because I'm not going anywhere,' Eden advised her brother-in-law, disconcerting him with a sharp retort such as he had never received from her before. But then Eden had already decided that the days when she had allowed Damiano's siblings to snub and embarrass her were long behind her.

'Oh, for goodness' sake,' Cosetta exclaimed, throwing Nuncio a look of stark impatience. 'This secrecy has gone on long enough. Annabel's being very silly keeping herself in the background but we're supposed to be here to put things right for her!'

Eden blinked in surprise at that reference to Damiano's former fiancée. Why on earth was Damiano's sister rabbiting on about Annabel Stavely?

'What are you trying to put right for Annabel?' Eden enquired but even Cosetta, who was normally a far from sensitive being, coloured and looked away from her, sooner than answer her directly.

'We wanted Annabel to come out to Brazil with us...Annabel and her son, Peter,' Nuncio began stiffly, his heavy face flushed as he concentrated his attention on his elder brother. 'But she became quite hysterical when we suggested that—'

'Of course, she did. She has her pride. Naturally she didn't want to be the one to make the first move. Any woman would feel the same in her position!' Cosetta proclaimed in heated defence of her best friend.

Eden slowly shook her head in silent wonderment. Damiano's family never failed to astonish her. Not only had they left her behind when they had flown out to greet their long-lost brother in Brazil, but they had also evidently attempted to persuade Annabel to take what should have been Eden's place! As for Cosetta's fond contention that Annabel was too proud to make the first move with Damiano...well, Eden almost laughed out loud at that claim. In her efforts to win Damiano back even after his marriage, Annabel had been blatant.

Admittedly, it had never seemed to get the redhead anywhere, Eden conceded. She might have envied Annabel because she believed that Damiano had once sincerely loved the other woman. But even thinking that Damiano might well have married her on the rebound,

Eden had recognised that he'd no longer been in love
with his former fiancée. Indeed, had she had a better
sense of humour five years earlier, she might well have
reaped a lot of macabre enjoyment from Annabel's attempts to attract Damiano when he'd been so patently
detached from her.

'What is this farrago of nonsense?' Damiano enquired very drily of his brother and sister. 'Why would
you have invited Annabel to come out to Brazil with
you? Why the hell would I have wanted to see her?'

'So that you could be tempted afresh,' Eden could
not resist pointing out to her husband, a slight wobble
in her voice. 'Your family obviously thought it was too
good an opportunity to miss. After all, you had spent
all those years locked up and were sure to be at a low
ebb of restraint!'

An appreciative smile curved Damiano's mouth and
he closed his arm round Eden. 'Why do you think that
I'm still complaining that *you* weren't on the flight?' he
teased before turning his attention back to his brother.
'Come on, Nuncio. Do try to come to the point.'

Nuncio cleared his throat like a bullfrog and stood
up. 'Annabel has had a child, Damiano...'

Eden's spine tingled and stiffened. Only now did she
recall Tina smugly telling her that she had a huge shock
coming her way. Common sense told her what had to
be coming next but she just couldn't credit the explanation that her mind was serving up to her.

'*So?*' Damiano elevated a sardonic dark brow.

'Annabel told us that you and she had got back together again shortly before you went out to Montavia,'
Cosetta delivered and the brunette slung a triumphant
smile at Eden's astonished face. 'We weren't at all surprised but poor Annabel didn't feel she could tell us the

truth until your wife had moved out of the town house. By then Annabel was five months pregnant and, with her father having been declared bankrupt, she was very much in need of our support—'

'Annabel will be in even greater need of your support when she finds herself hauled up in court for slander,' Damiano broke in with icy disbelief, his outrage etched in every angle of hard bone-structure. 'How *dare* you bring this tissue of lies into my home? If Annabel has had a child, it was *not* fathered by me!'

Eden had gone way beyond amusement now. She felt sick with shock. And she thought strickenly for an instant, *Could* it be true? Might Damiano have turned to Annabel again before he'd gone missing and when their marriage had been under strain? She looked up at him and found him gazing down intently at her. She met his eyes head on, those stunning clear dark golden eyes. She recognised the honest anger there, the pure exasperation with which one met a fantastic story, and not the smallest shade of discomfiture. Her momentary stab of concern vanished to be replaced with outrage. It was his wretched family again, she decided furiously, still set on having another go at dividing them!

'That's quite some story, Cosetta,' Eden commented tightly, her green eyes sparkling with scorn. 'Very offensive in its content but just a little too like a soap opera to impress anyone with any wit!'

'Annabel *said* that Peter was Damiano's son!' Cosetta argued shrilly.

In the face of his elder brother's outraged rebuttal, Nuncio had turned a pasty colour and fallen silent. Now he said uneasily, 'Ever since Damiano came home, Annabel has done nothing but beg us to mind our own business and keep quiet about this, Cosetta. I told you

I wasn't happy with the odd way she's been behaving—'

'That's only because Annabel wanted Damiano to make a free choice between her and Eden,' Cosetta argued even more frantically. 'Annabel *wouldn't* have lied to me!'

'What you seem to forget is that your brother made that choice when he married me,' Eden retorted with crisp dismissal. 'It's long past time that his family accepted that and, if you can't accept it, then leave us alone.'

'I couldn't have put it better myself,' Damiano stated flatly, curving Eden even closer to his big powerful frame as he surveyed their three visitors. 'And, sadly, you, my family, really *do* deserve Annabel. Indeed Annabel could not have ripped off a nicer set of people. I can barely believe how stupid you've all been—'

'Ripped off? Stupid?' Cosetta repeated incredulously. 'How can you say that?'

'Annabel waits until she thinks I'm dead and Eden has been driven from the family before she comes forward with her touching little confession…am I right?' Damiano prompted, sounding very bored.

'Well…yes,' Nuncio confirmed.

'She then told you she was expecting my child. Tell me, did anybody argue at that point? Did anybody seek any supporting evidence of her claim?' Damiano surveyed his siblings with questioning derision. 'So you just accepted that if Annabel was pregnant, the child was mine because she *said* so. Even though I was married—'

'Annabel said you were planning on getting a divorce.' Nuncio groaned.

'*Annabel said,*' Damiano stressed with angry contempt. 'Her father going bankrupt must've been a really nasty shock because Annabel has expensive tastes. Weren't you capable of adding two and two and making four, Nuncio? Didn't you smell the proverbial rat? How much money have you given her over the years?'

'I can't believe that Annabel could have made it all up just to get money off us! How could she *do* that to me?' Cosetta sobbed and she stalked over to the window and turned her back on them all.

'You used her to get at me, Cosetta,' Eden reminded the brunette ruefully. 'And she used you to stay in Damiano's radius.'

'Ouch...' Damiano groaned.

Looking hangdog, Nuncio muttered defensively, 'I was only trying to look out for *your* interests when I helped Annabel out, Damiano—'

'How? By hurting and humiliating my wife when she was at her most vulnerable? Tell me, how was *that* looking out for my interests?' Damiano demanded with a hard condemnation that made his younger brother flinch.

China-blue eyes cold as charity, Tina now spoke up with her usual hesitancy. 'I'm sorry but it's really not fair to blame Nuncio,' she said softly. 'None of us have wanted to mention it but Eden *did* have an affair with another man and obviously that upset all of us a great deal.'

Bitter anger flared in Eden at Tina's nerve in making that crack. She felt electric aggression power tension through every muscle in Damiano's lean, well-built length. 'Tina...' Damiano began not quite evenly, rage gritting from even those two single syllables, but he did not get the chance to continue.

Without the smallest warning, Cosetta erupted back

into the centre of the room and pitched a set of prints down onto Tina's lap. 'You lying, cheating little snake!' she spat furiously. 'It was *you* who had the affair with Mark Anstey! It was you all along and you lied all the way down the line!'

As Eden fixed appalled eyes on the photos she now belatedly recalled having left lying on the window-seat, close to where Cosetta had been standing, all hell broke loose. Nuncio made a sudden grab at the photographs and broke into an aghast exclamation while Cosetta continued her ranting attack on her former ally.

'You can stage this confrontation elsewhere,' Damiano drawled with chilling clarity. Striding over to the door, he flung it wide. 'All of you...*out!*'

Shattered silence fell.

'I'm prepared to get physical,' Damiano warned.

Their unwelcome visitors departed but they were all shouting at each other again before the front door even closed behind them. Eden sagged with relief.

'They will never set foot in any residence of ours again,' Damiano swore with vehemence. 'But when did my kid sister turn into such a shrew?'

Eden sighed and, turning round, rested her brow against his broad chest, feeling his arms close round her and revelling in the warmth and solidity of him. 'I think her friendship with Annabel turned her in that direction. Annabel is a lot older and she influenced her a good deal. Oh, dear...I feel so awful about leaving those dreadful photos just sitting there where anyone could find them!'

'I noticed them long before Cosetta did. I was sub-consciously *willing* Nuncio to go over there and see them, *cara mia*,' Damiano confided grimly, strongly disconcerting her. 'Tina has not been good company for Cosetta either—'

'But what about Nuncio? He looked so stricken, Damiano—'

'He's miserable with her or hadn't you noticed that yet? Let them work out their own problems,' Damiano advised. 'I don't have any sympathy to spare after that outrageous spiel about Annabel. Listening to them, I honestly wondered if my brother and sister had more than one brain cell apiece—'

'But you'll note that I had *total* faith in you,' Eden informed him with the kind of sweetness that carried a slight sting in its tail.

Dark colour accentuated his blunt cheekbones just as a knock sounded on the door and it opened. Their housekeeper began to speak but was silenced by the woman pushing impatiently past her to gain entrance to the room.

It was Annabel Stavely and Annabel as Eden had never seen her before. The redhead had no make-up on, swollen eyes and a look of desperation etched on her still beautiful face.

'You've got to let me explain myself!' Annabel exclaimed pleadingly.

'Do you think you could make it brief?' Damiano enquired very drily.

'I passed the limo at the end of the driveway,' Annabel confided in a rush and bit at her full lower lip. 'I hoped I'd get here first so that I could explain but I know that Nuncio and Cosetta must already have told you about the story I made up—'

'Children make up stories. Adults tell lies.' Damiano shot Annabel a derisive appraisal. 'And when an adult lies to commit a fraud, it is rather more serious. So let's not pretend that you involved yourself in some playful little charade—'

Annabel was very pale. 'I didn't see that it was going to hurt anybody—'

'You didn't *care* whether it did or not,' Eden cut in helplessly. 'For you to have pretended that your child was my husband's is about as low as any woman could sink—'

'How many other people are suffering from the same delusion?' Damiano demanded with sudden harshness, that aspect clearly not having occurred to him until Eden mentioned it.

'Only your family,' Annabel hastened to assure him. 'It really was a big secret—'

'It had better have been or you will find yourself in court,' Damiano spelt out in hard warning. 'If one rumour of this appears in print, call your solicitor because you're going to need him.'

Annabel surveyed him with appalled eyes and then dropped her head.

'Does your son believe that Damiano is his father?' Eden had to ask.

'No! Really, you're making far too much of this,' Annabel contended shakily. 'It was wrong and it was stupid but I was so broke I couldn't even settle the rent on my apartment! Don't you realise the *hell* I've gone through this last month since Damiano turned up alive?'

At that plea for sympathy on such a count, Eden's lips parted company and then sealed together again for she dared not have spoken.

'I mean I just couldn't *believe* you coming back from the dead like that!' Annabel wailed accusingly at Damiano. 'Do you think I'd have lied if I'd known there was any chance of that happening? I had to take myself off to a friend's villa in Turkey to hide. I didn't know what I was going to do to get myself out of this mess. And Cosetta kept on phoning and phoning and *phoning* me to demand that I fly out to Italy to see you! You were the very *last* person I wanted to see!'

'You've had a really dreadful time,' Eden muttered soothingly but she was challenged to keep her face straight.

Damiano murmured tautly, 'I don't think we need to discuss this any further, Annabel—'

'You mean you forgive me?'

Damiano sighed. 'Annabel...unless I've very much mistaken you have managed to defraud my brother of thousands of pounds over the last few years. You ripped him off and what *he* chooses to do about that is nothing to do with me.'

Apparently shaken by the realisation that she could not magically solve her every problem by begging Damiano to forgive her, Annabel departed with a lot less drama than she had arrived.

'We're out,' Damiano then instructed their house-keeper. 'I don't care who comes to the door. We're not here.'

Eden was feeling incredibly sleepy. Damiano took one look at her wan face and drooping head and he scooped her off her seat and carried her back upstairs. 'This has all been too much for you, *cara*—'

'Actually I'm so grateful I didn't miss out on hearing what an unwelcome shock you gave Annabel with your return from the dead!' Eden laughed helplessly at that recollection. 'I didn't *dare* look at you in case I went off into whoops. Are you finally going to tell me why you broke off your engagement to her?'

Damiano winced. 'Do I have to?'

'You *owe* me,' Eden told him playfully.

'I overheard a conversation she had with her sister. Her sister had just got engaged and she asked Annabel what she liked *most* about me,' Damiano related with a pained smile. 'And there was this huge silence and then Annabel finally said, "he's loaded and he's great in bed." That is the moment when the rot first set in.'

'She was probably joking—'

'Having had the pleasure of hearing that opinion, I naturally began paying closer attention to our relationship. I then found out that she wasn't at all averse to slipping into other men's beds when I was abroad,' Damiano shared wryly as he laid her down on the bed.

'Oh...' Eden rubbed her cheek against his shoulder, understanding why he had had no desire to tell her that particular tale before.

'I didn't tell my family why I'd ditched her. That *was* a mistake,' Damiano acknowledged. 'But I'd learned by then that my own feelings for Annabel were pretty shallow and I didn't care enough to disabuse them of their illusions.'

'Then you met me...' Eden was tiring of the subject of Annabel which had now been for ever shorn of further interest.

'That was love at first sight. Absolutely terrifying!' Damiano confided.

'Eden sat up with a start. 'Say that again—'

'Do I *have* to?' A charismatic smile curved Damiano's sensual mouth. 'Post-Annabel I was convinced that I was the coldest fish alive as far as women were concerned. I was very cynical and then I saw you and I swear that both my brain and my body went haywire the same second.'

'I don't believe I'm hearing this,' Eden framed in a daze.

Glittering dark eyes rested on her bemused face and he muttered ruefully, 'You're not going to like hearing the rest of it. In those days, I *hated* feeling like that and that added a certain hostility to our every encounter. I wanted to be in control...'

'And you thought you weren't in control because I wouldn't sleep with you,' Eden filled in for him with a sigh.

'No, there you're wrong, *amore*. As far as I was concerned, if you didn't want to make love with me, you couldn't possibly care about me or want me anything like as much as I cared about and wanted you.'

Even five years on, Eden was stricken by that revealing confession. She looked at him with reproachful eyes. 'Oh, *no*...'

'Oh, yes,' Damiano told her levelly. 'When I fell for you, love and sex were quite indivisible in my estimation. I'd never been in love in my life before but I couldn't believe you *could* love me and keep on freezing me out—'

Eden traced a regretful fingertip along his hard jawline. 'I had no idea that I could make you feel insecure back then. You always seemed so incredibly confident—'

Damiano caught her into his arms and held her fast, shimmering dark golden eyes scanning her with tender amusement. 'Call it like it was, *tesoro mio*,' he urged. 'I was arrogant and I just could not credit that a virgin could run rings round me—'

'I was very nervous of that kind of intimacy...but I think that if I'd known you loved me after we married, I would have felt very different,' Eden said slowly. 'Unfortunately, your sister told me about Annabel and then, when I came back from our honeymoon and finally *saw* Annabel, I thought that you most likely *had* married me on the rebound—'

'You and I were engaged for all of one week. I was engaged to her for two years and never got myself to the point of fixing a wedding date,' Damiano pointed out. 'I love you very, very much. Even when I was acting like a jerk, I never doubted that. I couldn't have handled it if I'd come home and you hadn't been here for me.'

Eden glowed with happiness. She rested her head down on his chest, listening to the slow, solid thump of his heart beating, drinking in the familiar scent of him. Then she smiled. 'How do you feel about having a baby?'

'On a scale of one to ten—ten being the height of keen,' Damiano informed her teasingly. 'Ten.'

'Sounds promising—'

Damiano vented a laugh. 'I have now finally reached the pinnacle of male maturity where I can consider a baby without being gripped by the devastating fear that you might feel *more* for the baby than you feel for me!'

'Even better. Are you aware that I haven't been on the contraceptive pill for years?'' Eden enquired, slowly raising her head to study him.

A slight frown-line drew his ebony brows together. 'I have to confess that I hadn't got around to thinking about technical stuff like that yet—'

'Technical stuff?' Eden queried chokily.

'When I'm in bed with you, I'm not exactly grounded...' Lustrous dark golden eyes suddenly settled on her with raw intensity. '*Accidenti!* If you're *not*...and *I* haven't been using—'

'You're going to be a father,' Eden told him softly.

Damiano rolled her gently flat against the pillows and stared fixedly down at her. 'Are you teasing me?'

'I'm pregnant,' Eden declared.

At that confirmation, Damiano hastily released her from a good half of his weight. 'That's fantastic!' he breathed, visibly stunned.

'But *not* breakable,' Eden added, hauling him back to her with possessive hands.

One year and one month later, Eden walked into the nursery at the Villa Pavone. Diamonds glittering at her wrist and in her ears, she was wearing a fabulous pale green ball gown in readiness for the big party they were throwing that evening.

Damiano was tucking in the twins. Their son, Niccolo, lay still like a little prince, big sleepy green eyes pinned to his father, but his twin sister, Chiara, was still wriggling. Damiano was endeavouring to mesmerise his infant daughter into more restful mode with the use of the musical mobile above the cot.

Eden smiled. She could still barely believe that she was the mother of two children. She had been a couple of months along before a scan had picked up the fact that she'd been carrying two babies, rather than just one. She had been delighted at the news but Damiano had been concerned that a twin pregnancy would be more risky. However, although Niccolo and Chiara had come into the world a little early as did most twins, both Eden and their children had come through fine.

The past year had been very eventful from start to finish. They had spent a lot of time in Italy, enjoying the rather more relaxed pace of their lifestyle there. Damiano had been re-elected Chairman of the Braganzi

Bank but he delegated much more, worked from home when he could and took her with him when he went abroad. Indeed, Eden had once or twice felt ever so slightly guilty that what had been a truly stupendous, wonderfully happy and successful year for her and Damiano had been something less for others.

Although there *had* been one light moment. Annabel Stavely had rushed off and married an elderly peer of the realm after Nuncio had informed her that he expected all the money he had given her repaid. Six months later, she had become a reasonably wealthy and, it had to be admitted, a fairly merry widow according to the gossip columns.

Then, just three months ago, Damiano had passed Eden a newspaper and had indicated a small article about Mark Anstey. Mark had been sent to prison for embezzling a huge amount of money from the unfortunate owners of the organic farm company. The biggest shock for Eden had been the discovery that that had *not* been Mark's first offence.

In the past year also, Nuncio and Tina had failed to mend their differences and had ended up going through a bitter divorce. During a heated quarrel, Tina had really lost her temper and had told Nuncio that their daughter, Allegra, was *not* his child. Nuncio had been devastated. Tina had then thought better of her honesty and had tried to persuade him that she had only been lying to hurt him. However, Nuncio had had DNA testing done and that had proved that Allegra could not be his. Even so, Nuncio had still insisted that he wanted to maintain contact with the little girl because he was very fond of her.

Damiano and Nuncio were now behaving like brothers again simply because Nuncio had become so de-

pressed after that bombshell about Allegra that Damiano
had had no choice but to offer sympathy and support.
Eden had then persuaded Damiano to invite Cosetta to
the twins' christening. Ignored by Damiano for months,
his sister had been on her best behaviour and anxious
not to cause offence. Eden was content to settle for politeness at their occasional meetings.

'*Dio mio*.' Damiano rhymed, turning from his now
sleeping daughter to appraise Eden in her ball gown
with deeply impressed eyes of gold. 'You look fantastic.'

Eden did a little twirl to ensure that he got the full
effect of her bare shoulders and the low-cut back. He
wolf-whistled. She grinned, her own attention roving
with equally keen appreciation over his beautifully cut
dinner jacket, silk shirt and narrow black trousers, all
of which accentuated his commanding height, his athletic physique and his sheer sexiness. She tried really
hard to wolf-whistle back but Damiano started laughing
and she couldn't manage it.

'Happy, *cara mia*?'

'Absolutely fizzing with it!' Eden assured him cheerfully as he settled his hands to her slim waist and drew
her into the circle of his arms. 'It's not every woman
who gets to celebrate two wedding anniversaries a
year!'

Exactly a year ago, they had renewed their wedding
vows in a church ceremony which had meant a great
deal to both of them. Damiano, however, also liked to
celebrate their original wedding anniversary as well.
Over fifty people were joining them for dinner that evening and a couple hundred more for a massive ball
which would last until dawn.

Taking a last proud and loving look at their sleeping

children, they walked downstairs and strolled into the main salon, now furnished with far from authentic comfy sofas and armchairs. Damiano uncorked a bottle of champagne and sent it foaming into glasses.

'Shouldn't we wait for our first guests?' Eden enquired in surprise.

Damiano passed her a heart-shaped leather jewel case.

She flipped up the lid. Damiano could not apparently stand the suspense of waiting for her reaction and he reached out and lifted out the gorgeous sapphire and diamond pendant to turn it over to display the inscription.

'"To the only woman I have ever loved, Damiano",' Eden read out loud, her eyes misting over.

'I adore you, *tersoro mio*,' Damiano murmured huskily, fastening the beautiful necklace at the nape of her neck.

'I just *adore* the way you keep on telling me,' Eden whispered dreamily, spinning back to him, meeting his burnished eyes and just melting back into his arms. 'I love you too.'

CONTRACT BABY

Lynne Graham

CHAPTER ONE

FROM the slim document case clasped in one strong brown hand, Raul Zaforteza withdrew a large glossy photograph. 'This is Polly Johnson. In six weeks' time she will give birth to my child. I *must* find her before then.'

Somehow primed to expect a gorgeous blonde with a supermodel face and figure, Digby was disconcerted to find himself looking at a small, slim girl with a mane of hair the colour of mahogany, soulful blue eyes and an incredibly sweet smile. She looked so outrageously young and wholesome he just could not imagine her in the role of surrogate mother.

As a lawyer with a highly respected London firm, Digby Carson had dealt with some very difficult cases. But a surrogacy arrangement gone wrong? The surrogate mother on the run and probably determined to keep the baby? He surveyed his most wealthy and influential client with a sinking heart.

Raul Zaforteza's fabled fortune was founded on gold and diamond mines. He was a brilliant business tycoon, a legendary polo player and, according to the gossip columns, a notorious womaniser. He was already prowling like a black panther ready to spring. Six feet two inches tall, with the sleek, supple build of a born athlete and the volatile temperament of his colourful heritage, he was an intimidating sight, even to a man who had known him from childhood.

'Digby...I understood that my lawyer in New York had already briefed you on this situation,' Raul drawled with barely concealed impatience.

'He said the matter was far too confidential to discuss on the phone. And I hadn't the slightest suspicion that you

5

were planning to become a father through surrogacy,' the older man admitted. 'Why on earth did you embark on such a risky venture?'

'*Por Dios*…you watched me grow up! How can you ask me that?' Raul countered.

Digby looked uncomfortable. As a former employee of Raul's late father, he was well aware that Raul had had a pretty ghastly childhood. He might be rich beyond avarice, but he had not been anything like as lucky in the parent lottery.

His bronzed features taut, Raul expelled his breath in a slow hiss. 'I decided a long time ago that I would never marry. I wouldn't give any woman that amount of power over me *or*, even more crucially, over any child we might have!' Fierce conviction roughened his rich, accented drawl. 'But I've always been very fond of children—'

'Yes…' An unspoken *but* hovered in the tense silence.

'Many marriages end in divorce, and usually the wife gets to keep the children,' Raul reminded the lawyer with biting cynicism. 'Surrogacy impressed me as the most practical way in which to father a child outside marriage. This wasn't an impulsive decision, Digby. When I decided to go ahead, I went to a lot of trouble to ensure that I would choose a suitable mother for my child.'

'Suitable?' Digby was keen to hear what Raul, with his famed love of fast, glitzy society blondes, had considered 'suitable' in the maternal stakes.

'When my New York legal team advertised for a surrogate mother, they received a flood of applications. I employed a doctor and a psychologist to put a shortlist of the more promising candidates through a battery of tests, but the responsibility for the final choice was naturally mine.'

The older man frowned down at the photograph of Polly Johnson. 'What age is she?'

'Twenty-one.'

Digby's frown remained. 'She was the *only* suitable candidate?'

Raul tautened. 'The psychologist did have some reservations but I decided to overlook them.'

Digby looked shaken.

'Everything that the psychologist saw in Polly I *wanted* in the mother of my child,' Raul stressed without a shade of regret. 'It was a gut feeling and I acted on it. Yes, she was young and idealistic, but she had the right moral values. She wasn't motivated by greed but by a desperate need to try and finance surgery which she hoped might extend her mother's life.'

'I wonder how that desperation affected her ability to make a rational decision about what she was getting involved in,' Digby remarked.

'Wondering is a pointless exercise now that she is pregnant with my child,' Raul countered very drily. 'But I *will* find her soon. Her background was exhaustively investigated. I now know that, just two months ago, she was at her godmother's home in Surrey. I don't yet know where she went from there. But before I do find her I need to know what my rights are in this country.'

Digby was in no hurry to break bad news before he had all the facts. British law frowned on surrogacy. If the mother wanted to keep the baby instead of handing it over, no contract was likely to persuade a British judge that taking that child from its mother was in the child's best interests.

'Tell me the rest of the story,' he advised.

While running through the bare facts for the older man's benefit, Raul stared unseeingly out of the window, grimly recalling his first sight of Polly Johnson through a two-way mirror in the New York legal office. She had reminded him of a tiny porcelain doll. Fragile, unusual and astonishingly pretty.

She had been brave and honest. And so impressively *nice*—not something Raul had ever sought in a woman before, but a trait he had found very appealing when he had considered all the positive qualities a mother might hand down to her child. Certainly Polly had been younger and less worldly wise than was desirable, but he had recognised her quiet inner strength as well as her essentially tranquil nature.

And the more Raul had watched Polly, the more he had learnt about Polly, the more he had wanted to *meet* Polly face to face, in the flesh, so that some day in the future he could comfortably answer his child's curious questions about her. But his New York lawyer had said absolutely not. Strict anonymity would be his only defence against any form of harassment in later years. But Raul had always been a ruthless rule-breaker, with immense faith in his own natural instincts, nor had he ever hesitated to satisfy his own wishes...

And acting on that essential arrogance, he conceded grudgingly now, was how everything had begun to fall apart. Worst of all, he who prided himself on his intelligence and his shrewd perceptive powers had somehow failed to notice the warning signs of trouble on the horizon.

'So once you knew that the girl had successfully conceived, you installed her in a house in Vermont with a trusted family servant to look after her,' Digby recapped, because Raul had fallen silent again. 'Where was her mother while all this was going on?'

'As soon as Polly signed the contract her mother went into a convalescent home to build up her strength for surgery. She was very ill. The woman knew nothing about the surrogacy agreement. When Polly was only a couple of weeks pregnant, her mother had the operation. Polly had been warned that her mother's chances of survival were at best only even. She died two days after surgery,' Raul revealed heavily.

'Unfortunate.'

Raul slung him a fulminating glance of scorn. *Unfortunate?* Polly had been devastated. And Raul had been uneasily conscious that her sole reason for becoming a surrogate had died that same day. Aware from the frustratingly brief reports made by the maid, Soledad, that Polly was deeply depressed, Raul had reached the point where he could no longer bear to stay at a supposedly sensible distance from the woman carrying his baby.

Understandably he had been concerned that she might miscarry. He had sincerely believed that it was his responsibility to offer her support. Isolated in a country that wasn't her own, only twenty-one-years old, pregnant with a stranger's baby and plunged deep into a grieving process that her optimistic outlook had not prepared her to face, the mother of his child had really *needed* a sympathetic shoulder.

'So I finally made contact with her,' Raul admitted tautly. 'Since I could hardly admit that I was the father of her baby, I had to employ a certain amount of deception to make that contact.'

Unseen, Digby winced. Raul should have avoided any form of personal involvement. But then Raul Zaforteza was a disturbingly complex man. He was a merciless business opponent and a very dangerous enemy. More than one woman had come to grief on the rocks of his innate emotional detachment. But Raul was also a renowned philanthropist, the most genuine of friends to a chosen few and a male still capable of powerful emotional responses.

Raul compressed his firm lips. 'I took a weekend place near where she was staying and ensured that our paths crossed. I didn't conceal my identity; I didn't need to…the Zaforteza name meant nothing to her. Over the following months, I flew up there regularly and called on her. I never stayed long…she just needed someone to talk to.' Radiating tension now, in spite of that studiously nonchalant explanation, Raul shrugged, his accented drawl petering out into another brooding silence.

'*And?*'

'And nothing!' As he swung round from the window, Raul's hard, dark eyes were sardonic in their comprehension. 'I treated her like a little sister. I was a casual visitor, nothing more.'

Digby restrained himself from pointing out that since Raul was an only child he could only have the vaguest notion of how one treated a little sister. And Digby had three daughters, every one of whom swooned at the mere mention of Raul's name. Indeed, the last time he had taken Raul home for dinner it had been a downright embarrassing experience, with all three daughters dressed to kill and competing for Raul's attention. Even his wife said that Raul Zaforteza might well have been packaged by the devil specifically to tempt the female sex.

He pictured a lonely young woman who might only have faced up to what surrogacy really *meant* in the aftermath of her mother's death. When that nice, naive young woman had suddenly found herself entertaining a member of the international jet set as self-assured, sophisticated and charismatic as Raul, what effect had it had on her?

'When did she go missing?' Digby prompted.

'Three months ago. She disappeared one day... Soledad went out shopping and left her alone,' Raul confided grimly. 'Do you realize that in three months I have hardly slept a night through? Day *and* night I have been worried sick—'

'I suppose there *is* a strong possibility that she may have gone for a termination—'

'*Por Dios...*' Raul dealt the older man a smouldering look of reproof. 'Polly wouldn't abort my child!'

Content to have issued that warning, Digby didn't argue.

'Polly's very soft, very feminine, very caring...she would *never* choose that option!' Raul continued to argue fiercely.

'You asked about your rights.' Digby breathed in deep, straightening his shoulders to brace himself for the blow he was about to deliver. 'I'm afraid unmarried fathers don't have any under British law.'

Raul stared back at him with rampant incredulity. 'That isn't possible.'

'You couldn't argue that the girl would make a bad mother either. After all, you *chose* her,' the older man pointed out ruefully. 'You described a respectable girl, drawn into a surrogacy agreement only because she was trying to help her mother. As the rich foreigner who used his wealth to tempt her into making a decision which she later regretted, you wouldn't look good in court—'

'But she has reneged on a legal contract,' Raul spelt out harshly. '*Dios mio!* All I want is the right to take my own child back to Venezuela. I haven't the slightest desire to take this into a courtroom! There has to be some other way in which I can get custody.'

Digby grimaced. 'You *could* marry her…'

Raul gave him a forbidding look. 'If that was a joke, Digby…it was in the worst possible taste.'

Henry pulled out a chair for Polly to sit down to her evening meal. His mother, Janice Grey, frowned at the young woman's shadowed blue eyes and too prominent cheekbones. At eight months pregnant, Polly looked drawn and ill.

'You should be resting at this stage of your pregnancy,' Janice reproved. 'If you married Henry now, you could give up work. You could take things easy while he helped you get your godmother's will sorted out.'

'It would be the best move you could make.' Solid and bespectacled, with thinning fair hair, Henry nodded in pompous agreement. 'You'll have to be careful that the Inland Revenue doesn't take too large a slice of your inheritance.'

'I really don't want to marry anybody.' Beneath her wealth of rich, reddish brown hair, Polly's delicate features were becoming stiff and her smile strained.

An awkward silence fell while mother and son exchanged meaningful glances.

Polly focused on her nicely cooked meal with a guilty

lack of appetite. It had been a mistake to take a room in Janice's comfortable terraced home. But how could she ever have guessed that her late godmother's trusted house-keeper had had an ulterior motive for offering her some-where to stay?

Janice and her son *knew* the strange terms of Nancy Leeward's will. They *knew* that Polly would inherit a mil-lion pounds if she found a husband within the year and stayed married for at least six months. Janice was deter-mined to persuade Polly that marrying her son would mag-ically solve her every problem.

And, to be fair to Janice, calculating she might be, but she saw such a marriage as a fair exchange. After all, Polly was an unmarried mum-to-be and couldn't claim her god-mother's money without a husband. Henry was single, and in a job he loathed. Even a small share of a million pounds would enable Henry to set up as a tax consultant in a smart office of his own. Janice would do just about anything to further Henry's prospects, and Henry wasn't just attached to his widowed mother's apron strings, he was welded to them.

'Babies can be very demanding,' Janice pointed out when her son had left the room. 'And, talking as someone who has done it, raising a child alone isn't easy.'

'I know.' But at the mere mention of the word 'baby' a vague and dreamy smile had formed on Polly's face. There was nothing practical or sensible about the warm feeling of anticipation which welled up inside her.

Janice sighed. 'I'm only trying to advise you, Polly. You're not in love with Henry, but where did falling in love get you?'

Polly's blissful abstraction was cruelly punctured by that reminder. 'Nowhere,' she conceded tightly.

'I've never liked to pry, but it's obvious that the father of your child took off the minute you got pregnant. Unreliable and irresponsible,' the older woman opined thinly. 'You certainly couldn't call my Henry either of those things.'

Polly considered Henry's joyless and stolid outlook on life and suppressed a sigh.

'People don't always marry for love. People get married for all sorts of other reasons,' Janice persisted. 'Security, companionship, a nice home.'

'I'm afraid I would need more.' Polly got up slowly and heavily. 'I think I'll lie down for a while before I go to work.'

Breathless from climbing the stairs, Polly lay down on her bed in the prettily furnished spare room. She grimaced. Never in a million years would she marry Henry just to satisfy the terms of Nancy Leeward's will and inherit that money.

She was too shamefully conscious that a craving for money had reduced her to her present predicament. Her late father, a strongly religious man, had been fond of saying that money was the root of all evil. And, looking back to the twisted, reckless decision she had made months earlier, Polly knew that in her case that pronouncement had proved all too true.

Her mother had been dying. But Polly had refused to accept the reality that the mother she had grown up without and had barely had time to get to know again *could* be dying: she hadn't believed the hand of fate could be that cruel. Armed by that stubborn belief, Polly had gone that extra mile that people talked about, but she had gone that extra mile in entirely the wrong direction, she acknowledged wretchedly.

How could she *ever* have believed that she would find it possible to give her baby up to strangers? How could she *ever* have imagined that she could surrender all rights, hand over her own flesh and blood and agree never, ever to try and see her own child again? She had been incredibly stupid and immature. So she had run away from a situation which had become untenable, knowing even then that she would be followed and eventually *traced*...

As the ever-present threat of being found and called to account for her behaviour assailed Polly, her skin turned clammy with fear. In her own mind she was no better than a criminal. She had signed a contract in which she had promised to give up her baby. She had sat back while an unbelievably huge amount of money was expended on her mother's medical care and then she had fled. She had broken the law, yet she had been wickedly and savagely deceived into signing that contract...but what proof did she have of that fact?

Sometimes she woke from nightmares about being extradited to the USA and put on trial, her baby taken from her and parcelled off to a life of luxury with his immoral and utterly unscrupulous father in Venezuela. Even when she didn't have bad dreams, it was becoming increasingly hard to sleep. She was at that point in pregnancy when she couldn't get comfortable even in bed, and she was often wakened by the strong, energetic movements of her baby.

And in her mind's eye then, when she was at her weakest, she would see Raul. Raul Zaforteza, dark, devastating and dangerous. What a trusting and pathetic victim she had been! For she had fallen in love with him, hopelessly, helplessly, blindly in love for the first time in her life. She had lived only from one meeting to the next, frantically counting the days in between, agonised if he didn't turn up and always tormented by the secret she had believed she was still contriving to keep from him. A jagged laugh was torn from her lips now. And all the time Raul had known she was pregnant. After all, he was the father of her baby...

An hour later, Polly headed to work. It was a cool, wet summer evening. She walked past the bus stop. She was presently struggling to save every penny she could. Soon she wouldn't be able to work any more, and once she had the baby she would need her savings for all sorts of things.

The supermarket where she worked shifts was a bright beacon of light and activity in the city street. As Polly disposed of her coat and her bag in the rest room, the manageress popped her head round the door and frowned. 'You look very tired, Polly. I hope that doctor of yours knows what he's doing when he tells you that it's all right for you to be still working.'

Polly flushed as the older woman withdrew again. She hadn't actually seen a doctor in two months, but at her last visit she had been advised to rest. How could she rest when she had to keep herself? And if she approached the social services for assistance they would ask too many awkward questions. So she lived in a state of permanent exhaustion, back aching, ankles swollen, and if she pushed herself too hard she got blinding headaches and dizzy spells.

By the end of her shift on one of the checkouts Polly was very tired, and really grateful that she was off the next day. Tomorrow, she decided, she would pamper herself. Shouldering her bag, she left the shop. The rain had stopped. The street lights gleamed off the wet pavements and cars swished by splashing the kerbs.

Polly didn't even try to close her coat. Only a tent would have closed round her swollen stomach, and the weight of her own body contributed to her fatigue. Not long now, she consoled herself. She felt as if she had been pregnant for ever, but soon she would be getting to know her baby as a separate little person.

Engaged in her thoughts of the near future, head downbent, Polly didn't register the existence of a large obstacle in her path. Only at the last possible moment, when she almost cannoned into the impossibly tall and solidly built male blocking her passage, did she notice the presence of another human being and seek to sidestep him.

As she teetered dangerously off balance, a cry of dismay escaping her, a pair of strong hands shot out to catch her by the shoulders and steady her. Heart pounding with fright, she reeled as he held her there, her head tipping back from a view of her rescuer's silver-grey silk tie to look up.

Raul Zaforteza gazed down at her from his great height, his facial muscles locking his staggeringly handsome features into a bronze mask of impassivity that was uniquely chilling.

In severe shock, Polly trembled, soft mouth opening and closing again without sound, a look of pure panic in her gaze as she collided with eyes that had the topaz golden brilliance of a tiger ready to claw the unwary to the bone.

'There is no place in this whole wide world where you could hope to stay hidden from me,' Raul spelt out in a controlled tone of immense finality, his rich, accented vowel sounds tingling in her sensitive ears, throwing up a myriad of despoilt memories that could only torment her. 'The chase is over.'

CHAPTER TWO

'LET me go, Raul!' Polly gasped convulsively, her heart thudding like a trapped animal's behind her breastbone, nervous perspiration beading her short upper lip.

'How can I do that?' Raul countered with level emphasis. 'You're expecting my baby. What sort of a man *could* walk away?'

Without warning, pain flashed in a scorching burst across Polly's temples, provoking a startled moan from her parted lips. Her hand flew up to press against her throbbing brow. Nausea stirred nastily in her stomach as the overpowering dizziness washed over her.

'*Por Dios*...what is the matter with you?' Raul tightened his hold on her as she swayed like a drunk, straining with every sinew to stay upright and in control.

In another moment he bent and swept her up into his arms, cradling her easily into the strength and heat of his big, powerful frame. As the street light shone on the greyish pallor of her upturned face, Raul emitted a groan and said something hoarse in Spanish.

'Put me down...' Polly was not too ill to appreciate the cruel irony of Raul getting that physically close to her for the very first time.

Ignoring her, chiselled profile aggressively clenched, Raul jerked his imperious dark head and the limousine parked across the street filtered over to the kerb. The chauffeur jumped out and hurried to open the passenger door. Raul settled her down on the squashy leather back seat, but before he could climb in beside her Polly took him by surprise and lurched half out again, to be violently sick in the

17

gutter. Then she sagged back on the seat, pressing a tissue to her tremulous lips and utterly drained.

As she lay slumped on her side, a stunned silence greeted her. Momentarily, a dull gleam of amusement touched her. Raul Zaforteza had probably got to the age of thirty-one without ever having witnessed such a distasteful event. And she hated him for being there to witness her inability to control her own body. Although she was the kind of person who automatically said sorry when other people bumped into *her*, a polite apology would have choked her.

'Do you feel strong enough to sit up?'

As she braced a slender hand on the seat beneath her, Raul took over, raising her and propping her up like a rag doll. Involuntarily she breathed in the elusive scent of him. Clean, warm male overlaid with a hint of something more exotic.

'So you finally ran me to earth,' Polly acknowledged curtly, refusing to look at him, staring into space with almost blank blue eyes.

'It was only a matter of time. I went first to the house where you're staying. Janice Grey wasn't helpful. Fortunately I was already aware of where you worked,' Raul imparted flatly.

She could feel the barrier between them, high and impenetrable as toughened frosted glass, the highwire tension splintering through the atmosphere, the restive, brooding edge of powerful energy that Raul always emanated. But *she* felt numb, like an accident victim. He had found her. She had made every possible effort to remain undetected— moved to London, even lied to friends so that nobody had a contact address or phone number for her. And all those endeavours had been in vain.

As a spasm of pain afflicted her, she squeezed her eyes tight shut.

'What *is* it?' Raul demanded fiercely.

'Feel like my head's splitting open,' she mumbled sickly, forcing her eyes open again.

Raul was now studying the pronounced swell of her stomach with a shaken fascination that felt deeply, offensively intrusive.

In turn, Polly now studied him, pain like a poisonous dart piercing her bruised heart. His hair—black as midnight now, but blue-black in sunlight—the strong, flaring ebony brows, the lean, arrogant nose, the magnificent high cheekbones and hollows, the wide, perfectly modelled mouth so eloquent of the raw sensuality that laced his every movement. A devastatingly attractive male, so staggeringly good-looking he had to turn heads wherever he went, and yet only the most audacious woman would risk cornering him. There was reinforced steel in those hard bones, inflexible control in that strong jawline.

The baby kicked, blanking out her mind, making her wince.

His incongruously long and lush black lashes swept up, and she was pinned to the spot by glinting gold eyes full of enquiry.

'May I?' he murmured almost roughly.

And then she saw his half-extended hand, those lean brown fingers full of such tensile strength, and only after a split second did she register in shock the source of his interest. His entire attention was on the giant mound of her stomach, a strangely softened expression driving the tension from his firm lips.

'May I feel my child move?' he clarified boldly.

Polly gave him a stricken look of condemnation, and with shaking, frantic hands tried somewhat pointlessly to try and yank her coat over herself. 'Don't you *dare* try to touch me!'

'Perhaps you are wise. Perhaps touching is not a good idea.' Nostrils flaring, Raul flung himself back in the corner of the seat, hooded eyes betraying only a chilling glint of intent gold, his bronzed face cold as a guillotine, impassive now in icy self-restraint.

And yet Polly was reminded of nothing so much as a

wild animal driven into ferocious retreat. He had never
looked at her like that in Vermont, but she had always
sensed the primal passion of the temperament he restrained.
Then, as now, it had exercised the most terrifying fascination for her—a male her complete opposite in nature, an
outwardly civilised sophisticate in mannerism, speech and
behaviour, but at heart never, ever cool, predictable or tranquil.

'Take me home,' she muttered tightly. 'I'll meet you
tomorrow to talk.'

He lifted the phone and spoke in fluid Spanish to his
driver. Polly turned away.

She remembered him in Vermont, addressing Soledad in
Spanish. She remembered the maid's nervous unease, her
undeniable servility. When Raul had been around, Soledad
had tried to melt into the woodwork, too unsophisticated a
woman to handle the cruel complexity of the situation he
had unthinkingly put her in. In his eyes she had only been
a servant after all. Raul Zaforteza was not a male accustomed to taking account of the needs or the feelings of
lesser beings...and in Soledad's case he had paid a higher
price than he would ever know for that arrogance.

The powerful car drew away from the kerb and shot
Polly's flailing and confused thoughts back to the present.
While Raul employed the car phone to make a lengthy call
in Spanish, she watched him helplessly from below her
lashes. She scanned the width of his shoulders under the
superb fit of his charcoal-grey suit, the powerful chest, lean
hips and long muscular thighs that not the most exquisite
tailoring in the world could conceal.

'*I* can't touch *you* but every look you give me is a visual
assault,' Raul derided in a whiplash aside as he replaced
the phone. 'I'd eat you for breakfast, little girl!'

Her temples throbbed and she closed her eyes, shaken
that he could speak to her like that. So many memories
washed over her that she was cast into turmoil. Raul,
tender, laughing, amber eyes warm as the kiss of sunlight,

without a shade of coldness. And every bit of that caring concern aimed at the ultimate well-being of the baby in her womb, at the physical body cocooning his child *not* at Polly personally. She had never existed for him on any level except as a human incubator to be kept calm, content and healthy. But how could she ever have guessed that shattering truth?

'You look terrible,' Raul informed her tautly. 'You've lost a lot of weight and you were very slim to begin with—'

'Nobody could ever accuse me of that now.'

'Your ankles are swollen.'

Polly rested her pounding head back wearily, beyond caring about what she must look like to him now. It scarcely mattered. She had been ten times more presentable in Vermont and he had not been remotely attracted to her, although she had only recognised that humiliating reality in retrospect. 'You're not getting my baby,' she warned him doggedly. 'Not under any circumstances.'

'Calm yourself,' Raul commanded deflatingly. 'Anxiety won't improve your health.'

'*It* always comes first, right?' Polly could not resist sniping.

'*Desde luego*...of course,' Raul confirmed without hesitation.

She winced as another dull flash of pain made her very brain ache. She heard him open a compartment, the hiss of a bottle cap released, liquid tinkling into a glass, and finally another unrecognisable sound. And then she jerked in astonishment when an ice-cold cloth was pressed against her pulsing brow.

'I will take care of you now. Did I not do so before? And look at you now, like a living corpse...' Raul condemned, his dark drawl alive with fierce undertones as he bent over her. 'I wanted to shout at you. I wanted to make you tremble. But how can I do *that* when you are like this?'

Her curling lashes lifted. Defenceless in pain, she stared up into frustrated and furious golden eyes so nakedly at variance with the compassionate gesture of that cool, soothing cloth he had drenched for her benefit. Being kind to her was killing him. She understood that. Suffering that grudging kindness was killing *her*.

'You taught me to *hate*,' she whispered, with a sudden ferocity alien to her gentle nature until that moment.

The stunning eyes veiled to a slumberous gleam. 'There is nothing between us but my baby. *No* other connection, *nada más*...nothing more,' he stressed with gritty exactitude. 'Only when you can detach yourself from your emotional mindset and recall that contract will we talk.'

Hatred flamed like a shooting star through Polly. She needed it. She needed hatred to race like adrenalin through her veins. Only hatred could swallow up and ease the agonizing pain Raul could inflict.

'You bastard,' Polly muttered shakily. 'You lying, cheating, devious bastard...'

At that precise moment the limo came to a smooth halt. As the chauffeur climbed out, Polly gaped at the well-lit modern building with its beautifully landscaped frontage outside which the car had drawn up. 'Where are we?' she demanded apprehensively.

A uniformed nurse emerged from the entrance with a wheelchair.

In silence Raul swung out of the limo and strode round the bonnet to wave away the hovering chauffeur. He opened the door beside her himself.

'You need medical attention,' he delivered.

Her shaken eyes widened, filling with instantaneous fear. Not for nothing had she visited the library to learn all she could from newspapers about Raul Zaforteza's ruthless reputation. 'You're not banging me up in some lunatic asylum!' she flung in complete panic.

'Curb your wild imagination, *chica*. I would do nothing to harm the mother of my child. And don't you *dare* try to cause a scene when my only concern is for your wellbeing!' Raul warned with ferocious bite as he leant in and scooped her still resisting body out of the luxurious car as if she weighed no more than a feather.

'The wheelchair, sir,' the nurse proffered.

'She weighs nothing. I'll carry her.' Raul strode through the automatic doors, clutching her with the tense concern of someone handling a particular fragile parcel. *The mother of his child.* Cue for reverent restraint, she reflected bitterly. Restraint and concern that the human incubator should be proving less than efficient. But, weak and sick from pain, even her vision blurring, she rested her head down against a broad shoulder.

'Hate you,' she muttered nonetheless, and would have told him that with her last dying breath because it was her only defence.

'You're not tough enough to hate,' Raul dismissed as a grey-haired older man in a white coat moved towards them.

Raul addressed him in a flood of Spanish. Scanning her with frowning eyes, the doctor led the way into a plush consulting room on the ground floor.

'Why does nobody speak English? We're in London,' Polly moaned.

'I'm sorry. Rodney Bevan is a consultant who worked for many years in a clinic of mine in Venezuela. I can talk faster in my own language.' Raul laid her down carefully on a comfortable treatment couch.

'Go away now,' Polly urged him feverishly.

Raul stayed put. The consultant said something quiet in Spanish. Raul's blunt cheekbones were accentuated by a faint line of dark colour. He swung on his heel and strode out to the waiting area, closing the door behind him.

'What did you say?' Polly was impressed to death.

As the waiting nurse moved forward to help Polly out of her coat, the older man smiled. 'You're the star here, not him.'

The nurse took her blood pressure. Why were their faces so solemn? Was there something wrong with her blood pressure? Her body felt like a great weight pulling her down.

'You need to relax and keep calm, Polly,' the doctor murmured. 'I want to give you a mild sedative and then I would like to scan you. Is that all right with you?'

'No, I want to go home,' she mumbled fearfully, knowing she sounded like a child and not caring, because she didn't feel she could trust anybody so friendly with Raul.

The voices went away. Raul's rich, dark drawl broke into her frantic barely half-formed thoughts. 'Polly...*please* let the medics do what they need to do,' he urged.

She forced her eyes open, focusing on him with difficulty, seeing those lean bronzed features through a blur. 'I can't trust you...or them...you *know* him!'

And even in the state she was in she saw him react in shock to that frightened accusation. Raul turned pale, the fabulous bone structure clenching hard. He gripped her hand, brilliant eyes shimmering. 'You *must* trust him. He's a very fine obstetrician—'

'He's a friend of yours.'

'*Sí, pero*...yes, but he is also a *doctor*,' Raul stressed with highly emotive urgency.

'I don't want to go to sleep and wake up in Venezuela... Do you think I don't know what you're capable of when you're crossed?' Polly managed to frame with the last of her energy.

'I've never broken the law!'

'You *would* to get this baby,' Polly told him.

The silence smouldered, fireworks blazing under the surface.

Raul stared down at her, expressive eyes veiled, but she knew she had drawn blood.

'You're not well, Polly. If you will not believe my assurances that you can trust the staff here, then at least think of the baby's needs and put those needs first,' he breathed, not quite levelly.

A pained look of withdrawal crossed her exhausted face.

She gave a jerky nod of assent, but turned her head to the wall. A minute later she felt a slight prick in her arm and she let herself float, and would have done anything to escape that relentless pounding inside her skull and forget that unjust look of cruel reproach she had seen in Raul's gaze.

As she drifted like a drowning swimmer, all the worst moments of her life seemed to flash up before her.

Her earliest memory was of her father shouting at her mother and her mother crying. She had got up one morning at the age of seven to find her mother gone. Her father had flown into a rage when she'd innocently tried to question him. Soon after that she had been sent to stay with her godmother. Nancy Leeward had carefully explained. Her mother, Leah, had done a very silly thing: she had gone away with another man. Her parents were getting a divorce, but some time, hopefully soon, when her father gave permission, her mother might come to visit her.

Only Leah never had. Polly had got her mothering from her godmother. And she had had to wait until she was twenty years old and clearing out her father's desk, days after his funeral, to discover the pitiful wad of pleading letters written by the distraught mother who had to all intents and purposes abandoned her.

Leah had gone to New York and eventually married her lover. She had flown over to England half a dozen times, at an expense she could ill afford, in repeated attempts to see her daughter, but her embittered ex-husband had blocked her every time—not least by putting Polly into boarding school and refusing to say where she was. Polly had been shattered by what she'd uncovered, but also overjoyed to realise that her mother had really loved her, in spite of all her father's assertions to the contrary.

In New York, she had had a tearful, wonderful reunion with Leah, whose second husband had died the previous year. Her mother had been weak, breathless, and aged far beyond her years. The gravity of her heart condition had been painfully obvious. She had been living on welfare, what health insurance she had had exhausted. The harassed doctor at the local clinic had reluctantly told Polly under pressure that there *was* an operation performed by a world-famous surgeon which might give her mother some hope, but that it would take a lottery win to privately finance such major surgery.

Up, down—too much down in her life recently, and not enough up, she thought painfully as she wandered through her own memories.

And then she saw Raul, strolling through the glorious Vermont woods where she had walked every day, escaping from Soledad's kind but fussing attentions to cry in peace for the mother she had lost. Raul, garbed in faultlessly cut casual clothes, smart enough to take Rodeo Drive by storm and so smooth, so impressively natural in his surprise at stumbling on her that it was a wonder he hadn't cut himself with his own clever tongue.

And she had met those extraordinary eyes of amber and bang...crash...*pow*. She had been heading for a down that would take her all the way to hell, even though she had naively felt she was on an up the instant he angled that first smouldering smile at her.

Polly woke up the following morning wearing a hideous billowing hospital gown. She had a room to herself with a private bathroom. Her head no longer hurt, but tiredness still filled her with lethargy.

The nurse who came in response to the bell cheerfully ran through routine checks, efficiently helped her to freshen up and neatly side-stepped most of her anxious questions. She consulted her chart and informed Polly that she was to have complete bedrest. Mr. Bevan would be in around lunchtime, she confided, just as breakfast was delivered.

A couple of hours later Raul's chauffeur arrived, like an advance party before him. He settled down a suitcase that Polly recognised because it was her own. The case bulged with what struck her as very probably every possession she had last seen in her room at the Greys'. A maid in an overall came in and helped her change into one of her own nighties. Polly then retrieved a creased brown envelope from the jumble of items in the foot of her case. It was time to confront Raul with the worst of the deceptions practised on her.

By the time mid-morning arrived, Polly was sitting bolt upright with wide, angrily impatient eyes and, had she but known it, the first healthy colour in her cheeks for weeks. She raked restive fingers through the silky mahogany hair tumbling round her shoulders and focused on the door expectantly, like someone not only preparing to face Armageddon but overwhelmingly eager to meet it.

The ajar door finally spread wide, framing Raul.

Her breath caught in her throat.

Sleek and powerful, in a summerweight double-breasted beige business suit, he looked sensationally attractive, supremely poised and shockingly self-assured. Polly lost her animated colour, ashamed of that helpless flare of physical response to those dark good looks and that lithe, lean, muscular physique. He was a ruthless and unashamed manipulator.

Black eyes raked over her, black eyes without any shade of warm gold. Emotionless, businesslike, not even a comforting hint of uncertainty about his stance. 'You look better already,' he remarked levelly.

'I feel better,' Polly was generous enough to admit. 'But I can't stay here—'

'Of course you can. Where else could you be so well cared for?'

'I've got something here I want you to explain,' Polly delivered tautly.

His attention dropped to the envelope clutched between her tense fingers. 'What is it?'

A shaky little laugh escaped Polly. 'Oh, it's not real proof of the manipulative lies I was fed...you needn't

worry about that! Your lawyer was far too clever to allow
me to retain any original documents, but I took photo-
copies—'

Raul frowned at her. '*Dios mio*, cut to the base line and
tell me what you're talking about,' he incised impatiently.
'You were told no lies at any time!'

'Off the record lies,' Polly extended tightly. 'It was very
clever to give me the impression that I was being allowed
a reassuring glimpse at highly confidential information.'

Raul angled back his imperious dark head. 'Explain
yourself.'

Polly tossed the envelope to the foot of the bed. 'How
you can look me in the face and say that I will never know.'

Raul swept up the envelope with an undaunted flourish.

'And don't try to pretend you didn't know about it.
When I was asked to sign that contract, I said I couldn't
sign until I was given some assurances about the couple
who wanted me to act as surrogate for them.'

'The...*couple*?' Raul queried flatly, ebony brows drawing together as he extracted the folded pages from the envelope.

'Your lawyer said that wasn't possible. His clients
wanted complete anonymity. So I left. Forty-eight hours
later, I got a phone call. I met up in a café with a young
bright spark from your lawyer's office. He said he was a
clerk,' Polly related jerkily, her resentment and distaste blatant in her strained face as she recalled how easily she had
been fooled. 'He said he *understood* my concern about the
people who would be adopting my child, and that he was
risking his job in allowing me even a glance at such confidential documents—'

'Which confidential documents?' Raul cut in grittily.

'He handed me a profile of that *supposed* couple from
an accredited adoption agency. There were no names, no
details which might have identified them...' Tears stung
Polly's eyes then, her voice beginning to shake with the
strength of her feelings. 'And I was really moved by what

I read, by their own personal statements, their complete honesty, their deep longing to have a family. They struck me as wonderful people, and they'd had a h-heartbreaking time struggling to have a child of their own…'

'*Madre mía…*' Raul ground out, half under his breath, scorching golden eyes pinned to her distraught face with mesmeric force.

'And you see,' Polly framed jaggedly, 'I really *liked* that couple. I felt for them, thought they would make terrific parents, would give any child a really loving home…' As a strangled sob swallowed her voice, she crammed a mortified hand against her wobbling mouth and stared in tormented accusation at Raul through swimming blue eyes. 'How *could* you sink that low?' she condemned strickenly.

Raul gazed back at her, strikingly pale now below his olive skin, so still he might have been a stone statue, a stunned light in his piercing dark eyes.

With the greatest difficulty, Polly cleared her throat and breathed unevenly. 'I asked the clerk to let me have an hour reading over that profile and I photocopied it without telling him. That afternoon, I went in and signed the contract. I thought I was doing a really good thing. I thought I would make that couple so happy… I was inexcusably dumb and shortsighted!'

The heavy silence stretched like a rubber band pulled too taut. And then Raul unfroze. In an almost violent gesture, he shook open the pages he still held. He strode over to the window, his broad back turned to her, his tension so pronounced it hummed like a force field in a room that now felt suffocatingly airless.

Polly sank wearily back against the pillows and fought to get a grip on the tears still clogging her aching throat.

Timeless minutes later, Raul swung back, his darkly handsome features grim and forbidding. 'This abhorrent deception was not instigated by me,' he declared, visibly struggling to contain the outrage blazing in his eyes, the revealing rawness to that harshened plea in his own de-

fence. 'I had no knowledge of your request for further information *or* of your initial reluctance to sign that contract.'

'How am I supposed to believe anything you say?'

'Because the guilty party will be called to account,' Raul
asserted with wrathful bite. 'At no stage did I give any
instruction which might have implied that I would coun-
tenance such a deception. There was no need for me to
stoop to lies and manipulation. There were other far less
scrupulous applicants available—'

'Were there?' Polly breathed, not best pleased to realise
that she had featured as one of many.

He was shocked and furious, so furious there was a slight
tremor in his fingers as he refolded the pages she had given
him. His sincerity was fiercely convincing.

'So now I know why you have no faith in my word. It
wasn't only my decision to conceal my identity as the father
of your child in Vermont that made you change your mind
about fulfilling the contract.'

It was an unfortunate reminder. He only had to mention
that cruel masquerade to fill Polly with savage pain and
resentment. She surveyed him with angry, bitter eyes. 'I
would never, ever have agreed to a single male parent for
my child, and when I found out who you really were, I was
genuinely appalled—'

Raul skimmed a startled glance at her. '*Dios
mio*…''appalled''? What an exaggeration—'

'No exaggeration. I wouldn't give a man with your reputation a pet rabbit to keep, never mind an innocent, helpless
baby!' Polly fired back at him.

Raul gazed back at her with complete incredulity. 'What
is wrong with my reputation?'

'Read your own publicity,' Polly advised with unconcealed distaste, thinking about the endless string of glamorous women who had been associated with him. There was
nothing stable or respectable about Raul's lifestyle.

Outrage sizzled round Raul Zaforteza like an intimidating aura. He snatched in a deep shuddering breath of re-

straint. 'What right do you have to stand in judgement over me? So subterfuge was employed to persuade you into conceiving my child—I deeply regret that reality, but nothing will alter the situation we're in now. That child you carry is *still* my child!'

Polly turned her head away. 'And mine.'

'The Judgement of Solomon. Are you about to suggest that we divide him or her into two equal halves? Let me tell you now that I will fight to the end to prevent that obnoxious little nerd I met last night raising my child!' Raul delivered with sudden explosive aggression.

Polly blinked. 'What little nerd?'

'Henry Grey informed me that you're engaged to him,' Raul imparted with a feral flash of white teeth. 'And you may believe that that is your business, but *anything* that affects my child's welfare is also very much *my* business now!'

Stunned to realise that Henry should have claimed to be engaged to her, Polly surveyed the volatile male striding up and down the room, like a prowling tiger lashing his tail at the confines of a cage. Why did she want to hold Raul in her arms and soothe him? she asked herself with a sinking heart.

'I think you should leave, Raul.' As that dry voice of reproof cut through the electric atmosphere, Polly tore her mesmerised attention from Raul. In turn, Raul swung round. They both focused in astonishment on the consultant lodged in the doorway.

'Leave?' Raul stressed in unconcealed disbelief.

'Only quiet visitors are welcome here,' Rodney Bevan spelt out gravely.

Dressed in an Indian cotton dress the same rich blue as her eyes, Polly turned her face up into the sun and basked, welded to the comfy cushioning on the lounger. The courtyard garden at the centre of the clinic was an enchanting spot on a summer day. Even Henry's unwelcome visit couldn't detract from her pleasure at being surrounded by greenery again.

Henry gave her an accusing look. 'Anybody would think you were enjoying yourself here!'

'It's very restful.'

Until Polly had escaped Henry and his mother for three days, she hadn't appreciated just how wearing their constant badgering had become. She was tired of being pressurised and pushed in a direction she didn't want to go. Now that Raul had found her, she was no longer in hiding. After she had sorted out things with Raul, she would be able to take control of her own life again.

'Mother thinks you should come home,' Henry told her with stiff disapproval.

'You still haven't explained *why* you told Raul we were engaged.'

Henry frowned. 'I should've thought that was obvious. I hoped he'd go away and leave us alone. What's the point of him showing up now? He's just complicating things, swanning up in his flash car and acting like he owns you!'

Strange how even a male as insensitive as Henry had recognised that Raul behaved as if he owned her. Only it wasn't her, it was the baby he believed he owned. Dear heaven, what a mess she was in, Polly conceded worriedly. There was no going back, no way of changing anything. Her baby was also Raul's baby and always would be.

'It was kind of you to call in, Henry,' she murmured quietly. 'Tell your mother that I really appreciate all her kindness, but that I won't be coming back to stay with you—'

'What on earth are you talking about?' Henry had gone all red in the face.

'I just don't want to marry you...I'm sorry.'

'I'll visit later in the week, when you're feeling more yourself.'

As Henry departed, Polly reflected that she was actually

feeling more herself than she had in many weeks. Stepping off the treadmill of exhaustion had given her space to think.

As she slowly, awkwardly raised herself, Raul appeared through a door on the far side of the courtyard. He angled a slashing, searching glance over the little clusters of patients taking the fresh air nearby. Screened by the shrubbery, Polly made no attempt to attract his attention.

His suit was palest grey. He exuded designer chic. In the sunlight, his luxuriant hair gleamed blue-black. His lean, strong face possessed such breathtaking sexy symmetry that her breathing quickened and her sluggish pulses raced. Raul radiated raw sexuality in virile waves. The media said that men thought about sex at least once a minute. One look at Raul was enough to convince her.

But a feeling of stark inadequacy and rejection now threatened her in Raul's radius. How the heck had she ever believed that a male that gorgeous was interested in her? How wilfully blind she had been in Vermont! If a woman excited Raul, he probably pounced on the first date, or maybe he got pounced on, but he had never made a pass at *her*, or even tried to kiss her. At first he had made her as nervous as a cat on hot bricks. But before very long his exquisite manners and flattering interest in her had soothed her inexperienced squirmings in his presence and given her entirely the wrong impression.

Incredibly, she had believed that one of the world's most notorious womanisers was actually a cautious and decent guy, mature enough to want to get to know a woman as a friend before trying to take the relationship any further. Remembering that fact now made Polly feel positively queasy. She had thought Raul was perfect; she had thought he was wonderful; she had thought he was really attracted to her because he continued to seek out her company...

Far from impervious to Raul's cool exasperation when he finally espied her, lurking behind the shrubbery, Polly dropped her head, her shining fall of mahogany hair concealing her taut profile.

'What are you doing out of bed?' Raul demanded the
instant he got within hailing distance. 'I'll take you back
up to your room.'

'I'm allowed out for fresh air as long as I don't overdo
it,' Polly said thinly.

'We'll go inside,' Raul decreed. 'We can't discuss confidential business here.'

Polly swung her legs off the lounger and got up. 'Business? I've learnt the hard way that my baby is not a piece
of merchandise.'

'Do you really think I feel any different?' Raul breathed
with a raw, bitter edge to his rich, dark drawl. 'Do you
really think you're the only one of us to have learnt from
this mess?'

She couldn't avoid looking at him in the lift. He stood
opposite her, supremely indifferent to the two nurses in the
corner studying him with keen female appreciation. He
stared at Polly without apology, intense dark eyes welded
broodingly to her heart-shaped face and the heated colour
steadily building in her cheeks.

She had one question she desperately wanted to ask him.
Why did a drop-dead gorgeous heterosexual male of only
thirty-one feel the need to hire a surrogate mother to have
his child? Why hadn't he just got married? Or, alternatively, why hadn't he simply persuaded one of his innu-
merable blonde bimbo babes into motherhood? Why surrogacy?

The minute Polly settled herself down on the sofa in her
room, Raul breathed with a twist of his expressive mouth,
'You're still angry with me about Vermont. We should deal
with that and get it out of the way…it's clouding the real
issues at stake here.'

At that statement of intent, Polly stiffened, and her skin
prickled with shrinking apprehension. 'Naturally I'm still
angry, but I see no point in talking about it. That's in the
past now.'

Raul strolled over to the window. He dug a lean brown

hand into the pocket of his well-cut trousers tightening the fit of the fine fabric over his narrow hips and long, muscular thighs. Polly found herself abstractedly studying a part of the male anatomy she had never in her life before studied, the distinctively manly bulge of his manhood. Flushing to the roots of her hair, she hurriedly looked away.

But it was so peculiar, she thought bitterly. So peculiar to be pregnant by a man she had never slept with, never been intimate with in any way. And Raul Zaforteza was *all* male, like a walking advertisement for high testosterone levels and virility. Why on earth had he chosen to have his child conceived by an anonymous insemination in a doctor's surgery?

'If I'm really honest, I wanted to meet you and talk to you right from the moment you signed the contract,' Raul drawled tautly, interrupting her seething thoughts.

'Why, for heaven's sake?'

'I knew my child would want to know what you were really like.'

A cold chill of repulsion trickled down Polly's spine. So impersonal, so practical, so utterly unfeeling a motivation.

'After your mother died, I was aware that you were in considerable distress,' Raul continued levelly. 'You needed support...who *else* was there to provide that support? If you hadn't discovered that I was the baby's father, you wouldn't have been so upset. And isn't it time you told me how you *did* penetrate that secret?'

In her mind's eye, Polly pictured Soledad and all the numerous members of her equally dependent family being flung off the ancestral ranch the older woman had described in Venezuela. She gulped. 'You gave yourself away. Your behaviour...well, it made me suspicious. I worked the truth out for myself,' she lied stiltedly.

'You're a liar...Soledad told you,' Raul traded without skipping a beat, shrewd dark eyes grimly amused by her startled reaction. 'A major oversight on my part. Two women stuck all those weeks in the same house? The barriers came down and you became friendly—'

'Soledad would never have betrayed you if you hadn't come into my life without admitting who you were!' Polly interrupted defensively. 'She couldn't cope with being forced to pretend that she didn't know you.'

'I was at fault there,' Raul acknowledged openly, honestly, taking her by surprise. 'I'm aware of that now. Vermont *was* a mistake…it personalised what should have remained impersonal and compromised my sense of honour.'

A mistake? A gracious admission of fault, an apology underwritten. Gulping back a spurt of angry revealing words, Polly swallowed hard. He was so smooth, so reasonable and controlled. She wanted to scratch her nails down the starkly handsome planes of those high cheekbones to make him feel for even one *second* something of what she had suffered!

'So, now that you know how I found out, are Soledad and her family still working for you?' Polly enquired stiffly.

Raul dealt her a wry smile. 'Her family is, but Soledad has moved to Caracas to look after her grandchildren while her daughter's at work.'

A light knock at the door announced the entry of a maid, bearing Polly's afternoon tea. Raul asked for black coffee, it not occurring to him for one moment that as a visitor he might not be entitled to refreshment. Blushing furiously, the maid literally rushed to satisfy his request.

Cradling the coffee elegantly in one lean hand, Raul sank down lithely into the armchair opposite her. 'Are you comfortable here?'

'Very.'

'But obviously it's a challenge to fill the empty hours. I'll get a video recorder sent in, some tapes, books…I know what you like,' Raul asserted with complete confidence. 'I should've thought of it before.'

'I'm not happy with what this place must be costing

you,' Polly told him in a sudden rush. 'Especially as I am not going to honour that contract.'

Raul scanned her anxious blue eyes. A slight smile momentarily curved his wide, sensual mouth. 'You need some time and space to consider that decision. Right now, I have no intention of putting pressure on you—'

'Just having you in the same room is pressure,' Polly countered uncomfortably. 'Having you pay my bills makes it even worse.'

'Whatever happens, I'm still the father of your baby. That makes you my responsibility.'

'The softly, softly, catchee monkey routine won't work with me... I'm so fed up with people telling me that I don't know what I want, or that I don't know what I'm doing.' Polly raised her small head high and valiantly clashed with brilliant black eyes as sharp as paint. 'The truth is that I've grown up a lot in the last few months...'

Raul held up a fluid and silencing hand in a gesture that came so naturally to him that she instinctively closed her lips. 'In swift succession over the past year or so you have lost the three people you cared about most in this world. Your father, your mother and your godmother. That is bound to be affecting your judgement *and* your view of the future. All I want to do is give you another possible view.'

Setting aside his empty coffee cup, he rose gracefully upright again. Polly watched him nervously, the tip of her tongue stealing out to moisten the dry curve of her lower lip.

Raul's attention dropped to the soft, generous pink curve of her mouth and lingered, and she felt the oddest buzzing current in the air, her slight frame automatically tensing in reaction. Raul stiffened, the dark rise of blood emphasising the slashing line of his hard cheekbones. Swinging on his heel, he strode over to the window and pushed it wider.

'It's stuffy in here... As I was saying, an alternative view of the future,' he continued flatly. 'You can't possibly *want* to marry that little jerk Henry Grey—'

Taken aback, Polly sat up straighter. 'How do you know?'

His chiselled profile clenched into aggressive lines. 'He's just being greedy...he wouldn't look twice at a woman expecting another man's child *unless* she was an heiress!'

Polly flinched at that revealing assertion. 'So you found out about my godmother's will...'

'Naturally...' Raul skimmed an assured glance in her direction. 'And the good news is that you don't have to marry Henry to inherit that money and make a new start. You're only twenty-one; you have your whole life in front of you. Why clog it up with Henry? He's a pompous bore. I'm prepared to *give* you that million pounds to dump him!'

In sheer shock, Polly's lips fell open. She began to rise off the sofa. 'I b-beg your pardon?' she stammered shakily, convinced he couldn't possibly have said what she thought he had said.

Raul swung fluidly round to face her again. 'You heard me. Forget that stupid will, and for the present forget the baby too...just ditch that loser!'

Her blue eyes opened very wide. She gaped at him, and then she took a step forward, fierce anger leaping up inside her. 'How dare you try to bribe me into doing what *you* want me to do? How *dare* you do that?'

Raul's cool façade cracked to reveal the cold anger beneath. He sent her a sizzling look of derision. '*Caramba!* Surely you'd prefer to stay rich and single when Henry's the only option on offer?'

Without an instant of hesitation, Polly snatched up the water jug by the bed with a feverish hand and slung the contents at him. '*That's* what I think of your filthy offer! I'm not for sale this time and I never will be again!'

Soaked by that sizeable flood, and astonished by both her attack and that outburst, Raul stood there dripping and downright incredulous. As his lean fingers raked his wet hair off his brow, his dark eyes flamed to a savage golden blaze.

'I'm not sorry,' Polly admitted starkly.

Raul slung her a searing look of scantily leashed fury. '*Por Dios*...I am leaving before I say or do something I might regret!' he bit out rawly.

The door snapped shut in his imperious wake. Polly snatched in a slow steadying breath and realised that even her hands were shaking. She had never met with a temper that hot before.

CHAPTER THREE

A VIDEO recorder arrived, complete with a whole collection of tapes, and was installed in Polly's room by lunchtime the following day.

As a gesture, it was calculated to make her feel guilty. That evening, Polly sat in floods of tears just picking through titles like *The Quiet Man* and *Pretty Woman* and *Sabrina*. All escapist romantic movies, picked by a male who knew her tastes far too well for comfort. She grabbed up another tissue in despair.

Raul Zaforteza unleashed a temper she hadn't known she had. He filled her to overflowing with violent, resentful and distressingly confused emotions. She hated him, she told herself fiercely. He was tearing her apart. She hated him even more when she felt herself react to the humiliating pull of his magnetic sexual attraction.

Worse, Raul understood her so much better than she understood him. In Vermont, she had trustingly revealed too many private thoughts and feelings, while he had been coolly evaluating her, like a scientist studying something curious under a microscope. Why? He had answered that straight off the top of his head and without hesitation.

So that he could answer her child's questions about her in the future.

Polly shivered at the memory of that admission, chilled to the marrow and hurt beyond belief. It wasn't possible to get more detached than that from another human being. But how many times had Raul already emphasised that there was nothing but that hateful surrogate contract between them? And why was she still torturing herself with that reality?

He had coolly, contemptuously offered her a million pounds to dump Henry and stay single. And why had he done that? Simply because he felt threatened by the idea of her marrying. Why hadn't she grasped that fact sooner? If she married, Raul would be forced, whether he liked it or not, to stand back while another man raised his child. So why hadn't she told him she wasn't planning to marry Henry?

Polly was honest with herself on that point. She hadn't seen *why* she should tell him the truth. What business was it of his? And she had been prepared to hide behind a pretend engagement to Henry, a face-saving pretence that suggested her life had moved on since Vermont. Only Raul had destroyed that pretence. Acquainted as he was with the intricacies of her godmother's will, he had realised that that inheritance was the only reason Henry was willing to marry her. It mortified Polly that Raul should have guessed even that. In his presence, she was beginning to feel as if she was being speedily stripped of every defence.

But then what did she know about men? It was laughable to be so close to the birth of her own child and still be so ignorant. But her father had been a strict, puritanical man, whose rules and restrictions had made it impossible for her to enjoy a normal social life. It had even been difficult to hang onto female friends with a father who invariably offended them by criticising their clothing or their behaviour.

She had had a crush on a boy in her teens, but he had quickly lost interest when her father refused to allow her to go out with him. When she had started the university degree course that she'd never got to finish, she had lived so close to the campus she had had to continue living at home. She had kept house for her father, assisted in his many church activities and, when his stationery business began to fail, helped with his office work.

She had sneaked out to the occasional party. Riven with guilt at having lied to get out, she had endured a few over-enthusiastic clinches, wondering what all the fuss was about while she pushed away groping, over-familiar hands, unable to comprehend why any sane female would want to respond to such crude demands.

She had met another boy while studying. Like his predecessors, he had been unwilling to come to the house and meet her father just to get permission to take her out at night. At first he had thought it was a bit of laugh to see her only during the day. Then one lunchtime he had taken her back to his flat and tried to get her to go to bed with him. She had said no. He had ditched her there and then, called her 'a pathetic, boring little virgin' and soon replaced her with a more available girl who didn't expect love and commitment in return for sex.

It had taken Raul Zaforteza to teach Polly what she had never felt before...a deep, dark craving for physical contact as tormenting to endure as a desperate thirst...

Polly was restless that evening. Aware that she wasn't asleep, one of the nurses brought her in a cup of tea at ten, and thoughtfully lent her a magazine to read.

As always, during the night, her door was kept ajar to allow the staff to check easily and quietly on her. So when, out of the corner of her eye, Polly saw the door open wider, she turned with a smile for the nurse she was expecting to see and then froze in surprise when she saw Raul instead. Visiting time finished at nine, and it was now after eleven.

'How did you get in?' Polly asked in a startled whisper.

Raul leant lithely back against the door until it snapped softly shut. In a black dinner jacket and narrow black trousers, a bow tie at his throat, he exuded sophisticated cool. 'Talked my way past the security guard and chatted up the night sister.'

Strolling forward, he set a tub of ice cream in front of her. 'Peppermint—your favourite...my peace offering,' he murmured with a lazy smile.

That charismatic smile hit Polly like a shot of adrenalin in her veins. Every trace of drowsiness evaporated. Her heart jumped, her mouth ran dry and burning colour started to creep up her throat. He lifted the teaspoon from the cup and saucer on the bed-table she had pushed away and settled it down helpfully on top of the tub.

'Eat it before it melts,' he advised, settling down on the end of the bed in an indolent sprawl.

It shook her that Raul should recall that peppermint was her favorite flavour. It shook her even more that he should take the trouble to call in with ice cream at this hour of the night when he had obviously been out somewhere.

With a not quite steady hand, Polly removed the lid on the tub. 'Henry lied,' she confided abruptly. 'We're not engaged. I'm not going to marry him.'

In the intimate pool of light shed by the Anglepoise lamp by the bed, a wolfish grin slashed Raul's darkly handsome features. Polly was so mesmerised by it, she dug her teaspoon into empty air instead of the tub and only discovered the ice cream by touch.

'You could do a lot better than him, *cielita*,' he responded softly.

Polly's natural sense of fairness prompted her to add, 'Henry isn't that bad. He was honest. It wasn't like he pretended to fancy me or anything like that...'

Slumberous dark eyes semi-screened by lush ebony lashes, Raul emitted a low-pitched laugh that sent an odd little tremor down her sensitive spine. 'Henry has no taste.'

The silence that fell seemed to hum in her eardrums.

Feeling that languorous heaviness in her breasts, the surge of physical awareness she dreaded, Polly shifted uneasily and leapt straight back into speech. 'Why did you decide to hire a surrogate?' she asked baldly. 'It doesn't make sense to me.'

His strong face tensed. 'I wanted to have a child while I was still young enough to play with a child...'

'And the right woman just didn't come along?' Polly assumed as the silence stretched.

'Perhaps I should say that I like women but I like my

freedom better. Let's leave it at that,' Raul suggested smoothly.

'I'm so sorry I signed that contract.' Troubled eyes blue as violets rested on him, her heart-shaped face strained. 'I don't know how I thought I could actually go through with it...but at the time I suppose I couldn't think of anything but how sick my mother was.'

'I should never have picked you. The psychologist said that he wasn't convinced you understood how hard it would be to surrender your child—'

'Did he?'

'He said you were too intense, too idealistic.'

Polly frowned. 'So why was I chosen?'

Raul lifted a broad shoulder in a slight fatalistic shrug that was very Latin. 'I *liked* you. I didn't want to have a baby with a woman I couldn't even like.'

'I was a really bad choice,' Polly muttered ruefully. 'Now I wish you'd listened to the psychologist.'

Raul vented a rather grim laugh. 'I never listen to what I don't want to hear. People who work for me know that, and they like to please me. That's why you were fed lies to persuade you into signing the contract. A very junior lawyer got smart and set you up. He didn't tell his boss what he'd done until *after* you'd signed. He expected an accolade for his ingenuity but instead he got fired.'

'Did he?' Polly showed her surprise.

'*Sí...*' Raul's mouth tightened. 'But my lawyer saw no reason to tell me what had happened. He had no idea that either of us would ever be in a position to find out.'

Polly ate the ice cream, lashes lowering as she savoured each cool, delicious spoonful. The seconds ticked by. Raul watched her. She was aware of his intent scrutiny, curiously satisfied by the attention, but extremely nervous of it too, as if she was a mouse with a hawk circling overhead. It was so quiet, so very quiet at that hour of the night, no distant buzzing bells, no quick-moving feet in the corridor outside.

And then Polly stiffened, a muffled little sound of discomfort escaping her as the baby chose that moment to give her an athletic kick.

Raul leant forward. '*Que*...what is it?' he demanded anxiously.

'The baby. It's always liveliest at night.' She met the question in his eyes and flushed, reaching a sudden decision. Setting down the ice cream, she pushed the bedding back the few necessary inches, knowing that she was perfectly decently covered in her cotton nightie but still feeling horrendously shy.

Raul drew closer and rested his palm very lightly on her stomach. As he felt the movement beneath his fingers, a look of wonder filled his dark, shimmering gaze and he smiled with sudden quick brilliance. 'That's amazing,' he breathed. 'Do you know if it's a boy or a girl yet?'

'Mr Bevan offered to tell me but I didn't want to know,' Polly admitted unevenly, deeply unsettled by that instant of intimate sharing but undeniably touched by his fascination. 'I like surprises better.'

Raul slowly removed his palm and tugged the sheet back into place. His hands weren't quite steady. Noting that, she wondered why. She could still feel the cool touch of his hand like a burning imprint on her own flesh. He was so close she could hardly breathe, her own awareness of him so pronounced it was impossible to fight. At best, she knew she could only hope to conceal her reaction, but though she was desperate to think of something to say to distract him her mind was suddenly a blank.

'You can be incredibly sweet...' Raul remarked, half under his breath.

Her intent gaze roamed over him, lingering helplessly on the glossy luxuriance of his black hair, the hard, clean line of his high cheekbones and the dark roughening of his jawline that suggested a need to shave twice a day. Reaching the wide, passionate curve of his mouth, she wondered as she had wondered so often before what he tasted like. Then, wildly flustered by that disturbing thought, her eyes lifted, full of confusion, and the dark golden lure of his gaze entrapped and held her in thrall.

'And incredibly tempting,' Raul confided huskily as he brought his sensual mouth very slowly down on hers.

She could have pulled back with ease; he gave her every opportunity. But at the first touch of his lips on hers she dissolved into a hot, melting pool of acquiescence. With a muffled groan, he closed his hand into the tumbling fall of her hair to steady himself and let his tongue stab deep into the tender interior of her mouth. And the whole tenor of the kiss changed.

Excitement so intense it burned flamed instantly through her, bringing her alive with a sudden shocking vitality that made her screamingly aware of every inch of her own humming body. And as soon as it began she ached for more, lacing desperate fingers into the silky thickness of his hair, palms sliding down then to curve over to his cheekbones. Only at some dim, distant, uncaring level was she conscious of the buzzing, irritating sound somewhere close by.

Raul released her with a stifled expletive in Spanish and sprang off the bed. With dazed eyes, Polly watched him pull out a mobile phone. And in the deep silence she heard the high-pitched vibration of a woman's voice before he put the phone to his ear.

'*Dios*...I'll be down in a moment,' Raul murmured curtly, and, switching the phone off, he dug it back into his pocket.

'I'm sorry but I have to go. I have someone waiting in the car.' He raked restive fingers through his now thoroughly tousled black hair, glittering golden eyes screened from her searching scrutiny, mouth compressed into a ferocious line. 'I'll see you soon. *Buenas noches*.'

The instant he left the room, Polly thrust back the bedding and scrambled awkwardly out of bed. She flew over to the window which overlooked the front entrance and pulled back the curtain. She saw the limo...and she saw the beautiful blonde in her sleek, short crimson dress pacing beside it. Then she watched the blonde arrange herself in a studied pose against the side of the luxury car so that she looked like a glamorous model at an automobile show.

Polly rushed back across the room to douse the lamp and then returned to the window. Raul emerged from the clinic. The blonde threw herself exuberantly into his arms. Polly's nerveless fingers dropped from the curtain. She reeled back against the cold wall and closed her arms round her trembling body, feeling sick and dizzy and utterly disgusted with herself.

Oh, dear heaven, why hadn't she slapped his face for him? Why, oh, why had she allowed him to kiss her? Feeling horribly humiliated and raw, she got back into bed with none of the adrenalin-charged speed with which she had vacated it. Tonight Raul had been out with his latest blonde. Now they were either moving on to some nightclub or heading for a far more intimate setting. She could barely credit that Raul had called in to see her in the middle of a date with another woman, as relaxed and unhurried as if he'd had all the time in the world to spend with her.

Polly felt murderous. She could still see the ice cream tub glimmering in the darkness. Gosh, weren't you a pushover? a sarcastic little inner voice gibed. Easily impressed, pitifully vulnerable. Her defences hadn't stood a chance with Raul in a more approachable mood. And he hadn't even kissed her because he was attracted to her—oh, no. Nothing so simple and nothing less flattering than the true explanation she suspected.

He had felt the baby move. That had been a disturbingly intimate and emotional experience for them both. For the first time they had crossed the barriers of that contract and actually *shared* something that related to the baby. And Raul was a very physical male who had, in the heat of the moment, reacted in an inappropriately physical way. The constraint of his abrupt departure had revealed his unease with that development. She was convinced he wouldn't ever let anything like that happen between them again.

Yet for so long Polly had ached for Raul to kiss her, and that passionate kiss had outmatched her every naive expectation. Without ever touching her, Raul had taught her to crave him like a dangerous drug. Now she despised herself and felt all the shame of her own wantonly eager response. She did hate him now, she told herself vehemently. Technically she might still be a virgin, but she wasn't such an idiot that she didn't know that sexual feelings could both tempt and confuse. Her response had had nothing to do with love or intelligence.

She had stopped loving Raul the same day that she'd discovered how he had been deceiving her in Vermont. But the complexity of their current relationship was plunging her into increasing turmoil. For what relationship *did* they have? She wasn't his lover but she was expecting his baby, and she couldn't even claim that they were friends, could she...?

A magnificent floral arrangement arrived from Raul the next day. Polly asked the maid to pass it on to one of the other patients. She didn't want to be reminded of Raul every time she looked across the room.

He phoned in the afternoon. 'How are you?'

'Turning somersaults,' Polly said brittly. 'Leafing through my frantically crammed social diary to see what I'll be doing today. Do I really need to stay here much longer?'

'Rod thinks so,' Raul reminded her. 'Look, I'll be away on business for the next week. I wanted to leave a contact number with you so that you can get in touch if you need to.'

'I can't imagine there being any need when I'm surrounded by medical staff and being waited on hand and foot.'

'OK. I'll phone *you*—'

Polly breathed in deep. 'Would you mind if I asked you not to?'

'I don't like having this type of conversation on the phone. It's a very female method of warfare,' Raul drawled grimly.

'I was just asking for a little space,' Polly countered tightly. 'In the circumstances, I don't think that's unreasonable. You may be the father of my child, but we don't have a personal relationship.'

'I'll see you when I get back from Paris, Polly.'

The line went dead. But Polly continued to grip the receiver frantically tight. She didn't want to see him; she didn't want to hear from him. Her eyes smarted. But the tears were nothing to do with him. Late on in pregnancy women were often more emotional and tearful, she reminded herself staunchly.

Mid-morning, late in the following week, Polly had just put on a loose red jersey dress with a V-neckline and short sleeves when Raul arrived to visit her. Hearing the knock on the door of her room, she emerged from the bathroom, still struggling to brush her long hair. She fell still in an awkward pose when she realised who it was.

Her heart skipped a complete beat. Raul was wearing a navy pinstriped business suit so sharply tailored it fitted his magnificent physique like a glove. Worn with a dark blue shirt and red silk tie, it made him look sensationally attractive and dynamic. Her throat closed over. It felt like a hundred years since she had last seen him. She wanted to move closer, had to forcefully still her feet where she stood.

Raul strolled forward and casually reached up to pluck the brush from her loosened hold. Gently turning her round by her shoulders, he teased loose the tangle she had been fighting with before returning the brush to her hand. 'I owe you an apology for my behaviour on my last visit,' he murmured with conviction.

Polly tensed. There was a mirror on the back of the bathroom door. She could see his reflection, the cool gravity of his expression, the dark brilliance of his assessing gaze.

Colour stained Polly's cheeks but she managed to laugh. 'For goodness' sake,' she said with determined lightness, 'there's no need for an apology. It was just a kiss...no big deal!'

Something bright flared in his dark eyes and then they were veiled, his sensual mouth curling slightly. '*Bueno*. I wondered if you would like to have lunch out today?'

In surprise, Polly swivelled round, all constraint put to flight by that unexpected but very welcome suggestion that she might return to the outside world for a few hours. 'I'd love to!'

In the foyer they ran into Janice Grey.

'Oh, dear, were you coming to visit me?' Polly muttered with a dismay made all the more pungent by a guilty sense of relief. 'I'm so sorry. I'm afraid we're going out for lunch.'

'That does surprise me.' Janice raised an enquiring brow. 'I understood you were here to rest.'

'I'm under the strictest instructions to see that she doesn't overtire herself, Mrs Grey,' Raul interposed with a coolly pleasant smile. 'I'm also grateful to have the opportunity to thank you for all the support you have given Polly in recent weeks.'

The middle-aged blonde gave him a thin smile and turned to Polly. 'Henry said that you weren't coming back to stay with us.' She then shot Raul an arch look that didn't conceal her hostility. 'Do I hear wedding bells in the air?'

Polly paled, and then hot, mortified colour flooded her cheeks. The silence simmered.

Raul stepped calmly into the breach. 'I'm sure Polly will keep you in touch with events, Mrs Grey.

'A tough cookie,' Raul remarked of the older woman as he settled Polly into the limousine a few minutes later. 'I'm relieved that you didn't choose to confide in her about our legal agreement. But why the hell did you look so uncomfortable?'

Polly thought of those crazy weeks in Vermont, when she had foolishly allowed herself to be wildly, recklessly in love with Raul. Her imagination had known no limits when every moment she could she'd tried to forget the fact that she was pregnant. Those stupid girlish daydreams about marrying Raul were now a severe embarrassment to recall. She had to think fast to come up with another explanation for her discomfiture.

'Janice *was* kind to me...but she'd never have offered me a room if she hadn't known about my inheritance. She couldn't understand why I wasn't prepared to marry Henry for the sake of that money. She thought I was being very foolish and shortsighted.'

'You don't need to make a choice like that now. In any case, *gatita*...you're far too young to be thinking about marriage.'

An awkward little silence fell. Polly was very tense. She was already scolding herself for having reacted to Raul's invitation as if his only aim was to give her a pleasant outing. Raul did nothing without good reason. Over lunch, Raul was undoubtedly planning to open a serious discussion about their baby's future. The subject could not be avoided any longer, and this time she would try to be as calm and rational as possible.

'Waiting to hear what you're going to say makes me very nervous,' she nonetheless heard herself confide abruptly. 'I may be pregnant, but I'm not likely to pop off at the first piece of bad news. Do you think you could just tell me right now up front whether or not you're planning to take me to court after the baby's born?'

Raul sent her a shimmering glance, his mouth curling. 'Much good it would do me if I did have such plans. Although it seems very wrong to me, in this country I have no legal rights as the father of your child.'

'Honestly?' Polly surveyed him through very wide and surprised blue eyes. 'But what about the contract?'

'Forget the contract. It might as well not exist now. Do you seriously think that I would even want to take such a personal and private matter into a courtroom?'

'I never thought of that,' Polly admitted, suddenly feeling quite weak with the strength of her relief. 'I just had nightmares about being extradited to the USA.'

An involuntary smile briefly curved Raul's lips. 'Force wouldn't work in a situation like this.'

Did he think that persuasion would? Polly worried about that idea. She knew that her own convictions ran so deep and strong he had no hope of changing her mind; she was determined to keep her baby. But she was burdened by the increasingly guilty awareness that that wasn't very fair to Raul, and that some way, somehow, they had to find a compromise that would be bearable for them both.

Yet where could they possibly find that compromise? Raul had chosen surrogacy because he wanted a child, but not a child he had to share in a conventional relationship. Raul had opted for a detached, businesslike arrangement without strings. But no matter what happened now he had no hope of acquiring sole custody of his own child. How could she not feel guilty about that?

Raul took her back to a luxury apartment in Mayfair. Polly felt intimidated by the grandeur of her surroundings. A light and exquisitely cooked lunch was served by a quiet and unobtrusive manservant. Throughout the meal, Raul chatted about his business trip to Paris. He was very entertaining, a sophisticated and amusing raconteur. But, while she laughed and smiled in response, all she could really think about was how easily he had fooled her with that charismatic polish in Vermont.

It meant nothing. It just meant he had terrific social skills. She had learned to read Raul well enough to recognise that essential detachment just beneath the surface, not to mention his smooth ability to avoid giving personal information. All those visits in Vermont and what had she picked up about him? That he had no close family alive, that he was a businessman who travelled a lot, and that he had been born in Venezuela. Precious little.

Raul ran hooded dark eyes over her abstracted face. 'I feel like you're not with me.'

'Perhaps I'm tired,' she said uncomfortably.

Instantly Raul thrust back his chair and rose lithely upright. 'Then you should lie down in one of the guest rooms for a while.'

'No...we need to talk,' Polly acknowledged tautly. 'I want to get that over with.'

Leaving the table, she settled down into a comfortable armchair. The coffee was served. Raul paced restively over to the window and then gazed across the room at her. 'Don't look so anxious...it makes me feel like a bully,' he admitted grimly.

Polly clutched her cup. 'You're not that,' she acknowledged fairly. 'You've been very patient and more understanding than I could ever have expected.'

Raul spread lean brown hands with an eloquence that never failed to engage her attention. 'I have a possible solution to this situation. Please hear me out,' he urged.

Tense as a bowstring, Polly sat very still.

'The biggest difference between us is that I planned to be a parent from the very outset of our association,' Raul delineated with measured clarity. 'But *you* did not. When you became pregnant you did not expect to take on permanent responsibility for that child.'

Polly nodded in wary, reluctant agreement.

'I think you're too young to handle becoming a single parent. I understand that you have become attached to the baby, and that you are naturally very concerned about its future well-being. But if you choose to keep the baby you will have to sacrifice the freedom that most young women of your age take for granted.'

Polly gave him a stubborn look. 'I know that. I'm not

stupid. And I'm hardly likely to miss what I've never had—'

'But you *could* have that freedom now. You should be making plans to return to university to complete your degree,' Raul told her steadily. 'If you let me take my child back to Venezuela, I will allow you access visits, regular reports, photographs. I will agree to any reasonable request. My child will know you as his mother but you will not be the primary carer.'

Raul had taken her very much by surprise. Polly hadn't expected such a willingness to compromise from a male to whom she sensed 'compromise' was an unfamiliar word. On his terms, she guessed it was a very generous offer. He was offering to share their child to some extent, and that was a lot more than she had anticipated.

'I believe every child deserves two parents,' she responded awkwardly. 'Two parents on the spot.'

'That's impossible.'

'I was brought up by my father, and there wasn't a day I didn't long for my mother.'

'This child may be a boy.'

'I don't think that makes any difference. Because of my own experiences, I couldn't face being parted from my child. Whatever it takes, I need to *be* there for my baby and do the very best I can to be a good mother.' Polly was very tense as she struggled to verbalise her own deepest feelings. 'And, yes, it is a very great pity that I didn't work that out before I signed that contract…but my only excuse is that I honestly didn't even begin to understand how I would feel once I was actually pregnant.'

'That's in the past now. We need to concentrate on the present.' With that rather deflating assurance, Raul flung back his darkly handsome head, his dark eyes formidable in their penetration. 'If you really mean what you say when you protest that you intend to be the very best mother you can be…then you must move to Venezuela.'

'*Venezuela?*' Polly exclaimed, wildly disconcerted at

having that stunning suggestion flung at her in cool challenge.

'I will set you up in a house there. You will have every comfort and convenience, and your child as well.'

Polly blinked, still attempting to absorb a staggering proposition that entailed moving to the other side of the world. 'I *couldn't*—'

'*Por Dios*...ask yourself if you are being fair. If the child needs his mother, then he also needs his father. And that child will inherit everything I possess.' Raul spelt out that reminder with imperious pride and impatience.

'Money isn't everything, Raul—'

'Don't be facile. I'm talking about a way of life that you have not the slightest conception of,' Raul returned very drily, watching her flush. 'At least be practical, Polly. My child needs to know that Venezuelan heritage, the language, the people, the culture. If you won't come to Venezuela, what am I to do? With the claims on my time, I can't possibly visit the UK often enough to form a close relationship with my child.'

Polly tried to picture living in Venezuela, with Raul picking up all her bills, walking in and out of her life with one blonde babe girlfriend after another and eventually taking a wife. No matter how he might feel now, she was convinced that he would succumb to matrimony sooner or later. In such a situation she would always be an outsider, an interloper, neither family nor friend, and a lot of people would simply assume that she was his discarded mistress. She knew she would never be able to cope with such a dependent, humiliating existence on the fringe of Raul's world. She needed to get on with her own life. It was time to be honest about that reality.

'Raul...I want to stay in the UK with my baby. I don't want to live in Venezuela, having you oversee every move I make,' Polly admitted, watching him bridle in apparent disbelief at that statement. 'You have the right to be involved in your child's future...but what you seem to forget

is that that future is *my* life as well! Anyway, you may not
think it now, but some day you'll get married, have other
children—'

Raul released his breath in a charged hiss of frustration.
'I would sooner be dead than married!'

'But you see...I *don't* feel the same way,' Polly shared
with rueful honesty. 'I would like to think that even as an
unmarried mum I will get married eventually.'

'Saying that to me is the equivalent of blackmail, Polly,'
Raul condemned, pale with anger beneath his golden skin,
eyes hot as sunlight in that lean, dark, devastating face. 'I
do not want *any* other man involved in my child's upbringing!'

Temper stirred in Polly, and the more she thought about
that blunt and unashamed declaration the angrier she became. Did Raul really believe that he had the right to demand that she live like a nun for the next twenty years?
Lonely, unloved, celibate. She stared at him. Yes, that was
what he believed and what he wanted, if he was not to have
sole custody of their child.

Raising herself out of the armchair, Polly straightened
her slight shoulders and stood up. 'You are so *incredibly*
selfish and spoilt!' she accused fiercely.

Astonished by that sudden indictment, Raul strode across
the room, closing the distance between them. 'I can't believe that you can dare to say that to me—'

'I expect not...as you've already told me, you're accustomed to people who want to please you, who are eager to
tell you only what you want to hear!' Polly shot back with
unconcealed scorn. 'Well, I'm *not* one of those people!'

His eyes blazed. 'I have bent over backwards to be
fair—'

'At what *personal* sacrifice and inconvenience?' Polly
slung back, trembling with rage. 'You are a playboy with
a reputation as a womaniser. You enjoy your freedom,
don't you?'

'Why shouldn't I?' Raul was unmoved by that angle of

attack. 'I don't lie to the women who pass through my life. I don't promise true love or permanency—'

'Because you've never *had* to, have you? You know, listening to you, Raul...I despise my own sex. But I despise you most of all,' Polly confessed, with hands knotting into furious fists by her side. 'It's one rule for you and another for me—a hypocritical sexist double standard the belongs in the Prehistoric ages with Neanderthals like you! You say you want this child, but you didn't want a child badly enough to make a commitment like other men, did you? And what do you offer me—?'

'The only two possible remedies to the mess we're now in. I'm not about to apologise because you do not like the imperfect sound of reality,' Raul delivered with slashing bite.

'Reality? You call it "reality" to offer me a choice between giving up my child almost completely...and living like a *nun* in Venezuela?'

Raul flicked her a grimly amused glance. 'You want the licence to sleep around?'

'You know very well that's not what I'm trying to say!'

'But you wouldn't want me to share your bed without all that idealistic love, commitment and permanency jazz...would you, *querida*?' Raul breathed with sizzling golden eyes, watching her freeze in shock at that plunge into the more intimate and personal. 'You see, what you want and what I want we can't have, because we both want something different!'

Every scrap of colour drained from Polly's face. 'I *don't* want you...like that,' she framed jerkily.

Raul cast her a glittering appraisal that was all male and all-knowing. 'Oh, yes, you do...that sexual hunger has been there between us from the moment we met.'

Polly backed away from him. She could not cope with having his knowledge of her attraction to him thrown in her teeth. 'No—'

'I didn't take advantage of you because I knew it would end in your tears.'

'Don't kid yourself…I might've ditched you first!' Polly told him with very real loathing, her pride so wounded she wanted to kill him. 'And let me tell you something else too, I put a much higher price on myself than your interchangeable blonde babes do.'

'I admire that…I really do,' Raul incised with complete cool, his temper back under wraps again at disorientating, galling speed. 'You have such rigid moral values, *gatita*. Well, warned in advance, I was careful to keep my distance in Vermont.'

Polly shuddered with a rage that was out of control, a rage that had its roots in pain and violent resentment. She was shattered by the sudden ripping down of the careful barriers that had made it possible for them to skim along the surface of their complex relationship. Without those barriers, and shorn by Raul of all face-saving defences, she was flailing wildly.

A look of positive loathing written in her furious eyes, she snapped, 'Then you'll have no problem understanding that the only way you'll ever get me to Venezuela…the only way you'll *ever* achieve full custody of your child…is to marry me, Raul!'

A silence fell between them like a giant black hole, waiting to entrap the unwary.

Raul was now formidably still, brilliant dark eyes icy with incredulity. 'That's not funny, Polly. Take it back.'

'Why? Do you want me to lie to you? Say I didn't mean it?' Polly demanded rawly as she tipped her head back, mahogany hair rippling back from her furiously flushed face. 'I'm being honest with you. If I stay here in the UK, I will get on with my life and you will *not* interfere with that life! I am not prepared to go to Venezuela as anything *other* than a wife!'

Raul sent her a derisive look that said he was unimpressed. 'You are not serious.'

Polly studied him with so much bitterness inside her she marvelled she didn't explode like a destructive weapon. 'I am. Let's see how good you are at making sacrifices when you expect *me* to sacrifice everything! Why? Because I'm not rich and powerful like you? Or because I'm going to be the mother of your child and you have this weird idea that a decent mother has no entitlement to any life of her own?'

Raul jerked as if she had struck him, a feverish flush slowly darkening his hard cheekbones.

This time the silence that fell screamed with menace.

A tiny pulse flickered at the whitened edge of his fiercely compressed mouth. His hands had closed into fists, betraying his struggle for self-command. But, most frightening of all for Polly, for the very first time Raul stared back at her with very real hatred. Cold, hard, deadly loathing. And, in shock, Polly fell silent, mind turning blank, all the fight and anger draining from her, leaving only fear in their place.

'I'll take you back to the clinic,' Raul drawled with raw finality. 'There is no point in allowing this offensive dialogue to continue.'

CHAPTER FOUR

Two days later, Polly was still recovering from the effects of that catastrophic lunch out.

But her mind was briefly removed from her own problems when she picked up a magazine dated from the previous month and learnt that her childhood friend, Maxie Kendall, had got married, indeed had already been married for several weeks. Maxie and her husband, Angelos Petronides, had kept their marriage a secret until they were ready to make a public announcement. Polly read the article and scrutinised the photos with great interest, and a pleased smile on Maxie's behalf.

She had last met Maxie at the reading of Nancy Leeward's will. Her godmother had actually had three goddaughters, Polly and Maxie and Darcy. Although the girls had been close friends well into their teens, their adult lives had taken them in very different directions.

Maxie had become a famous model, with a tangled love life in London. Darcy had been a single parent, who rarely left her home in Cornwall. Polly had tried to keep in touch with both women but regular contact had gradually lapsed, not least because Darcy and Maxie were no longer friends.

'Isn't she gorgeous?' one of the nurses groaned in admiration, looking over her shoulder at the main picture of Maxie on the catwalk. 'I would give my eye teeth to look like that!'

'Who wouldn't?' Polly's smile of amused agreement slid away as she found herself reflecting that Maxie closely resembled what appeared to be Raul's ideal of a sexually attractive woman. Tall, blonde and stunning. And here she was, a five-foot-one-inch-tall, slightly built brunette, who had never looked glamorous in her life.

She grimaced, still angry and bitter about the options Raul had laid before her with a cruel air of understanding generosity. If she lived until she was ninety she would not forget her crushing sense of humiliation when Raul had dragged her attraction to him out into the open and squashed her already battered pride.

In Vermont, Raul had evidently seen her susceptibility and quite deliberately steered clear of encouraging her. That awareness now made her feel about a foot high. She had honestly believed that she hadn't betrayed herself, had fondly imagined that she had managed to match his cool and casual manner. She had deliberately avoided every temptation to do otherwise, biting her tongue many, many times in his presence.

She had always left it to him to say when or if he was coming again, had never once complained when he didn't show up, had never attempted to pry into his private life. And, boy, had she been wasting her time in trying to play it cool, she thought now in severe mortification. Raul had been ahead of her. 'Sexual hunger', he had called it! How gallant of him to pretend that he had been tempted too, because she didn't believe that—indeed, not for one second *could* she believe that!

And now she blamed Raul even more bitterly for her own painful misconceptions during that time. Why hadn't he mentioned the existence of other women in his life? Even the most casual reference to another relationship would have put her on her guard. But, no, Raul had been content to allow her to imagine whatever she liked. That had been safer than an honesty that might have made her question his true motive for seeking out her company.

So Raul needn't think that she was going to apologise for telling him that a wedding ring was the only thing likely to persuade her to move to Venezuela. It had been the honest truth. She hadn't expected him to like that truth, or even pause for a second to consider marriage as a possible option to their problem, but she *had* wanted to shock him just as he had shocked her, she conceded uncomfortably.

Yet the raw hostility and dislike she had aroused had not been a welcome result. In fact, his reaction had terrified her, and in retrospect even that annoyed her and filled her with shame. She had to learn to deal with Raul on an impersonal basis.

Raul arrived that evening while she was lying on the sofa watching the film *Pretty Woman*. He strode in at the bit where the heroine was fanning out a selection of condoms for the hero's benefit. Shooting the screen a darkling glance, he said with icy derision, 'I've never understood how a whore could figure as a romantic lead!'

Polly almost fell on the coffee table in her eagerness to grab up the remote control and switch the television off. Hot-cheeked, she looked at him then. He had never seemed more remote: fabulous bone structure taut, lean features cool, his dark and formal business suit somehow increasing his aspect of chilling detachment.

Eyes as black and wintry as a stormy night assailed hers. 'I've applied for a special licence. We'll get married here in forty-eight hours.'

In the act of lifting herself from the sofa, Polly's arms lost their strength and crumpled at the elbows. She toppled back onto the sofa again, a look of complete astonishment fixed to her startled face. 'Say that again—'

'You have made it clear that you will not accept any other option,' Raul drawled flatly.

'But I never expected.... I mean, f-for goodness' sake, Raul,' Polly stammered in severe shock. 'We *can't* just—'

'Can't we? Are you about to change your mind? Are you now prepared to consider allowing me to take my child back home with me?' Raul shot at her.

'No!' she gasped.

'Are you willing to try living in Venezuela on any other terms?'

'No, but—'

'Then don't waste my time with empty protests. You have, after all, just got exactly what you wanted,' Raul informed her icily.

'Not if you feel like this about it,' Polly protested unevenly. 'And it isn't what I precisely wanted—'

'Isn't it? Are you now telling me that you *don't* want me?'

Polly flushed to the roots of her hair, still very sensitive on that subject. 'I… I—'

'If I were you, I wouldn't argue on that point,' Raul warned, a current of threatening steel in his rich, accented drawl. 'In the space of one minute, I could make you eat your words!'

Already in shock, as she was, that level of blunt assurance reduced Polly to writhing discomfiture, but she still said, 'When I mentioned marriage, I didn't mean it as a serious possibility—'

'No, you laid it out as the ultimate price, the ultimate sacrifice.' Raul's hard sensual mouth twisted. 'And I'll get used to the idea. It will be a marriage of convenience, nothing more. I won't allow my child to grow up without me. I also hope I'm not so prejudiced that I can't concede that having both a mother and a father may well be better for the child.'

In a daze of conflicting feelings, Polly muttered, 'But what about…*us*?'

'That baby is the only thing that should matter to either of us. Why should he or she pay the price for this fiasco?'

That was a telling point for Polly. She bowed her head, guilty conscience now in full sway. Only she still couldn't prevent herself from muttering, 'I expected to marry someone who loved me—'

'I didn't expect to marry at all,' Raul traded, without an ounce of sympathy.

'I'll have to think this over—'

'No, you won't. You'll give me your answer now. I'm not in the mood for prima donna tactics!'

Polly experienced a powerful urge to tell him to get lost. And then she thought about being married to Raul, and other, infinitely stronger emotions swamped her. Over time they could work at building up a reasonable relationship, she told herself. They would have the baby to share. Surely their child would help to bring them together? And, all false pride laid aside, Polly was suddenly agonisingly conscious that she would do just about anything to at least have that chance with Raul. If she didn't make that leap of faith now, there would be no second opportunity.

'I'll marry you,' she murmured tautly.

'Muy bien.' Raul consulted his watch with disturbing cool. 'I'm afraid I can't stay. I have a dinner engagement.'

'Raul...?'

He turned back from the door.

Polly swallowed hard. 'You can *live* with this option?' she prompted anxiously.

His sudden blazing smile took her completely by surprise, and yet inexplicably left her feeling more chilled than reassured. 'Of course.... I only hope you're equally adaptable.'

Two days later, Polly, clad in a simple white cotton dress, waited in her room for Raul to arrive.

Rod Bevan had told her that he had suggested the courtyard garden for the wedding ceremony, but Raul had apparently wanted a more private setting. Something quick that wouldn't interfere with his busy schedule too much or attract the attention of others, Polly had gathered rather sourly. It was hard to believe that this was her wedding day. No flowers, no guests, nothing that might be construed as an attempt to celebrate the event. Had she been out of her mind to agree to marry Raul?

She had tossed and turned half the night, worrying about that. Absently she rubbed at the nagging ache in the small of her back. It had begun annoying her around dawn, presumably because she'd been lying in an awkward position. She felt like a water melon, huge and ungainly. She felt sorry for herself. She felt tearful. She felt that she might well be on the brink of making the biggest mistake of her life.

But Raul himself had put it in a nutshell for her. They were putting the baby first, and this way their baby would have two parents. That was very important to Polly, and she had with constant piety reminded herself of that crucial fact. There was just one cloud on the horizon…a cloud that got bigger and blacker every time her conscience stole an uneasy glance at it.

Raul didn't *want* to marry her. He had made no attempt to pretend otherwise. The occasional flash of sanity told Polly that that was all wrong, totally unacceptable as a basis even for a marriage of convenience. But what was the alternative? Polly couldn't see *any* alternative. Only marriage could give them both an equal share of their child.

She stretched awkwardly, and used her fingers to massage the base of her spine. At that moment, Raul strode in.

'*Dios*…let's get this over with as quickly as possible,' Raul urged impatiently as he reached down a strong hand to enclose hers and help her up off the sofa.

Thirty seconds later Rod Bevan arrived, accompanied by two other men. One was the registrar who would perform the ceremony, the other Raul introduced as his lawyer, Digby Carson. The service was very brief. When it was over, everybody shook hands and everybody smiled—with the exception of Raul. His cool impassivity didn't yield or melt for a second.

In the midst of an increasingly awkward conversation, a sharp, tightening sensation formed around Polly's abdomen. A stifled gasp was wrenched from her.

'What's wrong?' Raul demanded, anxiety flaring in his stunning dark eyes.

'I think we'd better forget the coffee and the scones,'

Rod Bevan concluded with a rueful smile as he showed the other two men out.

While he was doing that, Raul scooped Polly up in his arms and laid her down gently on the bed. The impassive look had vanished. His lean, proud face was full of concern. 'The baby's not due for another two weeks,' he told her tautly.

'Babies have their own schedule, Raul. I'd say this one has a pretty good sense of timing,' Rod asserted cheerfully.

'I'll stay with you, Polly,' Raul swore.

'No, you will not!' Polly exclaimed in instantaneous rejection. 'I don't want you with me!'

'I'd like to see my baby born,' Raul murmured intently, staring down at her with all the expectancy his powerful personality could command.

Dumbly she shook her head, tears of embarrassment pricking her eyes. She could not imagine sharing anything that intimate with a man she hadn't even shared a bedroom with.

As he rang the bell for a nurse, she heard the consultant say something in Spanish. Raul's response was quiet, but perceptibly edged by harshness. The door thudded shut on his departure.

'He's furious!' Polly suddenly sobbed, torn by both resentment and an odd, stabbing sense of sharp regret.

'No…he's *hurt*,' the older man contradicted, patting her clenched fingers soothingly. 'For a male as squeamish as Raul, that was one hell of a generous offer!'

Polly gazed down in drowsy fascination at her baby and fell head-over-heels in love for the second time in her life. He was gorgeous. He had fine, silky black hair and big dark eyes, and a cry that seemed to be attached by some invisible string to her heart. He looked so small to her, but the midwife had said he was big—a whole ten pounds one ounce worth of bouncing, healthy baby.

As the nurse settled him into the crib, Raul appeared with

Rod Bevan. Although medication had left Polly feeling sleepily afloat, and incapable of much in the way of thought or speech, she stared at Raul in surprise. His darkly handsome features were strained, his expressive mouth taut, his eyes shadowed. His tie was missing, the jacket of his suit crumpled and his white shirt open at his strong brown throat.

'What's wrong?' Polly asked worriedly.

Broodingly, Raul surveyed his sleeping son and thrust a not quite steady hand through his already rumpled black hair. 'He's wonderful,' he breathed with ragged appreciation. 'But supremely indifferent to the danger he put you in!'

The consultant absorbed Polly's frown of incomprehension. 'Raul equates a Caesarean section with a near death experience,' he explained with gentle satire as he took his leave in the nurse's wake.

Faint colour overlaid Raul's blunt cheekbones. He studied Polly's weary face and frowned darkly. He reached for her hand and coiled long fingers warmly round hers. 'I wasn't prepared for surgical intervention...why didn't you warn me?'

Polly slowly shook her head.

'Rod tells me you've known for months that the baby would probably have to be delivered that way,' Raul persisted.

'It's quite common,' Polly managed to slur, her eyelids feeling as if they had weights driving them downward.

'You're so tiny,' Raul muttered almost fiercely. 'I should've thought—'

'Bit late now,' Polly incised with drowsy wit.

'My son is beautiful,' Raul murmured. 'At least we got something right.'

'*Our*...son,' she mumbled.

'We'll call him Rodrigo—'

She winced.

'Jorge?'

She pulled a face.

'Emilio?'

She sighed.

'Luis?'

A faint, drowsy smile curved her lips.

'Luis…Zaforteza,' Raul sounded thoughtfully.

Polly went to sleep.

Polly studied the four confining walls of her room and
smiled. Tomorrow she was leaving the clinic. Her smile
faded, her eyes apprehensive. They were to spend a couple
of days in Raul's apartment and then fly to Venezuela.
Pulling on a luxurious thin silk wrap, she left her room.
Every day Luis went to the nursery for a while to allow
her to rest. Repossessing her son had become the highlight
of her afternoon.

A slight frown line drew her brows together. The day
Luis was born, Raul had seemed so concerned for her, so
approachable, she reflected ruefully. But over the past five
days the barriers had gone up again.

Raul's fascination with his son was undeniable. Yet what
she had believed might bring them closer together seemed
instead to have pushed them further apart. Why was it that
when Raul visited she often felt like a superfluous but extremely well-paid extra? Was it the fact that Raul never
came through the door without some outrageously extravagant gift, which he carelessly bestowed on her in the manner of a rather superior customer bestowing a tip?

Day one, a diamond bracelet. Day two, a half-dozen sets
of luxurious nightwear. Day three, a watch from Cartier.
Day four, a magnificent diamond ring. It had become embarrassing. Raul was rich. Raul was now her husband. But
it felt very strange to be receiving such lavish presents from
a male so cool and distant he never touched her in even
the smallest way.

As she turned the corner into the corridor where the
nursery was, Polly was dismayed to see Raul talking with

Digby Carson outside the viewing window. Neither man having heard her slippered approach, she ducked into an alcove out of sight. She was too self-conscious to join them when she was so lightly clad, and was thoroughly irritated that vanity had made her set aside her more sedate but shabby dressing gown.

'So how do you feel about this…er…development?' the older man was saying quietly, only yards away from her ignominious hiding place.

'Deliriously happy, Digby.'

'Seriously, Raul—'

'That was sarcasm, not humour, Digby. My little bride is much smarter than the average gold-digger,' Raul breathed with stinging bitterness. 'She used my son as a bargaining chip to blackmail me into marriage!'

Rigid with shock at that condemnation, Polly pushed her shoulders back against the cool wall to keep herself upright.

'But whatever happens now I will keep my son,' Raul completed with harsh conviction.

There was a buzzing sound in Polly's ears. She heard the older man say something but she couldn't pick out the words. Dizzily, she shook her head as the voices seemed to recede. When she finally peered out, the corridor was empty again.

Without even thinking about what she was doing, she fled back to the privacy of her room. A gold-digger…a blackmailer. Trembling with stricken disbelief at having heard herself described in such terms, Polly folded down on the bed, no longer sure her wobbly knees would support her.

The pain went deep and then deeper still. Raul despised her. *'Whatever happens now I will keep my son.'* A cold, clammy sensation crawled down Polly's spine. What had he meant by that? And this was the husband she was hoping to make a new life with in Venezuela? A husband who obviously loathed and resented her? In her turmoil, only one fact seemed clear. She could no longer trust Raul…and she couldn't possibly risk taking her son to Venezuela without that trust.

Minutes later, a nurse wheeled in Luis's crib. Seeing Polly already wearing her wrap and slippers, she smiled. 'I see you were just about to come and collect him. Your husband said you were still asleep when he looked in on you earlier, but I know you like to feed Luis yourself.'

Alone with her child again, Polly drew in a shivering, steadying breath. Fear still etched in her shaken eyes, she gazed down at her son's innocent little face, and then she got up in sudden decision.

From the cabinet by the bed she extracted her address book. Leafing frantically through it, she found the phone number her friend Maxie had insisted on giving her when they had parted after the reading of Nancy Leeward's will. 'Liz always knows where I am,' she had promised.

Using the phone by the bed, Polly rang Liz Blake. As soon as the older woman had established who she was, she passed on Maxie's number. When she heard Maxie's familiar husky voice answering her call, Polly felt weak with relief.

'It's Polly…' she muttered urgently. 'Maxie, I need somewhere to stay…'

An hour after that conversation, having left a note of explanation addressed to Raul, Polly walked out of the clinic with Luis in her arms and climbed into the taxi waiting outside. The receptionist was too busy checking in new patients to notice her quiet exit.

CHAPTER FIVE

POLLY wheeled the stroller in from the roof garden. Threading back her spectacular mane of blonde hair with a manicured hand, Maxie Petronides bent to look in at a warmly-clothed Luis and exclaimed, 'He's so cute I could steal him!'

Polly surveyed her sleeping son with loving eyes. He was four weeks old and he got more precious with every passing day. Remorsefully aware that Raul was being deprived of their son, she had twice sent brief letters containing photos of Luis to Rod Bevan at the clinic, knowing he would pass them on.

The fabulous penthouse flat which she was looking after belonged to Maxie and her husband, Angelos, who used an even more spacious central London apartment. Polly was acting as caretaker for the property while the floors below were transformed into similar luxury dwellings. When the work was complete, Angelos Petronides would put the building on the market with the penthouse as a show home.

'So how are *you* feeling?' Maxie prompted over the coffee that Polly had made.

'Guilty,' Polly confessed ruefully, but she forced a smile, determined not to reveal the real extent of her unhappiness. Every time Raul came into her mind, she forced him out again. He had no business being there. He had *never* had any business being there. Learning to think of Raul only in relation to Luis was a priority.

'You shouldn't be feeling like that,' Maxie reproved. 'You needed this time alone to sort yourself out. This last year, you've been through an awful lot.'

'And made some even more *awful* mistakes,' Polly

71

stressed with a helpless grimace. 'I shouldn't have married Raul. It was incredibly selfish and unfair. I *still* don't know what got into me!'

'Love has a lot to answer for. Sometimes you get so bitter and furious, you want to hit back hard,' Maxie proffered, disconcerting Polly with the depth of her understanding. 'And that just creates more strife. It's only when it all gets too much that you suddenly simmer down and come to your senses.'

'I wish I'd hit that point *before* I married Raul,' Polly muttered wretchedly.

'But Raul has made mistakes too,' Maxie contended firmly. 'He's also sent out some very confusing messages about exactly what he wants from you. But if you're honest with him when you contact him again, it should take some of the heat out of the situation.'

Polly tried to imagine telling Raul that she loved him and just cringed. Some excuse to give a man for forcing him into marrying her! That *was* what she had done, she acknowledged now. And admitting that even to herself still appalled her. But, whether she liked it or not, Raul had had grounds to accuse her of using their son to blackmail him into marriage. That wasn't what she had intended, but that, in his eyes, had been the end result.

In the clinic she had brooded over the hurt and humiliation Raul had carelessly inflicted in Vermont. If she had never seen Raul again she would have got over him eventually, but being forced into such regular contact with him again had plunged her right back into emotional turmoil. She'd been too proud to face up to her continuing feelings for him...a woman scorned? She shuddered at that demeaning label. Whatever, she had been stubbornly blind to what was going on inside her own head.

She had still been so bitterly angry with Raul. Instead of putting those dangerous emotions behind her, before trying to seriously consider their son's future, she had let herself glory in them that day at his apartment. Admittedly, Raul had provoked her with his refusal to even allow that she might be entitled to a life of her own. But marriage would only have been a viable alternative if Raul had been a willing bridegroom.

On their wedding day she had also become a new mother. That in itself would have been quite enough to cope with, but Raul's subsequent behaviour had increased her anxiety about what their future together might hold. That overheard conversation had pushed the misgivings she had been trying to repress and ignore out into the open.

'Initially Angelos wasn't that fussed about getting married either,' Maxie confessed, taking Polly by surprise.

'Did he ever say he would sooner be dead than married?'

'Well, no…'

Of course not. Angelos was besotted with his wife. And Maxie was besotted with her husband. But then Maxie was gorgeous, Polly reflected wryly, and naturally physical attraction had initially brought the couple together. Angelos hadn't looked at Maxie and thought, I *like* her…she'd make a good surrogate mother. So why on earth had she tried to make a comparison?

After Maxie's visit, Polly spent the rest of the day being extremely conscious of the presence of every phone in the apartment. She knew it was time to get in touch with Raul direct. It was now over three weeks since she had left the clinic on a surging tide of rage, pain and fear after hearing Raul's opinion of her. But as that anger had subsided she had gradually come to appreciate that Raul had more right to be bitter than she had initially been prepared to admit.

And at least she now knew what had to be done about the situation, she reflected while she showered in the palatial *en suite* bathroom off the master bedroom. She was ready to humbly acknowledge her mistake, ready to talk to Raul about having their ill-judged marriage annulled. That would put them right back where they had started, but surely it would at least eradicate Raul's hostility? Fearful of the response she was likely to receive, it was after nine that evening when she finally dialled the number Raul had given her weeks earlier in the clinic.

'It's Polly…'

Silence buzzed on the line, and then she heard some background noise she couldn't identify. 'Raul?' she queried uncertainly.

'I heard you,' Raul finally responded, the dark, rich timbre of his accented drawl washing over her with a familiarity that almost hurt. 'Where are you?'

'I thought we should clear the air on the phone first,' Polly admitted tautly. 'Did you get my note?'

'Three pages isn't exactly a "note".'

'I was very upset when I heard you talking about me like that,' Polly admitted tightly.

'I did get that message. But I was letting off steam that day. It never occurred to me that I'd be overheard.'

Polly relaxed slightly.

'Tell me about my son,' Raul urged.

'Could you…could you just once manage to say *our* son?'

'That would be difficult.'

'Why?' Polly pressed.

'"Our" suggests sharing…and right at this minute you are not sharing anything with me,' Raul traded.

Polly paled, but she still coiled round the phone as if it was a fire on an icy night. 'I didn't mean…I didn't *plan* to push you into a marriage you didn't want,' she told him unsteadily.

'You just accidentally fell into that wedding ring, *gatita*?'

Polly turned pink, scrutinising the narrow gold band where it sat in prominent isolation on the coffee table, removed the same day she'd faced up to the fact that it was the symbol of a farce. 'Where are you?'

'In my car…you were saying?' Raul prompted.

'We don't have to stay married!' Polly rushed to make

that point and redeem herself without touching on anything more intimate.

Silence greeted that leading statement.

Polly cleared her throat awkwardly in that interim. 'I suppose you're still very annoyed that I left the clinic...?' Her voice rose involuntarily, turning that sentence into a nervous question.

'It's possible...'

'All of a sudden I didn't feel I could trust you, and I felt trapped...I didn't think I had any alternative—but it was an impulsive decision—'

'You're distressingly prone to impulses, *gatita*,' Raul incised with sudden bite. 'And this dialogue is just irritating the hell out of me!'

The line went dead. With a frown, Polly shook the silent phone. Nothing. Taken aback that Raul should have cut off her call, Polly blinked and slowly straightened. The silence of the apartment enclosed her. Only one soft pool of lamplight illuminated the corner of the big lounge.

Rising, she smoothed down her satin and lace nightgown and went to check on Luis. He was sound asleep, but he was due for a feed soon. In the elegant kitchen she tidied up the remains of her supper and prepared a bottle for Luis. All the time she was doing that, she agonised over that conversation with Raul. He had sounded so strange. Strained, wary, then bitingly angry.

The doorbell went, making her jump and then as quickly relax again. Maxie was her only visitor, and Maxie had called in one other evening, when Angelos had had a business dinner. Polly hurried across the octagonal hall. Without bothering to use the intercom, she hit the release button on the security lock which barred access to the private lift in the underground car park.

Then she stilled with a frown. Why would Maxie come to see her twice in one day? Only if there was something wrong! Running an apprehensive hand through the fall of her mahogany hair, Polly waited impatiently. It seemed ages before she heard the low, distant hum of the approaching lift, then the soft ping as it reached the top floor. The doors purred back.

But it was *not* Maxie; it was Raul who strode out of the lift.

Polly went into startled retreat, aghast eyes pinned to his intimidatingly tall and powerfully male physique.

Scathing dark-as-night eyes flashed into hers. '*Dios mio*…you deserve a bloody good fright!' Raul informed her wrathfully. 'All that high tec security and you don't even *check* who your visitor is before you invite him up?'

In shock, Polly felt her teeth chatter together. 'I…I just assumed it was Maxie—'

'Don't you have any sense? I could've been a rapist, or a robber, and I bet you're alone in this apartment!'

Swallowing hard, Polly gave a jerky nod, her attention fully locked to him. He looked spectacular in a fabulous silver-grey suit, cut to enhance every sleek, muscular angle of his wide-shouldered, lean-hipped and long-legged frame. As her shaken gaze ran over him, her stomach flipped and her mouth ran dry. His magnetic dark good looks were like a visual assault on senses starved of him.

'How…how did you find out where I was?' Her bewilderment was unconcealed.

Raul's wide mouth curled with impatience. 'Once I had your phone number, it was a piece of cake to get the address. Why do you think I kept you on the line for so long?'

Since Polly hadn't been conscious until the end of that call that anyone but her had been controlling anything, she gulped.

'Angelos Petronides will answer to me for this,' Raul breathed with sudden chilling conviction, lean, strong face forbidding.

'Angelos… Maxie's husband? You *know* him?' Polly exclaimed in surprise.

'Of course I know him, and he owns this building. Here you are on Petronides ground. I thought better of Angelos.

I didn't think he'd get involved in hiding my wife from me, but now that he *has*—'

'No, he hasn't!' Polly protested vehemently. 'I've never even met Maxie's husband! I asked her to help me find somewhere to stay and she brought me here—said they needed someone to look after the place. Maxie's certainly not aware that you know Angelos. And, as I asked her to be discreet, she's only told Angelos that she has an old friend staying here for a while…'

As her voice faltered to a halt, she experienced the feeling that she had already lost Raul's full attention. As his dark golden gaze roamed over her scantily clad figure, Polly suddenly became intensely conscious of the revealing nature of her nightgown, the delicate straps which exposed her bare shoulders, the sheer lace covering her breasts, the light, clinging fabric which outlined her once-again-slim hips and slender thighs for his appraisal.

As the silence which had seemed to come out of nowhere pulsed, Polly felt her breasts swell with languorous heaviness. Her nipples pinched tight, as if a current of fire had touched them. As she folded her arms over herself in mortified discomfiture, she snapped, 'Has anybody ever told you that it's very rude to stare?'

The silence lay still and impenetrable as glass.

And then Raul flung his darkly handsome head back and laughed with a rich spontaneity that shook Polly. Laughter put to flight his gravity, throwing his innate charisma to the fore. Her heart lurched. She tried to give him a reproving look, needing him to show her a mood she recognised and stay in it long enough for her to respond accordingly. But at that moment she was like a novice actress without a script and unable to improvise.

'You've gone from voluptuously ripe and enticing to sinfully, sexily slender,' Raul murmured with husky amusement. 'And you think it's *rude* that I should stare at my own wife?'

A deep flush lit Polly's fair skin. She didn't know where

to look, but was pretty sure she was not going to look back at him while he was saying things like that. *Sinfully, sexily slender?* Now she knew what Maxie had meant when she had criticised Raul for giving her conflicting messages. An impersonal and detached relationship had to have firm boundaries. Raul had been both impersonal and detached after their wedding, politely concerned that she should be comfortable and content, but nothing more. He had made no attempt to behave like a normal husband who had a relationship with the mother of his child.

And then Polly called herself an idiot. Here she was, wondering why Raul was behaving so strangely! But wouldn't most men react differently to a woman standing around half-naked in front of them? Hot colour flooded her cheeks at that obvious explanation.

'I'll go and put something on and then we can talk,' Polly muttered in a rush.

'Let me see Luis first,' Raul countered, moving closer to catch her hand and check her before she could move.

'You're not still annoyed with Maxie's husband, are you?' Polly asked anxiously as she took him down the corridor.

'I have a certain tolerance for a man plunged unsuspecting into an embarrassing situation by his bride,' Raul imparted wryly. 'Angelos is Greek, traditional as they come. He'd come down on his wife like a ton of bricks if he realised that she'd been helping to hide *my* wife and child from me!'

'It wasn't like that—'

'Only violence or abuse on my part would justify such interference between a man and his wife.'

Was that the third or the fourth time that Raul had referred to her as *his wife* in as many minutes? Polly thought abstractedly. After three weeks of telling herself that their marriage was a pathetic charade, it seemed so odd to have Raul referring to her in such terms.

'Raul...I really needed some time and space to think,' she murmured tautly.

Raul released her hand. 'You've had months to think without me around.'

But their relationship had changed radically in recent weeks, Polly wanted to protest in frustration as she watched him fluidly cross the elegant guest room to where Luis lay in his cradle. Their marriage had been one of reckless haste, entered into without proper consideration or adequate discussion.

She hadn't simply taken umbrage and run away; she had known that ultimately she would have to face Raul again and deal with the situation.

But in her distress and turmoil she had been in no fit state to confront a male who had a naturally domineering and powerful personality—and, worst of all, a male who had everything to gain from putting pressure on her to still accompany him to Venezuela. She had known she had to have time to think away from Raul before she decided what to do next.

Raul sent her a cool, assessing glance. 'I've known Digby all my life. What you heard was a private conversation with a friend. I imagine you and your friend Maxie have been less than charitable about me on at least *one* recent occasion...'

Unprepared for that embarrassingly accurate stab, Polly was betrayed by the burning wave of colour which swept up her throat.

'Exactly,' Raul purred with rich satisfaction, removing his attention from her to study his infant son, who was squirming into wakefulness. 'Do you see me getting all worked up about a fact of life? Could you see me writing three vitriolic pages and vanishing into thin air on such slender proof of intent as the mood of a moment?'

'No, but—'

'There is no "but",' Raul broke in with derision. 'Only

women behave like that. Rod thought it might be the baby blues, or some such thing! I knew better.'

'I was in the wrong...I should've confronted you,' Polly conceded tightly, heart-shaped face fixed in a mutinous expression, revealing the struggle it was to voice those words of contrition.

'Instead of throwing a tantrum on paper,' Raul emphasised, subjecting her to a hard, steady appraisal. 'Because I warn you now, I will never, ever allow you to be in a position again where you can use our son as a weapon against me.'

At that opportune moment, Luis mustered his lungs into a cross little cry for attention. Pale and taut now, in receipt of that menacing warning, Polly was grateful for the opportunity to turn away. But Raul reached his son first, sweeping him up with complete confidence. Smiling down at Luis, he talked to him in soft, soothing Spanish.

In the blink of an eye Raul had gone from that chilling threat to an unashamed display of tenderness with their son, Polly registered. That was the most intimidating thing to watch—the speed and ease with which he could switch emotional channels. Although there had been nothing emotional about his determination to tell her how he felt about her flight from the clinic. Cool, scornful, cutting.

'I'll get his bottle,' Polly muttered.

She skidded down to the bedroom to pull on a fluttering silk wrap first. When she returned to the dimly lit bedroom, Raul rose from the armchair to let her take a seat. He settled Luis into her arms and then hunkered lithely down to watch his son greedily satisfy his hunger.

'*Dios mío!* No wonder he's grown so much!'

Polly cleared her throat awkwardly. 'I want you to know that I would never use Luis as a weapon—'

'You already have,' Raul told her without hesitation, smoothing an astonishingly gentle hand over Luis's little head before vaulting upright again. 'In disputes between couples, the child is often a weapon. You should understand that as well as I do. When your parents' marriage broke up, your father kept you and your mother apart. Why? He was punishing her for leaving him for another man.'

Polly was astonished that he should still recall that much information about her background. 'I suppose he was,' she conceded as she got up to change Luis.

'Love turns to hatred so easily. It never lasts,' Raul murmured with supreme cynicism.

'It lasts for a lot of people,' Polly argued abstractedly, down on her knees and busily engaged in dealing with her son's needs. But she gathered courage from not being forced to meet Raul's often unsettling gaze. 'You know what I said on the phone earlier...about us not having to stay married?'

Having expected an immediate response to that reminder, Polly looked up in the resounding silence which followed.

Raul was staring back at her with penetrating and grim eyes. 'I do.'

'Look, why don't you wait in the lounge while I settle Luis?' Polly suggested uncomfortably.

A few minutes later, Luis was back in the cradle, snug and comfy and sleepy.

'I love you, you precious baby,' Polly whispered feelingly, not looking forward to the discussion she was about to open but convinced that Raul would be extremely relieved when she suggested that they have their marriage annulled.

As she entered the lounge, Raul swung round from the fireplace. 'I don't like this room. It's claustrophobic with that conservatory built over the windows,' he said with flat distaste. 'It's insane to close out such magnificent views!'

'Maxie's terrified of heights. That's why it's like that...' Polly hovered awkwardly. 'Raul—?'

'I'm not giving you a divorce,' Raul delivered before she could say another word.

Was he thinking angrily about the prospect of having to offer a divorce settlement? Did he imagine she was planning to make some greedy, gold-digging claim on his legendary wealth?

Polly reddened with annoyance at that suspicion. 'We don't need to go for a divorce. We can apply for an annulment and everything will be put right. It will be like this wretched marriage of ours never happened.'

Raul had gone very still, dark eyes narrowing into watchful and wary arrows of light in his dark, devastating face. 'An annulment?' he breathed, very low, that possibility evidently not having occurred to him.

'Well, why not?' Polly asked him tautly. 'It's the easiest way out.'

'Let me get this straight…' Raul spread two lean brown hands with silent fluency to express apparent astonishment. 'Just one short month ago you married me, and now, without living a *single* day with me, you have changed your mind?'

'You're making me sound really weird,' Polly muttered in reproach. 'I was wrong to let you marry me, knowing that you didn't want that option. Now I'm admitting it—'

'But too late…you're admitting it too late,' Raul declared.

'But it's not too late…' Polly's brow furrowed with confusion, because the discussion was not going in the direction she had expected. 'It's not as if we've lived together…or anything like that. Why are you looking at me like I'm crazy? You don't *want* to be married to me.'

As he listened to that stumbling reminder, dark colour flared over Raul's slashing cheekbones and his stunning dark eyes suddenly blazed gold. 'But I have come to terms with the fact that I *am* married to you!'

'I think we both deserve a bit more than that out of marriage,' Polly opined in growing discomfiture. 'We rushed into it—'

'*I* didn't rush,' Raul interrupted. 'I just wanted to get it over with!'

'Yes, well…doesn't it strike you that that isn't a promising basis for *any* marriage?' Polly framed carefully, alarmingly awake to the angry tension emanating from his tall, commanding figure. 'I thought you'd be pleased at the idea of having your freedom back.'

'Freedom is a state of mind. I now see no reason why marriage should make the slightest difference to my life,' Raul returned with grating assurance.

Polly was momentarily silenced by that sweeping statement.

'You're my wife, and the mother of my son. I suggest you get used to those facts of life,' Raul completed, studying her in angry, intimidating challenge.

A bemused look now sat on Polly's face. Her lashes fluttered. The tip of her tongue crept out to nervously moisten the taut fullness of her lower lip. 'I don't understand...'

Hooded eyes of gleaming gold dropped to linger on the ripe pink contours of her mouth. 'Sometimes you talk too much, *gatita*...'

'What does that mean...that word you keep on using?' Polly whispered, because the very atmosphere seemed to sizzle, warning her of the rise in tension. Suddenly she was finding it very difficult to breathe.

'Gatita?' Raul laughed as he closed the distance between them in one easy stride. 'It means "kitten". The shape of your face, those big blue eyes...you remind me of a little fluffy cat, cute and soft with unexpected claws.'

Having spent a lifetime fighting the downside of being smaller than most other people, Polly was not best pleased to be linked with any image described by words like 'little', 'fluffy' or 'cute'.

'What do you think I am? Some kind of novelty?' she demanded, fighting not to be intimidated by his proximity and towering height.

'If I knew what it was that attracts me to you, the attraction probably would have died by now,' Raul said cynically.

Polly stilled, feathery brows drawing together. 'But you're *not* attracted to me…'

Raul dealt her a rampantly amused appraisal. 'I may have controlled my baser urges, but I've lost count of the times I almost succumbed to the temptation of hauling you into my arms in Vermont,' he admitted frankly. 'Then I believed your appeal was related to the simple fact that I knew you were carrying *my* child…'

'Yes?' Polly conceded breathlessly, with the aspect of a woman struggling to take a serious academic interest in a confession that had flung her brain into wild confusion. Her heart was now thumping like a manic hammer below her breastbone.

'But now I've finally worked out what got us into this in the first place,' Raul confided, and, without giving her a hint of his intentions, he lifted his hands and slowly tipped the wrap from her taut shoulders. 'Subconsciously I picked you to be Luis's mother because you appealed to my hormones… Once I'd reached that conclusion, suddenly everything that's gone wrong between us started making sense!'

In her complete bemusement at that declaration, Polly was standing so still the garment simply slid down her arms and pooled on the carpet. 'What…*what*?' she began with a nervous start.

Bending, Raul closed his strong arms round her and almost casually swept her up off her feet.

'*What are you doing?*' Polly shrieked in sheer shock.

Raul dealt her a slashing smile of unashamed satisfaction. 'Husbands don't need to control their baser urges.'

'Put me down—'

But Raul silenced that angry command by bringing his hungry mouth crashing down on hers without further ado.

Polly saw stars. Stars inside her head, stars exploding like hot sunbursts in all sorts of embarrassing places inside her. It wasn't like the only other kiss they had shared—a slow burner, cut off before it reached its height. Raul's devouring demand had an instant urgency this time, intensifying her own shaken response. He probed her mouth with tiny little darting stabs of his tongue. The raw sexuality of that intimate assault was shockingly effective. It set up a chain reaction right through her whole body, filling her with a wild, wanton need for more.

Polly uttered a strangled moan low in her throat, hands sweeping up to dig possessively into his luxuriant black hair and hold him to her. Without warning, Raul broke free to raise his head, dark golden eyes intent on her hectically flushed face as he strode out into the hall and started down the corridor. '*Dios*...I could make love to you all night, but I know you're not ready for that yet,' he groaned in frank frustration.

Surfacing in turmoil from that predatory kiss, Polly gasped, 'Where on earth do you think you're taking me?'

Unerringly finding the master bedroom, opposite the guest room in which Luis slept, Raul shouldered wide the door, strode across the carpet and deposited her with almost exaggerated gentleness on the vast divan bed. He hit the light switch by the bed, dimly illuminating the room. Then he straightened with an indolent smile.

Polly reared up, bracing herself on her hands, her hair tumbling round her pink cheeks, her eyes very blue as she studied him in shaken disbelief. 'Do you honestly think I'm about to go to bed with you?'

It didn't take Raul two seconds to respond to that question. Surveying her steadily, he jerked loose his silk tie. '*Sí*...you're my wife.'

'This is not a normal marriage!' Polly argued, still gazing at him with very wide and incredulous eyes.

'That's been our biggest problem. The sooner this marriage becomes ''normal'' the better,' Raul delivered, discarding his tie and sliding fluidly out of his jacket to pitch it on a nearby chair. 'It's time to forget how we started out—'

'But we didn't start *anything*!' Polly slung back, watching him unbutton his tailored silk shirt with the transfixed aspect of a woman unable to credit that he was actually undressing in front of her. 'I was pregnant before we even met!'

'Stop complicating things. You were pregnant with my baby. That created a special intimacy from the outset. Naturally that made a difference to how I reacted to you—'

'In Vermont?' Polly threw in helplessly. 'When you dropped in out of the blue whenever it suited you?'

'It's difficult to be casual any other way.'

'I bet you *always* suit yourself!' Polly condemned thinly.

Raul gave her a wondering and decidedly amused appraisal. 'Five-foot-nothing tall and you're nagging at me like a little shrew!' he marvelled.

Polly could feel her temper rising like a rocket desperate to go into orbit. 'I want you to treat me seriously, Raul.'

'Then say something relevant to the present,' he advised rather drily. 'Vermont was months ago. Vermont was when I still believed I was going to collect my child and walk away. We've moved on a lot since then.'

He peeled off his shirt.

Polly stared, throat closing, tongue cleaving to the roof of her dry mouth. He was incredibly beautifully built. All sleek bronzed skin and muscles, a hazy triangle of dark curls sprinkling his impressive torso. She blushed and averted her eyes. 'I'm not ready to share a bedroom with you yet,' she informed him tautly.

'I'm ready enough for both of us,' Raul said with amused assurance.

Without looking at him, Polly sat forward and linked her hands round her upraised knees. 'But I wasn't prepared for this... Before you came here tonight, I thought we'd be applying for an annulment to *end* our marriage,' she reminded him tensely. 'And sex isn't something I can treat casually—'

'*Bueno*...I'm delighted to hear it.'

'And...I haven't done this before,' Polly completed jerkily.

The silence spread for endless seconds that clawed cruelly at her nerves.

'*Como?*' Raul breathed in a near whisper.

Polly snatched in a shaky breath and simply squeezed her eyes tight shut. 'I've never had a lover.'

'That's not possible,' Raul informed her.

'Yes it is!' Polly said, almost fiercely in her embarrassment, desperate to drop the subject but registering by his audibly shattered responses that there was no current prospect of an easy escape.

'Look at me!' Raul commanded.

Her hot face a study of mingled chagrin and resentment, Polly glanced up and collided with incredulous dark golden eyes. 'Some women *don't* sleep around!' she snapped.

Raul moved closer to the bed, his frowning bemusement doing nothing to reduce her suspicion that he now saw her as some kind of freak. 'But you were at university...you must've had at least *one* relationship.'

'Not a physical one. I don't believe in intimacy without commitment,' Polly admitted stiffly, doggedly fighting her own discomfiture. 'And ''commitment'' is a dirty word to a lot of men these days. I may be out of step with the times, but I'm not ashamed of my views.'

'Technically still a virgin,' Raul murmured sibilantly, letting his glittering golden gaze roam over her with hungry intent. 'I'm very surprised—but, since I shall be your first lover, I think I can handle the situation. And, as my wife, you can hardly question the level of *my* commitment.'

That proud and confident assurance hovered there for a split second. Polly lost colour and dragged her troubled eyes from him to focus on the bare pink toes which protruded from below the hem of her nightgown. 'But you didn't *want* that commitment,' she reminded him in a strained tone.

'I'll get used to it.'

Polly swallowed hard and took her courage in both hands, determined to go to the heart of her misgivings and be frank. 'But if we share a bed, Raul…I expect you to be faithful.'

The silence thickened and lay heavily.

'No woman tells me what to do,' Raul countered with ferocious bite. 'And that includes you!'

Polly froze, and then stared at the fancy silk bedspread until it blurred below her shaken eyes. Then she angled her head back and forced herself to meet the onslaught of his chilling dark eyes. 'I think fidelity is the least commitment you could make.'

'*Dios*…' Raul growled, reaching for his discarded shirt in an abrupt movement and pulling it back on. 'So you have found another weapon. Off the top of my head I could name a dozen married men and women cheating on their spouses…do you think *they* didn't make promises?'

Polly's heart was beating so fast it felt as if it was sitting at the foot of her throat. 'But that's not—'

'This marriage is on trial, as every new relationship is. Do you think living together like brother and sister is a fair test of any relationship between a man and a woman?' Raul derided with lancing scorn, black eyes raking mercilessly over her disconcerted face. 'Do you fondly imagine that I will be a good little celibate boy while you sit back and smugly weigh up whether or not you can trust me enough to reward me with the right to share your bed?'

'I didn't mean it like that, Raul!' Polly argued strickenly as she sprang off the bed.

'So far you have had everything your way, but here it stops,' Raul delivered, his cold rage unconcealed. 'If you refuse to behave like a normal wife, *don't* expect me to behave like a husband!'

Shocked and distressed by the savage anger she had provoked, Polly clutched at his arm as he reached for his jacket, 'Raul, I—'

He swung back and closed a powerful arm round her

slight body, imprisoning her. He meshed long fingers into her hair, forcing her eyes to meet his. 'First you bargain with my son, then you bargain with sex.'

Breathless and trembling, she gazed up at him, lost herself in the brilliance of his shimmering dark eyes. *'No!'* she protested painfully.

Bending, Raul slid his arm below her slim hips and lifted her unceremoniously up to his level, crushing her swelling breasts into the muscular wall of his chest. Her nostrils flared on the enervating, hot, husky male scent of him. Hard black eyes assailed hers and held them by pure force of personality. 'You will not dictate terms to me. You will not demand empty and meaningless guarantees. A proper wife doesn't put a price on her body!'

'I…I wasn't doing that—'

'The marriage is on trial…*I am not!*' Raul stressed forcefully. 'I will not be judged on the basis of my past!'

Polly couldn't get breath into her lungs. Soft lips parting, she snatched in tiny little pants, drowning against her volition in the power of those compelling dark eyes.

'You're such a little hypocrite,' Raul delivered in a contemptuous undertone, scanning her dilated pupils and flushed cheeks. A sensually intent glitter flared in his assessing gaze, giving him the look of a tiger about to spring as he cupped her chin, lean fingers lingering to smoothly stroke the smooth curve of her jaw. 'This close to me, you're like a stick of dynamite hoping for a match!'

'I don't know what you're talking about—'

Striding over to the bed, Raul lowered her and followed her down onto the divan in one smooth, lithe motion. 'Then let me *show* you…'

Before she could even guess his intention, he had anchored her in place with one long, powerful thigh and brought his hard, mobile mouth crashing down on hers. With his tongue he plundered the sensitive interior with raw, erotic thoroughness. She groaned, plunged helplessly into the grip of mindless pleasure. He slid a hand beneath her, arching her up into contact with the aggressive thrust of his arousal, sending a cascade of fire trickling through her veins to accelerate every pulse.

Raul lifted his head. Her eyes were dazed, her ripe mouth reddened and swollen. Looking up at that lean, strong face, she trembled, caught up in a spell she was too weak to fight. With a slumberous smile, Raul flicked loose the tiny pearl buttons on the lace bodice of her nightie. And all the time Polly was involuntarily watching *him*, studying the black density and length of the lashes fanning his high cheekbones—the sole feminising influence in those hard-boned features—the luxuriant ebony hair tumbled by her fingers on to his brow, the blue-black shadow already roughening his strong jawline. All male, stunningly sexy.

'You have beautiful breasts,' Raul sighed.

Disconcerted, she followed the direction of his gaze. Thunderstruck, she stiffened and flushed at the sight of her own breasts, rising bare and shameless for his appraisal, her nipples already distended into wanton pink buds. 'Raul...?' she mumbled unevenly, lying there, wanting to cover herself, wanting to move, and yet inexplicably powerless to attempt to do either.

He allowed his thumb to delicately rub over one prominent peak, and her whole body jerked on the wave of sudden sensation that made her teeth grit in sensual shock and fired an insistent throb between her thighs.

'And you are *so* responsive,' he husked, angling back from her and then, without any warning whatsoever, smoothly sliding off the bed to spring upright again.

She suddenly found herself lying there alone and exposed, and a muffled cry of dismay escaped Polly. She rolled over onto her stomach, shaken, bewildered eyes pinned to Raul. Hooking his jacket on one forefinger, he glanced back at her from the door, bronzed face saturnine, black eyes several degrees below freezing.

'I could take you any time I wanted...and I *will*,' he swore, soft and low.

'You can't make me do anything I don't want to do!'

'Oh, yes, I can, *gatita*. Haven't the last five minutes taught you anything?' Raul skimmed back with merciless cool. 'You have an amazing capacity to lose yourself in passion. By the time I'm finished with you, you will be begging me to share the marital bed!'

Polly was already so devastated by what he had just done to her that she just gaped at him, heart sinking like a stone, stomach clenching sickly. A cruelly humiliating and deliberate demonstration of sexual power from a male who had homed in like a predator on her one weakness. *Him.* She was appalled by a depth of diabolic calculation alien to her own more open nature.

'A car will pick you up tomorrow evening. We're flying home,' Raul drawled indolently as he sauntered out through the door. '*Buenas noches*, Señora Zaforteza.'

She listened to him walk down the corridor, her hands bunched into fists. She wanted to scream with angry frustration and pain. She hated him, but she hated herself more. He had kissed her and nothing else had mattered. Now her body ached with guilty, unfulfilled passion, the enemy of every fine principle she had ever believed in. She was finally finding out how hard it was to withstand physical temptation.

And Raul? she thought furiously. Raul had simply walked away, content to have made his point in the most ego-crushing manner available.

CHAPTER SIX

POLLY sat in a comfortable seat in the spacious cabin of Raul's private jet and suppressed a sigh. Luis was asleep in his skycot and Raul had still to arrive. He had been delayed.

She glanced curiously at Irena, the young and pretty stewardess watching out for Raul's arrival. A sultry brunette, she looked like a model in her smart uniform, but in spite of the long wait she had coolly avoided any real contact with her employer's wife. A man's woman, uninterested in her own sex, Polly had decided.

Hearing the sound of feet on the metal steps outside, seeing Irena's face blossom into surprising warmth as she moved out of view to greet Raul, Polly was annoyed to recognise her own powerful sense of anticipation—and, mortifyingly, her childish stab of envy that the brunette should get to see him first. Swallowing hard on that lowering awareness, she studied the carpet, fighting to contain her own dangerously volatile emotions.

'Sorry, I'm late...' Raul drawled with infuriating cool, crossing the cabin to peruse his slumbering son and comment, in a tone of satisfaction and pride, 'Luis is always so peaceful.'

'You've never seen him any other way. Actually, your son kept me up half the night!' Polly complained thinly, before she could think better of it.

Disorientatingly, Raul laughed as he sank lithely down opposite her, forcing her to look at him for the first time. And his sheer stunning impact simply slaughtered her carefully prepared outer shield of tranquillity. Last night he had finally ripped away her defences and made her betray herself in his arms. Now she discovered there could be no pretense of indifference or detachment, not when her nails were already digging painfully into her palms, her skin dampening, her breathing quickening, her eyes unable to rest any place but on him.

Those bronzed features, already as familiar to her as her own yet still possessed of the most intense charismatic appeal. The lean, arrogant nose, the spectacular dark, deep-set eyes, the wide, hard mouth, the aggressive jawline. Drop-dead gorgeous, and yet every angle of that darkly handsome face was stamped with immense strength and character.

'At the *hato*…the ranch, the whole household will revolve round our son,' Raul promised with quiet amusement. 'He will be spoiled by so many willing helpers that your nights should be undisturbed from now on.'

Polly could see no reflection of her own highwire tension in him. He talked briefly, lightly about their destination. The isolated ranch where his ancestors had lived for generations was on the cattle plains he called the *llanos*. It would be very hot, possibly quite wet as the rainy season wasn't quite over yet, Raul warned in the sort of bracing, healthy, dismissive tone she suspected the hardy might use to refer to a hellhole they loved and honoured as home, regardless of its deficiencies.

Soon after the jet had taken off, Raul released his belt and leant forward to unsnap Polly's. Rising, he curved strong hands over her taut shoulders to urge her up into the circle of his arms.

'What are you—?'

'Lesson one on being a proper wife,' Raul murmured with amused dark eyes as he scanned her bewildered face. 'Even when you're really mad at me, you should always look glad to see me when we've been apart.'

That close to that lithe, lean body, Polly trembled. 'You are so changeable,' she condemned shakily. 'You were furious with me last night—'

'I'm just not used to a negative response in the bedroom,' Raul countered with velvet-soft satire. 'And when I've been forced to ride roughshod over my every reservation to become a legally wedded husband, that negative response took some swallowing.'

'But I tried to explain how I felt—'

'Not with an explanation I can take seriously, Polly,' Raul interrupted with conviction. 'You want me. I want you. You have a wedding ring to satisfy your principles. Sex is only a physical hunger, an appetite…not something important enough to become a divisive issue between us.'

Polly blinked, striving to think that through and shrinking from the feelings she experienced in response. *Not important?* An appetite, something to be casually, even carelessly satisfied as and when the need took him? Such terminology ensured that there was little danger of her overestimating the extent of her own attractions, she conceded in fierce pain.

A firm hand caught her chin, tipping up her face, making her meet the passionate gold of his intent gaze. 'If you expect too much from me, I am certain to disappoint you. Don't do that to us. Be satisfied with what we have,' Raul warned almost roughly.

Polly flung her head back. 'And what *do* we have?'

In answer, he attacked on her weakest flank. He lifted her up into his powerful arms, his sensual mouth took hers and she was lost, filled with the mindless pleasure of simply being there. All she was capable of at that moment was feeling—feeling what *he* could make her feel. The wild, sweet excitement as seductive as a drug, the shivering sensitivity of her own body crushed into the wonderfully masculine strength of his, heady sensation born at every point where they touched.

He released her lips and she discovered she was sprawled across his lap like a wanton, without any memory of how she had got there. Struggling to catch her breath, she stared into the stunning eyes level with her own. Long brown fingers framed her flushed cheekbones and eased her back from him.

'At least we have a starting point, *gatita*. It will be enough,' Raul swore with silken satisfaction. 'Now I think you should get some rest.'

'Rest?' she repeated unevenly.

'You look exhausted, and this is a very long flight.'

'Luis...?' she mumbled.

'I can manage him for a few hours,' Raul asserted with cool confidence.

Polly scrambled clumsily upright again, face burning under the onslaught of a wave of hot colour. Her legs were so wobbly she wasn't sure she could walk, and she felt dizzy, disorientated.

Raul watched her retreat to the sleeping compartment every step of the way, a slightly amused smile beginning to curve his expressive mouth. Polly shut the door and sagged, furious with him, furious with herself. First he treated her like a toy to be played with, then he dismissed her like a child after a goodnight kiss! It made her feel controlled and horribly vulnerable, because she literally didn't know at any given time what Raul was planning to do next. Just because he was experienced...and she wasn't!

Oh, dear heaven, no, she reflected, not wanting to even think about how and where he had gained all that cool sexual assurance. She curled up in a tight ball on the built-in bed. Until Raul had said it, she hadn't realised just how very tired she was. Hopefully she would be better equipped to deal with him when she felt a little more buoyant.

Polly woke up slowly, eyes opening blankly on her surroundings until she finally registered that she was still on the Zaforteza jet. Glancing at her watch, she groaned in disbelief. She had just enjoyed the equivalent of a full night's sleep for the first time since Luis had been born...*Luis!* Pushing her wildly tumbled hair off her brow,

Polly rolled off the bed and opened the door back into the main cabin.

A cosy and unexpected little scene met her startled eyes. Chattering in soft, intimate Spanish, Irena was leaning over Raul while he cradled Luis. She was as close to Raul as a lover. Her big brown eyes swept Polly's sleep-flushed face and crumpled clothing in a hostile look at the interruption.

'Why didn't you wake me up sooner?' Polly demanded curtly of Raul.

'You were exhausted, and Irena was happy to help out.' As Raul ran his stunning dark eyes over her tousled appearance, his ebony brows drew together in a slight but highly effective frown. 'You should get changed. We'll be landing at Maiquetia in an hour.'

The stewardess still had one possessive hand resting on Raul's shoulder. Polly was appalled to register that the source of her own ferocious tension was undeniably a hot nasty jealousy which fuelled instantly suspicious thoughts. What had they been doing all those hours while she was asleep and safely out of the way? Was that why Raul had been so keen to send her off to rest? Why did Irena look like a cat that had got the cream?

As Polly studied Raul with a highly combustible mix of suspicion, distrust and embittered shameful longing, he stood up and calmly settled their son into his neat little cot. 'I need a shave.'

'Did you get *any* sleep?' Polly muttered tautly.

'Enough. I don't need much.' Raul strode past her.

'Your husband is a real dynamo, *señora*. He has worked for most of the flight,' the young stewardess shared with a coy look of admiration, tossing her head with a husky little laugh. 'But don't worry, I ensured that he ate and took time out to relax.'

At that news, Polly paled and went back into the sleeping compartment, but Raul had already disappeared into the compact bathroom next door. She lifted the white lightweight dress she had laid out earlier and smoothed abstractedly at the remaining creases while she waited for Raul to emerge. Finally the door opened. She felt absolutely sick by then, suspicion and jealousy making mincemeat of all rational thought.

'Do you sleep with Irena?' That blunt question just erupted from Polly. It was inside her head, but she could not for the life of her work out how the question had got from her brain onto her tongue.

Raul studied her without any expression at all. 'Tell me you didn't ask me that.'

That eerie lack of reaction completely spooked Polly. She crimsoned, pinned her lips together and then opened them again, driven by an overwhelming need for reassurance. 'After what you said the night before last about not behaving like a husband...not to mention the way *she's* behaving around you...naturally I'm suspicious!'

'If I answer that insanely stupid question, I will lose my temper with you,' Raul warned, very soft and low, narrowed dark eyes flaming gold between lush black lashes.

'I don't trust you—'

'I will not live with jealous scenes. In fact nothing would disgust me more or alienate me faster. I do not sleep with my employees. The only woman in my life at present is you,' Raul stated with a feral flash of even white teeth which suggested that even making that admission went severely against the grain.

Polly relaxed ever so slightly. 'I want to believe that, but—'

'The truth is that *you* are jealous of Irena,' Raul condemned with whiplash cool. 'Could that be because she makes the effort to look like an attractive adult woman while you're still dressing like an adolescent who doesn't want to grow up?'

Utterly unprepared for that counter-attack, Polly felt her soft mouth fall wide.

Raul flicked the white sundress off the bed. 'A three-year-old could wear this! Embroidered flowers at the neck-line, ruched, shapeless—'

'It *was* bought in a children's department. Ordinary shops don't cater for women my height and size!' Polly shot at him shakily. 'And, since I don't want to dress like a precocious teenybopper, I have to choose the plain out-fits.'

Raul shrugged. 'OK...I'll remedy that.'

'I am not jealous of *that woman*...and you needn't think you can change the subject—'

'Oh, I'm not changing it, Polly...I'm just refusing to talk about it,' Raul incised with sudden grimness, shooting her a coldly derisive look. 'Use your brain. Irena is Venezuelan. Venezuelan women are naturally glamorous, confident and flirtatious—'

'My goodness, I can hardly wait to meet the Venezuelan men! What a fun time I'm going to have in your country!' Polly forecast furiously.

In a sudden movement that shook Polly inside out, Raul strode forward and closed a lean and powerful hand round her slender forearm, dwarfing her with his intimidating height and breadth. With his other hand, he pushed up her chin, subjecting her to a splintering look of burning outrage that made her stomach turn an abrupt somersault and her knees go weak and wobbly.

'What is mine is *mine*,' Raul stressed with barely sup-pressed savagery. 'I'd break you into little pieces for the jaguar to feed on before I would let any other man near you!'

Plunged willy-nilly into an atmosphere suddenly raw with scorching lightning currents of threat, Polly simply gazed up at him like a stupefied rabbit.

With equal abruptness, Raul released her again, a be-traying rise of blood delineating his proud cheekbones as he absorbed her bewilderment. 'I'm not a jealous man,' he asserted in a roughened undertone. 'But I am very conscious of my honour, and of my son's need for stability in his life.'

Polly nodded like a little wooden marionette, afraid to move too close to the hungry flickering flames of a bonfire.

Raul was pale now beneath his golden skin, his superb bone structure harshly prominent. 'I'm sorry if I overreacted...'

If, Polly reflected dizzily. Such a civilized term after so violent a loss of temper, brief though it had been. And she had discovered another double standard. The man who would be owned by no woman fully believed he owned his wife like a possession. But, ironically, what troubled her most at that instant was the stark awareness that she had really upset Raul. Yet she hadn't a clue why her silly sarcastic comments should have exploded his cool, controlled façade into a shocking blaze of primitive fury.

'Put it down to jet lag,' Raul added almost jerkily, pushing long brown fingers restively through his glossy blueblack hair. 'You are not *that* kind of woman. If you had been, I would never have agreed to marry you.'

What kind of woman? The unfaithful type? What a peculiar thought for a male like Raul to harbour! For, on the face of it, Raul Zaforteza was a real heartbreaker, possessed of every quality most likely to hold a woman's attention. Personality, looks, sex-appeal, wealth, power. How many women would risk losing Raul by betraying him in another man's bed?

'I will join you at the ranch in a couple of days,' Raul murmured flatly as he moved past her—suddenly, she registered, keen to abandon the dialogue...and *her*? The suspicion hurt.

'Join me?' Polly echoed uncertainly. 'What are you talking about? Where are you going?'

'Tonight I'm afraid I'll have to stay in Caracas. Tomorrow I'll be in Maracaibo, and possibly the next day as well. I have several urgent business matters to deal with. I've been abroad for many weeks,' he reminded her drily.

Alone again, Polly freshened up and slid with a distinct lack of enthusiasm into the simple white cotton dress. When she returned to the main cabin she could not avoid noticing Irena's frequent starstruck glances in Raul's direction, and her pronounced need to hover at his elbow as eager as a harem slave to satisfy his every wish. No longer did she marvel at her own suspicions earlier. The brunette had a real giant-sized crush on Raul. And possibly Raul was so accustomed to inviting female flattery and exaggerated attention that he genuinely hadn't noticed.

'OK, so there *is* a problem,' Raul breathed, disconcerting Polly with a dark satiric glance of acknowledgement in Irena's direction while she was gathering up Luis's scattered possessions at the far end of the cabin. 'We were both fifty per cent wrong, but, believe me, I have never given her the slightest encouragement.'

Polly nodded in embarrassed silence, feeling like an idiot over the fuss she had made but fearful of re-opening the subject lest she make things even worse.

Raul parted from her at the airport as coolly and politely as a distant acquaintance, a shuttered look in his brilliant dark eyes. Irena escorted Polly onto the light plane which would whisk her and her son out to the Zaforteza ranch. Polly's heart was already sinking.

Would it always be like this with Raul? Would she never *know* Raul? Would she never understand what went on inside that complex and clever head of his? And was it possible that that 'urgent business' he had mentioned had merely been a convenient excuse to leave her? How humiliating it was to suspect that Raul *had* actually intended to accompany her to his home until she'd treated him to that foolish scene! After all, hadn't he told her up front that jealousy disgusted him, and that nothing would drive him away quicker?

It was lashing with rain when Polly clambered off the plane, protected by a giant umbrella extended over her and

Luis by the pilot. He helped her into the waiting four-wheel drive. Neither he nor the driver appeared to have a word of English. Polly was now feeling less guilty and more angry with Raul. How did he think it felt for her to arrive at the *estancia* alone, where nobody knew her and where very possibly nobody would even be able to speak to her?

Through the streaming windows she caught glimpses of a large spreading collection of buildings. Palm trees were being battered in the torrential downpour. And yet the heat was intense, the humidity high. A hellhole, Polly decided, in the right mood to make that snap judgement. Raul had posted them out to the boonies to live in a hellhole and just gone on his own sweet way, just as he was used to doing, just as he no doubt expected to *continue* doing…

A huge colonial-style house adorned by fancy verandahs and an upper balcony wreathed with climbers loomed out of the rain. Clutching Luis like a parcel, Polly made a dive through the torrent when the car door opened, fled up the steps and surged indoors into the mercifully air-conditioned cool without a single sidewise glance or pause.

She had a split second to catch her breath on the magnificence of the vast reception hall she stood in before she focused on the huddle of female servants sheltering behind the front door, all staring at her and the baby she held wide-eyed. Silence hung for the space of twenty seconds.

A tall and stunningly beautiful blonde strolled into view. Frowning regally at Polly, she shot something at her in Spanish.

'I'm sorry, I don't speak—'

'I am the Condesa Melina D'Agnolo. Where is Raul?' the woman demanded in accented but perfect English.

'Still in Caracas.' Conscious of the staff now sidling out of a door to the left as fast as mice escaping a cat, Polly gazed enquiringly at the other woman. Sheathed in a superb cerise suit, glittering jewellery adding to her imperious air of well-bred exclusivity, the lady exuded angry impatience.

'*Caracas?*' It was an infuriated shriek of disappointment.

As the shrill sound echoed off the high ceiling, Luis jerked in fright and let out a loud, fretful wail.

Melina D'Agnolo stalked forward and surveyed him with unconcealed distaste. 'So this is the child I have heard rumours about. It *does* exist. Well, what are you waiting for? Stop it making that horrible noise!'

'He's just hungry—'

'When will Raul arrive?'

'In a couple of days.'

'Then I shall wait for him,' Melina announced, eyes hardening as Luis continued to cry noisily in spite of Polly's efforts to console him. 'But you will keep that child upstairs, out of my sight and hearing.'

'I'm afraid I have no intention—' Polly began angrily.

'I will not tolerate impertinence. You will do as you are told or you will very soon find yourself out of a job!' Melina informed her. 'In Raul's absence, I am in charge here.'

Realising that she had been mistaken for an employee, Polly raised her head high, intending to explain that she was Raul's wife. But the other woman had already walked away to utter a sharp command in Spanish. A middle-aged woman in a black dress appeared so quickly she must have been waiting somewhere nearby. Melina issued what sounded like a staccato stream of instructions.

The older woman glanced in open dismay at Polly.

'The housekeeper will take you upstairs to the nursery. You can eat up there. I don't want to be bothered by the child…is that understood?'

'Why do you say you're in charge here? Are you related to Raul?' Polly enquired stiffly, and stood her ground.

Melina's green eyes narrowed with suggestive languor, full lips pouting into a coolly amused smile. 'I've never been asked to identify myself in this house before. Raul and I have been intimate friends for a very long time.'

Every scrap of colour drained from Polly's face. There was no mistaking the meaning of that proud declaration.

Her stomach curdled. It was a judgement on her, Polly thought sickly. She had foolishly made that scene over the infatuated Irena and now fate had served up her punishment: she was being confronted by the real thing. A genuine rival...

'Why are you looking at me like that?' Melina D'Agnolo enquired haughtily.

'I think this is going to be embarrassing,' Polly muttered.

Melina dealt her an impatient frown of incomprehension.

'Raul and I got married a month ago.'

The thunderous silence seemed to reverberate in Polly's ears, and then Luis started crying again.

The svelte blonde stared at Polly with raised brows, her incredulity unfeigned. 'It isn't possible that you are *married* to Raul—'

'I'm afraid it is...' Polly cut in, and switched her attention ruefully to the housekeeper still waiting for her.

The older woman murmured gently, 'Let me take the little one upstairs and feed him for you, *señora*.'

Grateful for the chance to remove Luis from the hostile atmosphere, Polly laid her son in the housekeeper's arms with a strained smile.

'*Señora?*' Melina D'Agnolo echoed the designation with stinging scorn. 'I think we need to talk.'

Raul, where are you when I need you? Polly thought in furious discomfiture. This was his department, not hers! How could Raul possibly have overlooked the necessity of telling his mistress that he had acquired a wife? Polly turned reluctantly back to face the angry blonde. 'I don't think that would be a good idea.'

'If you prefer it, we can talk out here, where all the staff can hear us.'

Rigid with tension, Polly followed Melina into a gracious reception room filled with superb antique furniture. 'I don't see that we *have* anything to say to each other—'

'Obviously Raul married you because of the child. The oldest ploy of all. I expect you think you've been very clever.' Melina loosed a grim little laugh. 'Yes, I'm shocked, and I don't mind admitting it. Ten years ago Raul loved me, but he *still* wouldn't marry me, so I married someone else to teach him a lesson!'

Wanting no share of such confidences, Polly hovered, stiff with strain.

'So you needn't tell me that Raul loves you because I wouldn't believe it! I am the *only* woman Raul has ever loved,' Melina informed her with blistering confidence. 'I have never been concerned by his other little flirtations.'

'That's your business, not mine.'

'Your marriage won't last six months,' Melina said with dismissive certainty. 'Raul cherishes his freedom. When my husband died, I chose to be patient. I have never interfered with Raul's life—'

'Then don't do it now,' Polly slotted in tightly.

'If you think that is a possibility, you're even more of a child than you look!' Melina threw her a scornful look of superiority. 'And next month you'll be expected to deal with two hundred guests over the fiesta weekend. There'll be a rodeo, a friendly polo match and a non-stop party. Are you used to mixing with the wealthy élite? How good are you on a horse? I'm usually Raul's hostess, but now the job's yours…and if it doesn't go like clockwork, he'll be furious.'

Polly had paled. 'I'm sure I'll manage—'

'Raul will come back to me…of course he will. It's only a matter of time,' Melina asserted with contemptuous green eyes. 'If you're out of your depth with me, how much more out of your depth are you with him? I almost feel sorry for you. When Raul's bored, he is cruel and critical and callous—'

'I think it's time you left,' Polly interrupted flatly.

'If I were you, I wouldn't mention this meeting,' the blonde murmured sweetly as she strolled to the door. 'Raul detests jealous scenes. It would be much wiser for you to pretend that this meeting never took place.'

'Why should you be kind enough to give me that warning?'

Melina laughed unpleasantly. 'You already have all the problems you can handle. I shall enjoy watching you struggle to fill my shoes!'

Polly watched the blonde stalk across the hall and up the imposing staircase. She released her breath very slowly but she still felt utterly stunned. Melina D'Agnolo had been a severe shock. Raul's mistress—proud and unashamed of her position in his life and in no hurry to vacate his bed.

And one look at Melina had been sufficient to tell Polly that her misapprehension about the pretty stewardess on board the jet had been laughable. Melina was much more convincing in the role of mistress. Melina with her exquisite face, fabulous figure and tremendous elegance and poise. Mature, classy and sophisticated. Raul's kind of woman. And what even the greatest optimist would acknowledge as *seriously* challenging competition...

No, Polly scolded herself fiercely. She wasn't going to allow herself to start thinking that way. Raul had said that she was the only woman in his life now, and he had given her no cause to doubt his sincerity. OK, she had just suffered through a horribly embarrassing encounter and been forced to endure the other woman's spiteful attacks, but Melina would pack and depart and she would never have to see her again. She would put Melina right back out of her mind. Raul's past was none of her business, she reminded herself staunchly.

Upstairs, Polly wandered across a huge landing and picked a passageway. Finally, after a couple of wrong choices, she peered into a nursery as exquisitely furnished as a room in a glossy magazine. A crowd of smiling, whispering female staff surrounded the imposing antique four-poster cot. Freshly clothed and clearly content, Luis nestled within the cot's hand-embroidered bedding like a little king, giving an audience and basking in all the attention.

'It has been so long since there was a child here,' the housekeeper confided.

'Was this Raul's cot?' Polly asked, smiling.

The older woman looked away uncomfortably. 'No, *señora*...but it was his father's.'

Briefly wondering what she had said to disconcert the woman, Polly was led down a corridor lined with fabulous oil paintings and into a magnificent big bedroom. Realising that it had stopped raining, Polly opened the French windows and stepped out onto the sun-drenched balcony to gaze out appreciatively on the beautifully landscaped gardens. Lush lawns and colourful vegetation were shaded by clumps of graceful mature trees. In the distance an architectural extravaganza of a small building complete with turrets caught her attention.

'What's that used for?' she asked her companion.

The older woman stiffened. 'It is not used for anything, *señora*.'

'What a waste...it's so pretty.'

'It is full of ghosts, not a good place.' The housekeeper retreated back indoors, seemingly unaware that she had said anything that might cause Polly to stare after her in wide-eyed surprise and curiosity. 'I will fix you some breakfast, *señora*. You must be hungry.'

That evening, Polly rested back in the huge sunken bath in the *en suite* bathroom and felt like a queen lying in solitary state. She poked a set of pink toes up through the bubbles covering the surface of the water and sighed.

Melina D'Agnolo had vanished like the bad fairy. Only when she had disappeared had it occurred to Polly to wonder *how* she had gone, and to where. By car, by plane? The Zaforteza ranch was set in miles and miles of cattle country.

In the afternoon Polly had walked out to the furthest edge of the gardens and seen the plains stretching as far as the eye could reach in every direction, their monotony broken up by occasional clumps of trees, stretches of flood water that glinted in the hot sun and ground that seemed to sweep up and merge with the endless blue sky.

She closed her eyes and let herself think about Raul. Would he phone? Once she had told him not to bother and he hadn't given her a chance to say no a second time. But how the heck could she possibly measure up to a woman as gorgeous as Melina? The fear crept in and she tried to squash the thought and the feeling simultaneously.

'Lesson two on being a proper wife...' a silken drawl imparted lazily from the door. 'If you have to be in the bath when I come home, make it one I can share. Omit the heavily scented bubbles.'

CHAPTER SEVEN

POLLY'S mouth fell open at the same instant as her eyes shot wide. Raul stood in the doorway, a sizzling smile of amusement slashing his mouth as he absorbed her astonishment.

'But you look kind of cute…' Raul conceded, brilliant dark eyes roaming with unconcealed interest over the rose-tipped breasts pertly breaking through the bubbles for his scrutiny.

Wrenching free of her paralysed stillness, Polly sat up in a frantic rush and hugged her knees to her chest. Raul gave an extravagant wince. 'Sometimes you act like a ten-year-old, *gatita*.'

'Couldn't you have knocked on the door?' Polly demanded defensively.

'The door wasn't even closed,' he reminded her drily, and he leant back against the door, slowly pushing it shut, as if he was making some kind of statement.

Sooner than ask him what he was doing, and already having discarded as too dangerously provocative the idea of asking him to step outside while she vacated the bath and covered herself, Polly studied him anxiously from below her dark lashes.

A tide of terrifying longing swept over her in a stormy wave. Her own heartbeat thundered inside her ears, and all the time her eyes were roaming all over him in hungry, helpless little darts. He was so incredibly tall in his light grey suit, his white shirt throwing his bronzed skin into exotic prominence, his luxuriant black hair gleaming under the recessed lights above, eyes glinting wicked gold in that lean, dark, devastating face.

108

'You missed me,' Raul purred, like a jungle cat basking in sunlight, his husky accent thickening and sending a trail of reaction down her taut spinal cord.

'For heaven's sake, how could I have missed you? I last saw you in the early hours of this morning!' Polly snapped, but it was a challenge to snap when it was so outrageously difficult to even breathe normally in his radius.

'You don't just need lessons on how to be a proper wife...you need a bloody intensive training course!' Raul shot back at her with shocking abruptness. 'What does it take to get a pleasant response from you? Thumbscrews?'

Jolted by that sudden blaze of temper, Polly gazed up at him strickenly. She felt the most awful stinging surge of tears threatening at the back of her eyes. Hurriedly she bent her head. Maybe meeting your gorgeous mistress spoilt my day, she almost slung accusingly, but caution restrained her.

'Maybe I'm not used to sharing a bathroom,' she muttered ruefully.

'Then this is where we will start,' Raul delivered.

Start what, where? Polly wondered in complete confusion.

'*Dios*...I can hardly believe I flew back here just to *be* with you!'

'Did you? I thought your urgent business took precedence.'

'Possibly the prospect of getting my bride horizontal on the marital bed had greater appeal.'

'Oh...' Polly said after a startled pause. 'Do you have to be so crude?'

Without the slightest warning, strong hands curved under her arms and a split second later she was airborne. Raul straightened and held her ruthlessly imprisoned in mid-air as she dripped water and bubbles everywhere, her shaken face aghast. 'Not so shrewish now, are you?' he murmured with unconcealed amusement.

'Please put me back in the water,' Polly mumbled pleadingly.

Raul gazed into her shrinking blue eyes and slowly lowered her back into the bath with careful hands. 'You're such a baby sometimes...I wasn't going to hurt you!' he breathed in stark reproach.

Still trembling, Polly hugged the far side of the bath. 'I don't know why I'm so nasty with you,' she lied—because she knew very well. 'I'm not usually like this with anybody.'

'You were so sweet in Vermont. I didn't even know you had a temper, never mind that viper's tongue,' Raul admitted wryly. 'What went wrong?'

You did. At that stupid question Polly was tempted to throw something at him. She had fallen hopelessly in love, more deeply in love than she had ever believed possible, and nothing had ever been the same since. He didn't love her, he didn't believe in love, and she couldn't risk letting him find out how she really felt about him. Given an ounce of such ego-boosting encouragement, he would walk all over her and take her for granted the way he had in Vermont.

The female sex had spoilt Raul. For minimum input he had always received maximum benefit—everything on his terms, everything the way *he* wanted it. And their marriage still felt like a deadweight threatening ball and chain to him. He didn't have to tell her that. She *knew* it. She marvelled that he should believe that taking her to bed would miraculously change anything, particularly when he had already spelt out the fact that he didn't rate sex any higher than an 'appetite'.

And where did that leave her? The virginal bride with novelty value? A fresh body for his enjoyment?

Raul discarded his jacket on a chair and tossed his tie on top of it. Emerging from her insecure reverie, Polly gaped. Shoes and socks were summarily discarded.

'What are you doing?'

Raul sent her a gleaming glance of intent. 'Losing your virginity is not akin to a visit to a sadistic dentist.'

'What would you know about it?'

A wolfish grin slashed his mobile mouth. 'I'll fill you in on my impressions tomorrow morning.'

Off came his shirt, to be carelessly discarded in a heap. Polly's throat clogged up at sight of that magnificent brown torso and the triangle of all male dark curling hair outlining his powerful pectoral muscles. 'Is this my anatomy lesson?' she whispered shakily.

'You need one?' As free of inhibition as she was repressed, Raul flicked loose his belt and slid out of his well-cut trousers.

Although Polly wanted to look away, she couldn't. Her throat thickened, her mouth running dry. Her mesmerised attention locked on to the silky furrow of hair running down over his flat, taut stomach to disappear tantalisingly beneath the band of a pair of black briefs.

'You're beginning to embarrass *me*,' Raul censured mockingly.

Caught staring, Polly twisted her head away, cheeks flaming. 'I don't think anything embarrasses you!' she condemned unevenly.

'You really *are* shy…I thought it was an act in Vermont,' Raul confessed without warning. 'You were so open and forthright in every other way—'

'I don't put on acts,' Polly protested feverishly. 'I can't help the way I was brought up any more than you can.'

'What's that supposed to mean?' Raul breathed with sudden brooding darkness.

Involuntarily she shivered, catching the warning nuances in his accented drawl and spooked by what she could not understand. 'My father believed girls should be modest and quiet and strait-laced, and my godmother agreed with him—'

'Whatever happened to the "quiet"?' Raul cut in with unhesitating humour.

Her momentary ripple of foreboding ebbed, only to be replaced by a more pressing urge to leap out of the bath as

Raul stepped in. Arms wrapped tightly round her knees, Polly twisted her head back round and slung him an accusing glance as he settled fluidly down on the other side of the bath and rested his burnished dark head back against the inset cushioning.

'Look, why can't we just do it in bed like other people?' she suddenly launched at him in mortified condemnation. 'I think you're going out of your way to make this more difficult for me!'

Dealing her a briefly bemused appraisal, Raul suddenly flung his head back and burst out laughing without restraint. *'Caramba, cielito—'*

'That is *it*…that is *finally* it!' Polly raked at him, chagrin tipping over into a sudden empowering rage that enabled her to begin rising without any constraining fear of exposing her own body.

Raul leant forward and caught her hand, tipping her sufficiently off-balance to ensure that she was powerless to resist the ease with which he reached up his other hand and tumbled her down on top of him, water splashing everywhere.

Panting furiously for breath, Polly pulled herself back from him. 'Let go of me!'

Raul regarded her with deceptive languor. 'I wasn't actually planning to consummate our marriage here…I just wanted to talk…'

'T-talk?' Polly parroted weakly as she subsided back beneath the water to conceal herself, carefully avoiding the slightest contact with his long extended limbs.

'No need to panic…at least…not yet,' Raul drawled smoothly, the golden gleam deep in his shimmering dark eyes increasing the colour in her hot face. 'In my innocence I believed that this was a comparatively mild first step towards greater intimacy.'

'Do you normally just *talk* in the bath with your women?' Polly practically snarled in her discomfiture, knowing that any plea of innocence was not to be trusted in this instance, perfectly well aware that Raul was highly amused by her enervated state.

The golden gleam vanished, leaving her gazing in sudden fear into wintry cool dark eyes. '*Infierno!* You're obsessed. Jealousy is a very destructive thing. Do you want to destroy us before we even begin with these constant attacks?'

Pale now, Polly just closed her eyes. In the space of a moment she saw a dozen beautiful female faces skim cruelly through her mind's eye. Only then did she grasp the source of her jealousy, the day when it had been born to increase the bitterness she had experienced after leaving Vermont. To satisfy her driving need to know more about the father of her child, she had gone to the library and scanned through newspaper gossip pages and glossy society magazines...

Time after time she had come on photos of Raul with some gorgeous blonde babe on his arm. And that was the day when she had finally accepted how pitiful her love was, how hopelessly without foundation or any prospect of reciprocation.

Then, months on, to have that impression of Raul as a heartless womaniser reinforced all over again—to watch Raul leave that London clinic to walk into another woman's arms, to live through that mortifying misunderstanding about the stewardess and then the very same day to be confronted with the horrendous real shock of Melina D'Agnolo. Was it any wonder that she was desperately insecure, afraid to trust Raul and lashing out in an attempt to protect herself from further pain?

'I won't live like this with any woman,' Raul breathed with terrifying quietness. 'It's like trying to fight an invisible enemy... Whatever I do you'll always be suspicious!'

As he pulled himself upright, her lashes lifted. Stepping out of the bath, Raul snatched a fleecy towel from the rail and strode back into the bedroom without a backward glance.

And, just as suddenly, Polly's defensive attitude fell

away. She saw a marriage which hadn't even begun now going down the drain without fanfare. She saw the chance she had been given thrown away out of proud defiance and a refusal to face her own insecurities and faults.

Raul hadn't made love to her in Vermont. *She* had been the one who had misinterpreted *his* intentions. He had had the right to pursue other relationships. His freedom had been his own and she had had no claim on him. That was the reality which she had failed to accept all these months because *she* had fallen in love. And what was she doing now but driving Raul away from her, in spite of the fact that he had given her no cause to distrust him?

In a panic, now that she had seen herself at fault, Polly climbed out of the bath, tugged a black towelling robe off a wall hook and hurriedly dug her arms into the too long sleeves.

'Raul...I'm sorry!' she called in advance, afraid he might already have left the bedroom beyond.

'Forget it...I need some fresh air.'

Rolling up the sleeves of what she now realised had to be his robe, Polly edged apprehensively round the door and peered out. Damp black wildly tousled hair flopping over his bronzed brow, Raul was zipping up a pair of skintight cream jodhpurs.

In silence, she watched him yank highly polished leather boots out of a cupboard and sink down on the chaise longue at the foot of the bed to pull them on. 'You're going riding?' she muttered uncertainly. 'But it's getting dark.'

'Get back in your bath with your bubbles,' Raul advised with brooding satire. 'Immerse that little body you protect so assiduously...and leave me alone.'

'Look...I said I was sorry.' Polly lifted her chin. 'Do I have to crawl?'

Raul lifted his dark head and regarded her directly for the first time since she had entered the room. She was shaken by the black brooding distance etched with clarity in his spectacular dark eyes. 'How are you on disappearing?' he drawled in a tone like a silken whiplash. 'Because right now, I just don't want to be around you.'

Polly flinched from that brutal candour, the flush of pink in her cheeks receding to leave her paper-pale. Without warning, Raul was like a dark, intimidating stranger.

'So go back in the bathroom before I say anything else to hurt your sensitive feelings,' Raul told her harshly. 'I'm not in the mood to control my tongue!'

'I'm not afraid of what you have to say.'

'Then why the hell are you goading me like this?' Raul splintered back at her in frustration. 'I don't like being needled. I especially don't like snide comments. If you have something to say to me, have the guts to say it loud and clear, because I have no time for anything else!'

Melina loomed like the bad fairy in her mind's eye. Polly wanted to defend herself. She wanted to explain how upsetting and threatening she had found that encounter. But she had a greater fear that the mention of her own feelings in relation to yet another woman and him would be a dangerously provocative act that would simply send him through the roof. As he gazed expectantly back at her, Raul's eyes burned as gold as the flames in the heart of a fire.

'I haven't anything to say,' she stated, in what she hoped was a soothing tone likely to defuse the situation.

But, disconcertingly, that tone had the same effect as throwing paraffin on a bonfire. Raul sprang up, throwing her a blistering glance of derision. 'You have the backbone of a jellyfish! I'm ashamed to be married to such a spiritless excuse for a woman!'

'Maybe…m-maybe I have more control over my temper than you have,' Polly stammered through teeth clenched with restraint.

Raul slashed an imperious hand through the air in savage dismissal. 'This morning I left you at the airport. I walked away from conflict. I've spent the last ten years doing that quite happily. I watched my father do that all his life with women,' he grated in a raw, hostile undertone. 'And then it dawned on me that I was married to you, and that if I start closing you out when you anger me, what future can this marriage have?'

'Raul, I—'

'*Cállate!* I am talking,' Raul broke in with supreme contempt as he yanked a garment out of a drawer. 'I find your continuing jealousy irrational and disturbing. And for someone so repressed she shrinks from even sharing a bath with her own husband, I find it even stranger that you should want to know what I might or might not have done with other women when I was answerable to nobody!'

Lips bloodlessly compressed to prevent them from trembling like the rest of her shivering, woefully weak body, Polly watched him pull on a white polo shirt and whispered shamefacedly. 'I don't want to know…' She was stumbling wretchedly. 'I *mean*—'

'Never again will I make the smallest sacrifice to make this marriage work!' Raul swore with hard emphasis. 'I have my son…what else do I need? Certainly not a silly little girl who cowers at the idea of making love with me!'

'Raul, please…' Polly muttered strickenly as he strode towards the door and flung it wide.

All volatile energy and movement now, he yelled something down the corridor. On cottonwool legs, Polly followed him to the threshold and watched one of the maids coming at an anxious run.

Raul rapped out instructions in Spanish. The maid bobbed her head in instant acquiescence and then sped off down the corridor again.

Raul sent Polly a smouldering look of derision. 'You need no longer fear my unwelcome approaches, *mi esposa*. The maid will convey your possessions to another room!'

CHAPTER EIGHT

POLLY paced the floor in the beautiful guest room the housekeeper had allotted to her without once meeting her eyes. The shame of so new a bride being ejected from the marital bedroom had been fully felt on Polly's behalf.

Over the next couple of hours, Polly ran the gamut of fiercer emotions than she had ever known. She had never come across anyone with a temper as volatile as Raul's. She had never dreamt that Raul might speak to her like that—even worse, *look* at her as he had. As if she was nothing to him, less than nothing, even, nothing but a pain and a nuisance, beneath his notice and utterly unworthy of any further attention.

She went from rage at his having made such a public spectacle of their differences to sudden all-engulfing pain at the sheer strength of that rejection. They had been together perhaps twenty-four hours, yet everything had fallen apart. A voice in her mind just screamed that she couldn't cope, couldn't handle the situation. She wanted to take Luis and run...run and make Raul *sorry*, she registered. The tears flowed then, in shame at the manner in which her thoughts went round and round in circles but never lost the need to keep Raul at the very centre.

Calmer, if no more happy once she had cried, she took a good, hard look at her own behaviour and didn't like what she saw. And when she exerted herself to try and see things from Raul's point of view, she just groaned and squirmed at her own foolish prickly resentment and insecurity.

Gorgeous, woman-killing, much sought-after and fêted guy becomes unwilling husband but makes decent effort to paper over the cracks. What with? Sex. What else? He doesn't *know* anything else. Every other woman can't wait to get him between the sheets to check out that fabled reputation, but his bride is inexplicably and therefore offensively reluctant. Not only reluctant but also sarcastic, jealous, and seemingly incapable of behaving like a mature adult committed to getting their marriage of convenience up and running.

And why had she behaved like an idiot?

Because she loved him, Polly conceded painfully, and she wanted, needed to be so much more than a convenient body in Raul's bed. And, worst of all, a sexually ignorant partner when he had to be accustomed to lovers with a considerable degree of sophistication and expertise, not to mention lithe and perfect bodies. So, out of stubborn pride and resentment over her own sense of inadequacy, she had driven him away.

If she had told him straight off about that clash with Melina D'Agnolo, at least he would have understood why she was in such a prickly mood. But she had missed her opportunity and knew that it would be an act of insanity to risk opening such a subject with Raul now. In fact even the thumbscrews he had mentioned wouldn't dredge Melina's name from her lips...not when he already saw her as an obsessively jealous woman.

And all his self-preserving male antennae were in perfect working order, Polly acknowledged at the lowest ebb of self-honesty. She was and had been jealous, and no doubt would be jealous again, because jealousy thrived on insecurity. And she *did* want to own Raul, body and soul.

Seeing how swollen her eyes were in the mirror, she splashed her face over and over again with cold water. Then she washed her hair, put on a little light make-up, some perfume and slid into one of the silk nighties he had given her. Creeping down the corridor like a burglar sneaking under the cover of darkness, she walked back into the marital bedroom and clambered into the big wide bed to watch the moonlight slant across the ceiling through the undrawn curtains.

She must have fallen asleep, because she woke with a start later, hearing running feet and then raised anxious voices in the corridor outside. Thrusting her tumbled hair off her sleepy face, she switched on the light and lurched out of bed. Opening the bedroom door, she peered out.

A clutch of gesticulating staff surrounded Raul. Liberally daubed in mud, and far from his usual immaculate self, he looked frantic, shooting out questions at volume, expressive hands moving at volatile speed to indicate his level of angry concern.

'Raul...?' Polly called worriedly as he paused for breath. 'What's wrong?'

The staff huddle twisted round with a general look of astonishment.

'Where the hell have you been?' Raul thundered at her accusingly.

'In bed...sleeping,' Polly mumbled in bewilderment. 'Why?'

'Why?' Raul roared back in apparent disbelief.

The staff were now all slowly rolling back like a quiet tide in the direction of the stairs. Raul strode past her into the bedroom, shooting the rumpled bed a speaking glance of seeming amazement.

'Lesson three on being a proper wife.' Polly whispered her prepared opening sentence before she could lose her nerve. 'Never let the sun go down on a row.'

'It's rising...the sun,' Raul informed her half under his breath and, bending down, he scooped her unresisting body up into his arms, crossed the room and settled her back on the bed.

Frowning, not following that oddly strained if true remark, as the dawn light was indeed already burnishing the night sky, Polly gazed uncertainly up at him. 'What was going on out there?'

Dark colour flared over his superb cheekbones and his

wide, sensual mouth hardened. 'You weren't where you were supposed to be. I thought you'd bolted again.'

'B-bolted where?' Polly asked, with some difficulty squashing the incautious giggle trying to break free of her taut throat.

'How do I know? There's two helicopters out there, a whole collection of cars, a stable full of horses! If you wanted to bolt, it wouldn't be much of a challenge to find the means,' Raul informed her grimly as he stood over her, six foot plus of dark, menacing authority. 'My bed was the last place I expected to find you!'

So he hadn't even looked. He had jumped to conclusions. He had checked the bedroom she should have been in and immediately raised the alarm. Although she was deeply embarrassed by that candid admission that he hadn't dreamt she would have the nerve to take up residence in his bed, she was also rather relieved to register that Raul was not omnipotent. He could not yet forecast her every move. But she turned her head away from the light, fearful that he would see too much in her expressive face.

'Do you want me to go?' she asked with studied casualness.

'No...I can recognise an olive tree when I'm handed one.'

'You mean an olive *branch*,' she contradicted gently.

'No, when you put on silk, scent, mascara and lipstick for my benefit, and arrange yourself like a little bridal sacrifice in my bed...' Raul murmured almost roughly as he stared down at her, brilliant eyes reflecting only the light in his darkly handsome features '...it's definitely not just a branch, it's a whole tree...in fact, it might well be the equivalent of an orchard.' He thrust impatient fingers through his disordered hair and shook his head ruefully. '*Dios mío*...what am I talking about?'

Standing there, talking like that, he seemed disturbingly different. He was still regarding her with a piercing, narrow-eyed intensity that didn't seem to be making him any more comfortable than it was making her. In fact, he looked pretty pale beneath his healthy bronze skin. As Polly was already achingly self-conscious about lying there in his bed, his reactions were increasing her anxiety level. Here she was, offering an invitation to the best of her ability, but maybe he no longer even *wanted* that invitation!

The tense silence seemed to scream in her ears.

'You must've been out riding for a long time...' she commented, desperate to break that nerve-straining quiet.

'I went some distance. I called in with...with a neighbour.' His stubborn jawline clenched, handsome mouth compressing, strong face suddenly shadowing as he strode towards the bathroom. 'I'm filthy. I need a shower.'

Pink-cheeked now, Polly studied him the same way a crossword addict without talent studies the *crème de la crème* of challenges, desperate for a hint of true inspiration. He stepped out of view, and she listened then to the strangely intimate sounds of a man undressing: the thud of his boots hitting the tiled floor, the snap as he presumably undid the waistband of his jodhpurs...

Oh, dear heaven, if Raul no longer even wanted her to share his bed, how did she get out of this situation without losing face?

'Maybe I should go back to my room,' Polly practically whispered.

Sudden silence fell.

Bare-chested and barefoot, Raul appeared in the doorway, all rampant virility with rumpled hair and the jodhpurs which had an indecently faithful fit to his long, lean thighs undone at his waist. 'Whatever you feel most comfortable doing.'

On receipt of that refusal to state an opinion either way— which from a male of Raul's domineering temperament was particularly hard to take—Polly blinked in bemused chagrin.

'But you can sleep here just as easily,' Raul pointed out with a careless shrug.

'Fine…' Polly managed to splutter, turning over on her side to glower with stinging eyes at the dawn filling the sky with such vibrant colour. The unfeeling louse didn't *want* an orchard of olive branches. Her so sophisticated, sexy and immensely self-assured husband was trying to let her down gently. And now she was stuck, because if she jumped out of bed and fled she was going to look really stupid and pathetic! And, furthermore, Raul would then work out for himself that her olive branch had been rather more emotionally motivated than she'd chosen to admit.

She listened to the shower switching off and grimaced. The lights went out. The mattress gave at the other side of the bed.

'If you sleep any closer to the edge, you might fall out,' Raul remarked lazily.

'I don't want to get in your way!' Polly snapped childishly.

Raul released his breath in an audible hiss. 'You don't have anything to fear, *gatita*. I realise that I've been…inconsiderate,' he selected after an uncharacteristic hesitation.

Stiff as a board, Polly strove to work out the intent of that unexpected admission.

'Naturally I want you to be happy,' Raul informed her out of the blue.

'Do you?'

'Of course. Why so amazed?' Raul queried. 'What else would I want?'

'You want the best for Luis,' Polly breathed, not quite levelly. 'I understand that—'

'*Dios*…when I thought you'd gone I never even thought to check on our son!' His slightly dazed tone was that of a male belatedly making that connection and not best pleased by it.

Good heavens, Polly thought in shock over that astonishing admission. Raul had actually thought of *her* first, put *her* first? Instantly it was as if a tight little knot of resentment was jerked loose inside her. She no longer felt like an unwanted wife, to be tolerated only because their son needed his mother. And she wondered when Raul's single-minded focus on Luis had stretched to include her as a person of some import in his own life. But she really didn't care *when* that minor miracle had taken place, she was just so very grateful that it had.

'I wouldn't bolt again…as you put it,' she shared awkwardly.

'I can forgive you for Vermont. That was understandable. The clinic too…you panicked. That's all in the past now.'

Polly turned over. 'But coming here was still a big thing for me…'

'No less a challenge for me, *querida*.' Raul reached for her clenched fingers where they lay above the sheet, and calmly tugged her across the divide between them.

Her breath caught in her throat as he eased her into his arms. Gazing up at him, she drank in the hard bones forming that lean, strong face, her stomach fluttering, her heartbeat racing, every fibre of her body pitched in anticipation of his next move.

Raul rubbed a blunt forefinger gently over the ripe fullness of her parted lips and looked down at her. A sigh feathered in her throat, her eyes widening, dark blue pools of unconscious invitation. 'I…I was just nervous earlier,' she confided.

'You have beautiful eyes. That was the first thing I ever noticed about you.'

'In Vermont?'

'I saw you long before then.'

Her brow furrowed. 'But *how*?'

'Your photograph, then your initial interview with my lawyer. Trick mirror. I was in the office next door,' he confided without apology.

'Devious,' she said breathlessly, her heart hammering as she stared up into mesmeric golden eyes.

'Cautious,' Raul contradicted.

The hard heat of his lean, virile body was seeping into her by pervasive degrees. She was so outrageously conscious of his proximity that she was keeping her lungs going on tiny little pants. 'Kiss me,' she muttered, before she could lose her nerve.

'I'm burning up to possess you,' Raul breathed thickly. 'I won't stop at kissing.'

She trembled and, closing her eyes, reached up to press her lips against his. Teasingly he circled her mouth with his own, refusing to deepen the pressure, and in sudden driving impatience Polly sank her fingers into the depths of his luxuriant black hair to pull him down to her.

Vibrant amusement shimmered in his eyes as he held himself above her. 'Is that a yes?'

Shaken then by her own boldness, she met the reckless golden glitter of sensual threat in his gaze and started melting down deep inside, the weighted languor of anticipation sentencing her to stillness. Helplessly she nodded.

With a slashing smile that turned her heart over, Raul lowered his imperious dark head. 'You have to understand that this is a first for me too,' he shared silkily. 'I've never had a virgin in my bed. It makes you very special.'

'I never know whether you're being ironic or sincere,' Polly muttered tautly.

'Only a very stupid man would be ironic on his wedding night,' Raul asserted as he brought his hard, mobile mouth passionately down on hers.

He kissed her with innate eroticism, parting her lips, letting his tongue plunge deep into the honeyed warmth within, seeking out and finding every tender spot. Clutching at him, she was madly conscious of every slight movement he made, and wholly at the mercy of the wild, sweet, seductive feelings sweeping through her quivering body. It was a passionate, urgent exploration that betrayed his very masculine hunger, a growl of satisfaction escaping his throat before he lifted his head again, surveying her with shameless satisfaction.

'I told you that you would come to me, *mi esposa*.'

Her lashes fluttered up. She gave him a dazed look of reproach, too shaken by the effect he was having on her to muster a tart response. He came back to her again, tasting her, delving deep and then skimming the tender roof of her mouth in a flickering, provocative caress until she was gasping for breath but still hanging onto him.

Leaning back from her then, an unashamedly predatory smile on his sensual mouth, Raul trailed the ribbon straps of her nightgown slowly down over her slight shoulders, brushing them down her arms and then carefully slipping her hands free at the wrists.

'I want to look at all of you,' he breathed huskily. 'Touch all of you. Taste every smooth, silken inch of that pale, perfect skin and then sink so deep into you, you won't know where I end and you begin.'

Transfixed, and hectically flushed, Polly stared up at him, utterly overpowered by the tiny little tremors already racking her taut length, the tormenting throb of heat she could feel between her slender thighs. Torn between fascination and shyness, she watched him smoothly tug down the bodice of her nightgown so that her small, firm breasts sprang free, her nipples already wantonly distended rosy buds.

'Raul, please…' she moaned, hot with a debilitating and confusing mix of embarrassment and excitement.

'*Dios*…but you are exquisite.' His dark golden eyes blazed over her bare breasts with urgent appreciation and made her tremble.

With deft but impatient hands, Raul eased the nightgown tangled round her waist down over her slim hips, raising her knees to slide the garment finally free and discard it.

Smoothing a soothing hand over her shifting hips, he ran intent eyes over the slender length of her, her tiny waist, delicately rounded stomach, the cluster of dark curls crowning the juncture of her trembling thighs. As she made a sudden impulsive snatch at the sheet, he forestalled her, and gazed down at her with a wicked smile. 'I've waited a long time to see you like this.' Long brown fingers closed round her wrist and lingered. 'Your pulse is going crazy. Admit it…it's exciting to be looked at, appreciated and lusted over. What did you expect, *querida*? That I would fall on you like a clumsy, selfish boy and it would all be over in minutes? That is not how I make love…'

'No…' Polly conceded shakily, scarcely able to swallow, so constricted was her throat.

A dark line of colour lay over his superb cheekbones. 'I want this to be good for you…I want you to spend all day aching for the moment when I take you in my arms again…'

Trembling like a leaf, with the heat surging through her in waves, Polly mumbled, 'Ambitious…'

'Always…in everything. It's in my blood,' Raul husked in agreement, running an exploring hand lightly over her outrageously sensitive breasts and forcing a gasp of startled reaction from her.

Helplessly she strained up to him, and with the tip of his tongue he provocatively traced the already reddened curve of her lips, so that she tipped her head back, openly inviting the hot, hard pressure of his mouth which every sense craved.

With a roughened laugh he tasted her again, sliding a hand beneath her hips and pressing her into contact with the aggressive thrust of his own arousal, and excitement drenched her in a blinding, burning wave. She moaned beneath that devastating mouth of his, need rising like a greedy fire as he let his fingers finally stroke and tug her achingly sensitive nipples. Freeing her swollen lips, he slid down the bed and employed that expert mouth on her tender breasts instead.

Pushing up against him, she twisted wildly, unprepared for the raw tide of sensation engulfing her now. Every intimate caress felt so unbearably good, yet all the time she strained and yearned helplessly for more, intoxicated by physical feelings she had never experienced before and ruled by their demands.

'Easy, *gatita*,' Raul muttered softly, pulling her to him, stilling her helpless squirmings with the momentary weight of one long, powerful thigh. 'We're not running a race...'

Polly snatched in a long, shuddering breath, focusing on him in a dazed kind of wonderment. 'I didn't know it would be like this...'

'Like a raging fire in which two can burn up with pleasure?' Raul bent over her and let his lips brush tenderly over hers.

She jerked as he eased her thighs apart and embarked on a more intimate invasion, touching her where she had never been touched before, discovering the damp silken ache at the centre of her. And he caressed her with such shrewd comprehension of what would excite her most that she was overwhelmed by the uncontrollable pleasure, sobbing against his broad shoulder, always longing and needing and finally begging for more as the desperate need for greater fulfilment rose to screaming proportions inside her.

And then Raul came smoothly over her, and surged into her before she could even get the chance to fear the unknown. As he thrust deeper there was a short, sharp pain that made her cry out, and then, a split second later, the most extraordinary and intense feeling of physical pleasure as he abruptly stilled to gaze with rather touching anxiety down at her.

'I hoped it wouldn't hurt,' Raul confessed raggedly.

And Polly smiled a little dizzily up at him, at that moment loving him so much for caring that she was weak with the strength of the emotion shrilling through her.

'Doesn't matter,' she swore unsteadily.

And then he moved within her again, and her eyes slid shut on the rush of sensation which was so indescribably seductive and controlling. If he had stopped she would have died, and she wrapped herself round him, utterly lost within the surging domination of his possession. He drove her up to the heights and she splintered there in ecstasy, glorying in his groan of intense physical pleasure as he slammed into her one last time with compulsive driving force.

Eyes welling with tears from the sheer raw intensity of her emotions, Polly held him tight within the circle of her arms, revelling in the sweetness of her new right to do that, openly and unashamedly, without fear of revealing too much. And she marvelled at how much closer she felt to Raul now. She wanted those timeless, tranquil moments to last for ever. He was an absolutely fantastic lover, she decided. Lying in that gloriously intimate embrace and knowing that she had satisfied him, in spite of her inexperience, filled her with new pride and confidence.

In that same instant of heady contentment Raul pulled away from her and sprawled back against the pillows again. He flipped his tousled dark head over and surveyed her with deceptively indolent dark golden eyes that gleamed with satisfaction. 'You see, love isn't necessary to sexual gratification.'

Already hurt by the speed of his withdrawal from physical proximity, Polly gazed back at him with a sinking sensation in her stomach. 'Is there a point to that comment?' she asked tautly.

'I think you get the point.'

'It's a re-run of the "don't expect too much from me," escape hatch for the commitment-shy male, is it?' Polly condemned on a rush of bitter pain that filled her with a furious need to strike back. 'You are just so terrified of emotion I actually feel sorry for you, but why should you worry about disappointing me? After all, you've been disappointing me one way or another ever since the first day we met!'

Stunned by that ringing and unexpected indictment, any pretense of indolence now abandoned, Raul stared at her, eyes dangerous as black ice. 'Is that a fact?' he breathed unevenly—only so thick was his accent it sounded much more like, 'Ees-zat-a-fat?', so she knew she had hit home very hard.

Polly snatched up her nightie and pulled it over her head with trembling hands. 'Yes...but it hardly matters,' she assured him with a skimming look of scorn. 'I have nothing to lose and I'm not lowering my needs to the level of yours. You're on probation, Raul.'

So incensed was he by that patronising little speech, he threw back the sheet and sprang out of bed. 'I...Raul Zaforteza...on *probation*?' he gritted in savage disbelief.

Squaring her slight shoulders, Polly was unrepentant. 'And so far you are not doing very well. You seem to think you've done me one very big favour marrying me...but ask me how *I* feel five months from now—'

'*Por qué?* What the hell is going to happen in five months?' Raul raked at her across the depth of the bedroom.

'I will inherit my godmother's money, and if I'm not happy with you, I'm not spending the rest of my life in misery.'

'*Misery?*' Raul ground out in outrage.

'I'm not,' Polly told him, and meant it. 'You needn't think you can toss diamond jewellery at me to keep me happy. Diamonds are quite pretty, but not something I feel I have to have.'

'*Pretty?*' Raul echoed in rampant disbelief.

'Other things mean much more to me...respect, affection, caring. I do appreciate that you have probably spent the entirety of your adult life giving extravagant gifts to women because you can't cope with emotional demands, but—'

'How dare you say I cannot cope?' Volatile golden eyes slammed into hers in a look as hostile as a physical assault.

'You said it yourself. You said you walk away when things get difficult.' Polly made that incendiary reminder with reluctance.

Raul studied her with a seething, wordless incomprehension that twisted her heart inside out. Then he spun away, presenting her with the long golden sweep of his flawless back to wrench open a drawer and start to haul on a pair of black jeans. She knew he didn't even trust himself to speak. She knew he was infuriated by the sudden struggle speaking English had become because he was in such an ungovernable rage.

'I realize I'm far from perfect, and that a lot of things I do and say must irritate you...but I don't think I deserve to feel that you only came home tonight to have sex with me,' Polly told him, her eyes stinging so hard she had to open her eyes very wide to hold the tears back. 'Like I'm some sort of novelty act...and then, right after it, regardless of my feelings, you have to gloat—'

On that charge, Raul swung back. 'All I said was that love was not necessary to—'

Polly drew in a deep, shuddering breath. 'And why did you say that?' she whispered painfully, suddenly sick and tired of pretending. 'You knew it wasn't true. You *must* know how I feel about you. I think you've *always* known...'

Raul went very still. Dense black lashes dropped low, spectacular eyes betraying only a glint of gold, ferocious tension tightening his bronzed skin over his fabulous bone structure. 'You're going to regret this...'

'No, I won't. I'm past caring,' Polly muttered with perfect truth. 'I love you to death, and you probably knew it before I did! If you'd had a single shred of decency you would've backed off in Vermont. In the same way you knew exactly why I wanted to marry you...yet you told Digby I was a gold-digger and a blackmailer. It's like a big black secret you won't acknowledge, but I won't live a lie, Raul.'

Utterly drained by that stark baring of her own tormented emotions, Polly slid out of the bed and walked towards the door.

'*Dios*...I can't give you love!' Raul launched at her with positive savagery.

'But with a little effort you could make a reasonable stab at respect, if not anything else. Because if you don't,' Polly whispered jaggedly, torn in two with pain and the regret he had so accurately forecast she would feel, 'I'll stop loving you, and love is all you have to hold me. I won't be a doormat...I won't be walked on.'

Without looking back, she flipped the door shut behind her. She was in a complete daze, shock at what she had done and said hitting her all at once. She was shaking all over, moving towards the sanctuary of the guest room she had abandoned earlier on jellied knees. But somehow she didn't feel like crying any more. What had passed between her and Raul had been too devastating. A shame something she had found so wonderful, so beautiful, had had to end in such emotional agony.

Raul simply couldn't have allowed it to stay that good. He had had to open that smart mouth of his and blow everything apart. Make her feel like a one-night stand instead of a wife who loved him—and who he knew damned well loved him! In the clear dawn light she lay down on the bed, a giant, aching hole where her heart had been. She didn't want a heart that hurt her so much.

When the door opened again, she sat up with a start. Raul thrust the door shut behind him and studied her, brilliant black eyes incisive.

'I too have faults,' Raul murmured. 'But, unlike you, I acknowledge them.'

'What are you saying?' Feeling worn and drained, Polly simply bowed her head defensively over her raised knees.

'Yes, I disappointed you in Vermont...but then you disappointed me too.'

Disconcerted by that assurance, Polly lifted her head. Raul held her questioning look with unflinching cool.

'If you had been the truly honest woman you like to believe you are, you would have told me that you were pregnant then. But, when it suited your purposes to remain silent, you were as neglectful of the truth as I was about my real identity. I think we're about equal on the score of disappointing each other,' Raul completed drily.

A slow, painful pink had surged into Polly's cheeks. It shook her to be faced with the fact that she had also made mistakes—not least by ignoring reality when it seemed to be within her own interests to do so. She had never come close to telling Raul that she was a surrogate mum-to-be, had been too frightened he would reject her in disgust. How ironic it was that he had known all along, and even judged her on that cowardly silence!

'I suppose you're right,' she contrived to force out rather hoarsely.

'As for last night, and your conviction that I only returned to have sex with you—do you really think I am so immature *or* so desperate for sexual release?' At that searing demand, Polly twisted her head away, no longer caring how he translated such a reaction. 'I'm here now because I accepted that I shouldn't have left you in the first place, and that such behaviour would only reinforce your fears about our future.'

Polly linked her fingers fiercely tight together. All rage put behind him, Raul's ice-cool and rational rebuttal of her angry accusations was a cruelly effective weapon of humiliation. 'OK,' she got out, when she couldn't bear his expectant silence any longer.

'And do you really think that threatening to leave me in five months' time is likely to add to the stability of our marriage?'

Polly flinched as if he had cracked a whip over her. She felt like a child being told off for bad behaviour.

'Now I think you're going to sulk,' Raul forecast, with an even more lowering air of adult restraint.

Polly struggled, and finally managed to swallow the enormous lump in her throat. 'I think you're probably right.'

CHAPTER NINE

RAUL'S equestrian centre was a vastly impressive installation set about a mile from the ranch. Polly settled Luis into his stroller and wandered down the asphalt lane in the sweltering heat, striving not to look like a woman out in search of her husband. But the truth was she was getting desperate, for she had seen virtually nothing of Raul over the past few days.

Indeed, after those twin earth-shattering scenes at dawn, she had initially expected to find Raul a good thousand miles away on business by the time he appeared the following day. Why? Because he was thoroughly fed up with her! Fed up with the virtual minefield she had already made of their marriage of convenience and fed up with her over-emotional reactions. What had happened to patience? Calm? Reasoned restraint?

But in the cruellest possible way she had Raul trapped. He might not be able to respond to emotional demands, but, challenged with an accusation of cowardice, sheer horror that she might be right would keep him on the spot. Only 'on the spot' at the ranch unfortunately seemed to mean that he could avoid her just as effectively.

He had a suite of rooms he used as offices on the ground floor, and staff who flew in and out as if helicopters were buses. He rose at dawn and went riding every morning and never returned to the ranch for breakfast. Either he was engaged in business the rest of the day or down at the equestrian centre. But every evening they dined together in the stifling formality of the dining room.

And, terrifyingly, it was as if that confrontation several days earlier had never happened—only now there was a divide the width of the Atlantic ocean between them. Raul didn't need to walk away to hold her at a distance. He could make civil conversation, express a courteous desire to know what she had done with her day, discuss Luis and generally treat her like an honoured house guest with whom, regrettably, he didn't have very much time to spend. Oh, yes, and leave her to sleep in a guest room bed without a visible ounce of regret.

So now, when Polly espied Raul chatting to a fair-haired man in front of the state-of-the-art stables, she attempted to appear slightly surprised to run into him. She wanted to behave normally, but without giving him the impression she had deliberately sought him out.

Embarrassingly sexual butterflies erupted in her tummy as she watched him lithely straighten from his elegant lounging position against the rail. As always, he looked stupendous, black hair flopping over his bronzed brow, dark, deep-set eyes narrowed, wide shoulders outlined by a black polo shirt, lean hips and long powerful thighs sheathed in skintight jodhpurs, polished boots gleaming in the sunshine.

'Fancy seeing you here' might well be interpreted as sarcasm, so she gave Raul a purposely casual smile. Her heartbeat thundered with suppressed excitement against her breastbone, ensuring that she swiftly removed her attention from him again. 'Luis and I are just out for a walk,' she announced, and then wanted to bite her tongue out because she sounded positively fatuous.

'This is Patrick Gorman, Polly.' Raul introduced the slim, fair-haired younger man already extending his hand to her. 'He runs the breeding programme for the polo ponies.'

'Delighted to meet you, Mrs Zaforteza.'

'You're English!' Polly registered with surprise and pleasure. 'And I think I recognise that accent. Newcastle?'

'Spot on!'

Polly laughed. 'I was born in Blyth, but my parents moved south when I was six.'

'That's why you don't have a hint of a Geordie accent.' Giving her an appreciative grin, Patrick bent over the stroller. 'I'm crazy about babies!' he exclaimed, squatting down to get a closer look at Luis, where he was contentedly drowsing under the parasol. 'He's incredibly little, isn't he?'

'He's actually quite big for his age,' Polly asserted proudly, thinking how wonderfully well this supposedly accidental meeting with Raul was going, because Patrick was the chatty type which naturally helped to break the ice.

'My niece is a year old, and quite a handful last time I saw her,' Patrick told her cheerfully.

'Luis doesn't do much more than eat and sleep at the minute.'

'You have a lot of fun ahead of you,' Patrick Gorman smiled. 'Since Raul has some calls to make, would you like me to show you around this operation?'

'The calls will wait. I'll do the guided tour,' Raul slotted in smoothly, his attention darkly fixed to his animated and chattering companions.

Polly risked a glance at Raul. Brooding tension had hardened his lean, dark face. In receipt of a smouldering look, she flushed. 'Are you sure you can spare the time?' she pressed anxiously.

Disconcertingly, Raul dropped a casual arm round her taut shoulders. 'Why not?'

'Did I say something wrong back there?' Polly asked as he walked her away from the younger man.

'You talked more in two minutes to a complete stranger than you have talked to me in three entire days,' Raul delivered silkily. 'However, I would advise you to maintain a certain formal distance with Patrick.'

'Why?'

'Don't be misled by all that boyish charm. Patrick is a serial womaniser.'

Polly blinked. 'He seemed very nice. He was so interested in Luis.'

'It was just a light word of warning,' Raul drawled dismissively, his blunt cheekbones accentuated by a slight darkening of colour as she frowned at him in patent confusion over why he should have found it necessary to give that warning.

He changed the subject. 'Actually, I thought you would've been down to the stables long before now. Country-bred Englishwomen are always mad about horses. They even take their ponies to boarding school with them!' He laughed with husky appreciation. 'I expect you ride pretty well yourself.'

Conscious of the approving satisfaction he didn't attempt to conceal in his assumption that she was used to being around horses, Polly muttered, 'Er...well—'

'I've never met an Englishwoman who didn't,' Raul confided, making her tense even more. 'And, as horses are a major part of my life, that's one interest we can share.'

'I'm probably a bit rusty...riding,' Polly heard herself say, when she had *never* been on a horse in her entire life. But any wish Raul might express to share anything other than a bed deserved the maximum encouragement.

A split second later, she realised that she had just told a very stupid lie which would be easily exposed, but she had been so delighted at his talk of wanting to share his love of horses with her that she hadn't been able to bring herself to disappoint him. She would teach herself to ride, just enough to pass herself. It couldn't be that difficult, could it? In the meantime, all she had to do was make excuses.

He showed her round the stables. She copied every move he made with the horses poking their heads out over the doors. Mirroring worked a treat. Just about everything he told her went right over her head, because her knowledge of horseflesh began and ended with a childhood love of reading *Black Beauty*.

'It's all so fascinating,' she commented with a mesmerised smile while he talked about polo—an incomprehensible commentary on chukkas, throw-ins and ride-offs. His lean brown hands sketched vivid impressions to stress the fast and furious action. It occurred to her that even if he had been talking in Spanish she would still have been utterly hooked. His sheer enthusiasm had a hypnotic effect on her.

Registering the glow in her dark blue eyes as she listened to him, Raul smiled. 'You look happier today, *querida*.'

The silence that fell as he uttered the endearment seemed to thump in time with Polly's hopelessly impressionable heart. The tip of her tongue snaked out to dampen her dry lower lip. His stunning dark golden eyes homed in on the tiny movement and her tummy simply flipped. In the hot, still air, a storm of such powerful desire engulfed Polly that she quivered with embarrassment.

A slow smile curved Raul's beautiful mouth. Striding forward with confidence, he reached for her, a sudden burning brilliance blazing in his gorgeous eyes. 'You're trembling...'

And he knew why. He radiated an answering sexual heat that overwhelmed her every attempt to conceal her own reactions. And when he hauled her close with hungry hands, and plunged his mouth down passionately hard on hers, she felt as if the top of her head was flying off with excitement, and she simply went limp, eyes sliding shut, struggling to breathe, heart pounding like a manic triphammer.

'Oh, boy...' she gasped, as Raul lifted his imperious dark head again, pressing her shaken face against his shoulder. Feverishly she drank in his hot, clean scent, torn by a devouring need for him that was shatteringly intense.

But it was balanced by an awareness of *his* hunger, the jerky little shudder racking him as he snatched in a fractured breath. The barriers had come down, she sensed. He was touching her again. She was no longer off limits, like an ornament sheltering under a glass bell jar. And he wanted her, oh, yes, he wanted her, and this time that was going to be enough, she told herself urgently.

As he set her back from him, brilliant eyes veiled, Raul murmured lazily, 'I'll pick you up for a picnic lunch around three. Leave Luis at home.'

A little fretful squalling cry erupted like a comical complaint from the stroller. Raul burst out laughing. Surveying his wakening son's cross little face with a luminous pride he could not conceal, he sighed, 'We made a wonderful son together...I just wish we had made him between the sheets.'

Polly blushed, but she was touched that he should think along the same lines as she had done. 'Not much we can do about that.'

'But we'll do it the normal way the next time,' Raul asserted with amusement, and before she could even blossom at that reassuring implication that they would have another child some day, he added with deflating practicality, 'One of the grooms will run you back to the ranch. You shouldn't be out in this heat without a hat. Sunstroke is not a very pleasant experience.'

When she walked into her bedroom, two of the maids were hanging a rail of unfamiliar new garments in the wardrobe. Polly hovered, fingering rich fabrics, recognising wildly expensive designer tailoring. Dear heaven, Raul had bought her clothes. No asking, What do you like? No suggestion that she go and choose for herself. She eased a sleek dress in a smoky shade of blue from a padded hanger and held it against herself. Lordy, she'd never worn anything that short in her life!

But she was smiling, because she was already walking on air. *Next time.* Two little words that told her that Raul regarded their marriage as a lasting development. She put on the blue dress and then tracked down the housekeeper and asked for the keys of the curious little turreted building on the south boundary of the gardens. She had a couple of hours to kill, and yesterday had peered in through the shrouded windows and found the doors securely locked.

'No one goes there now, *señora*.' The older woman muttered something anxious in Spanish about *el patrón*, her kindly face strained as she finally passed over the keys with marked reluctance.

The staff might be superstitious about the place, but Polly was unconcerned by that troubled reference to '*el patrón*'. Raul wouldn't give two hoots if she went and explored. This was supposed to be her home now, and that picturesque building intrigued her.

She opened the Gothic front door and walked into a split-level, surprisingly spacious room with dust-covered furniture. The walls were faded and stained, the curtains in an advanced state of disintegration. She wandered through silent rooms, coming on a dated kitchen layered with dust before she walked up the cast-iron staircase.

There was a large bedroom, a bathroom, and then one other bedroom. She stopped in the doorway of the third room. It was a child's room, with little rusty cars still sitting on shelves, yellowing photos curling up on a noticeboard, as if the little boy had just gone away and never come back. It was eerie.

She peered at the photos. One she recognised as Raul's father. There were two portraits at the ranch that she had assumed were of Raul's parents. Eduardo, who bore a marked resemblance to Raul, and Yolanda, a regal blue-eyed blonde, who resembled him not at all. She didn't recognise the laughing brunette with the exotic tigerish eyes, although those eyes reminded her of…Raul's eyes?

The sounds of steps on the metal stairs sent Polly hurrying back out onto the landing. It was Raul, still dressed in his riding gear, breathing shallowly as if he had been hurrying.

'What are you doing poking around in here?' he demanded rawly, a savage glitter in his golden eyes, harsh lines of strain bracketing his sensual mouth.

Polly was thoroughly disconcerted by his reaction. 'I wasn't "poking around"...I was just curious. Who lived here? I didn't realise anyone had actually lived here until I came inside.'

Raul studied her fiercely and then finally lifted a wide shoulder in a jerky shrug of grudging acceptance. 'I thought you knew. Everyone knows... My family background has been exhaustively dug up and raked over by the media.'

A sense of foreboding touched Polly then, her stomach muscles clenching tight. Raul was reacting like someone in shock, his eyes flickering uneasily over their surroundings and then skimming away again, a far-away look of grim vulnerability in his eyes until he shielded them, his facial bones ferociously prominent beneath his bronzed skin.

'I lived here with my mother until I was nine,' Raul told her flatly.

'Your parents separated?' she asked in bewilderment.

Raul vented a hollow laugh. 'My mother was my father's mistress, Polly, *not* his wife!'

Floundering in shock, Polly stammered, 'B-but the blonde woman in the picture in the hall—?'

'My father's wife, Yolanda. Our lifestyle was somewhat dysfunctional.'

With a mistress in a flamboyant little house at the foot of the garden? He wasn't joking.

Raul explained in a very few words. His mother, Pilar, had been the daughter of a *llanero*, who'd worked on a neighbouring tenant's ranch. Pilar had already been pregnant with Raul when Eduardo Zaforteza married his beautiful oil heiress bride.

'When Yolanda found out about my mother, she locked the bedroom door, and my father used that as his excuse to bring us here to live,' Raul shared tautly. 'After my mother's death, he gave Yolanda half of everything he possessed to agree to my adoption.'

'What age were you when your mother died?' Polly muttered.

'Nine. There used to be a swimming pool out there. She drowned in it when she was drunk. She was frequently drunk,' Raul admitted flatly. 'What my father called "love" destroyed her...in fact it destroyed all our lives.'

'Yolanda never had any children?'

'Frequent miscarriages...*sí*, the bedroom door was unlocked eventually.' Raul grimaced. 'I think my father enjoyed having two women fighting over him. When it became a hassle, he just took off and left them to it for a while. He and Yolanda died in a plane crash almost ten years ago.'

Nausea was stirring in Polly's sensitive stomach. All of a sudden she was seeing and understanding so much, but recoiling from a vision of the distressing scenes which Raul must have witnessed as he grew up. An unhappy mother with a drink problem. No normal family life, no secure childhood, nothing but tangled adult relationships and constant strife.

She was imagining how much the wronged wife must have loathed Raul and his mother, and didn't even want to consider what it had been like for Raul to live in the same house with Yolanda from the tender age of nine. An embittered woman, who had forced her husband to pay for the right to adopt his illegitimate son. Little wonder Raul found it a challenge to believe in love or the deeper bonds of marriage.

'You should have this place cleared out.' Polly strove for a brisk tone.

'I haven't set foot here in years. It was my father who insisted it stay as it was. He liked to come here when he felt sentimental,' Raul said with lethal derision.

Polly was frankly appalled by what he had told her, but working hard to hide it. She was annoyed that she had blundered in to rouse such unpleasant memories, and exasperated that she hadn't had more interest that long-ago day at the library in learning about Raul's background rather than about the women in his life. She started down the curving staircase, eager to be out in the fresh air again.

'I'll have this place emptied, then…OK?' Polly pressed, seeking agreement for what she saw as a necessary act.

Raul shrugged with comforting unconcern. The distant look had gone from his eyes as he scrutinised her appearance and his mouth quirked. 'So the clothes have arrived…I chose them when I was in Caracas. At least you've got something decent to wear until you do your own shopping,' he pointed out, for all the world as if she had been walking around in rags.

Half an hour later, they got into a four-wheel drive to head out for the picnic he had promised. They left the asphalt lanes that criss-crossed the vast spread of the ranch buildings to hurtle down a dusty trail and then out across the grassy plains. All sign of modern civilisation was left behind within minutes. Yellow poplars, gum trees and the ubiquitous palm grew in thickets on higher ground, where the floodwater hadn't reached. Great flocks of exotic multi-coloured birds rose from the trees with shrill cries as they passed.

The sky was a clear, cloudless turquoise over the sun-drenched savannah. It was a strange and unfamiliar terrain to Polly, yet the *llanos*, teaming with wildlife in their isolation, had a haunting, fascinating beauty.

'Where are we going?' she finally asked.

'Wait and see,' Raul advised lazily.

He brought the car to a halt and sprang out. As she followed, all she could see was a dense line of trees. Raul pulled a hamper out of the back seat. They walked under the trees, and then she caught her breath. In a gently sloping hidden valley below them, a waterfall tumbled down over ancient weathered rocks into a reed-edged lagoon.

'Once a tributary of the Orinoco river ran through here…this is all that remains.' Raul set the hamper down on the lush grass in the shade of the coconut palms.

Polly was enchanted. 'It's so peaceful.'

'My mother brought me here as a child. This place was special to her,' Raul confided. 'I suspect I might have been conceived here.'

'Don't you have any family left alive?' Polly asked as she sat down.

Raul swung round to look at her, his fabulous bone structure tensing, dark eyes sombre in the sunlight. 'My grandfather, Fidelio.' Raul shrugged. 'He disowned my mother. He's a very proud old man, and still refuses to acknowledge our relationship, but I told him about Luis last week.'

'I'm sorry I've been so prickly and awkward,' Polly said abruptly.

Raul gave her a slanting smile as he sank down beside her. 'I've been awkward too. This...you and I...it's all new to me.'

That rueful smile touched something deep inside her. Rising up on her knees, Polly took her courage in both hands. Planting her palms against his chest, she pushed him flat.

Startled, Raul gazed up at her, and then a wolfish grin slashed his face. 'And I was going to be a gentleman, *gatita*. I was planning to wait until you'd eaten! But, since we are both of one mind...' Raul murmured, taking pity on her as she hovered above him, uncertain of what to do next, and reaching up to slowly draw her down to him.

He sent his hands skimming down to her slim hips and eased her into the cradle of his long, muscular thighs with an erotic suggestiveness that was as bold as it was unashamed. Melded to every virile line of his powerful body, Polly turned boneless. He undid the zip on her dress and tipped it down off her shoulders.

Her firm breasts rose and fell inside the delicate cups of her lace bra. He unclipped the bra and curved appreciative hands over the pale, pouting curves that tumbled out. She gave a muffled gasp as he tugged at her straining nipples and arched her back, excitement seizing her in its hold.

Raul flipped her over gently onto her back. Vaulting upright, he proceeded to remove his clothes with a lack of cool that only excited her more. She lifted her hips, tugged down the dress, sat up to shyly dispose of her remaining garments—but all the time she was covertly watching him. As that superb bronze body emerged she was enthralled, mouth bone-dry, pulses accelerating.

A delicious little quiver of anticipation made her ache. Just looking at him, seeing the potent evidence of his desire for her, stole her breath away. He was so aroused she could feel herself melting into a liquid pool of submission. And when he returned to her she was already on fire, the swollen pink buds of her breasts begging for his attention, a sensation of damp heat throbbing almost painfully between her thighs.

His stunning eyes read the message in hers. He came down to her and kissed her breathless with a force of hunger that overwhelmed her own. 'I feel wild...' he groaned with a ragged laugh. 'One more night watching you across the dining table and I would've pulled you under it!'

'It didn't show.'

'*Infierno*...I get as hard as a rock just being in the same room with you,' Raul growled rawly. 'I don't think I have ever been so frustrated in my life! I was tempted to take you into the stables earlier and...' As her dark blue eyes widened in open shock at that series of blunt revelations, he compressed his lips, a dark rise of blood emphasising his cheekbones. 'I just want you so much I can't think of anything else right now.'

Polly was dazed by that almost apologetic conclusion. She had never once dreamt that Raul might come to desire her to such an extent. Colliding with devouring golden eyes, she shivered. He meshed a not quite steady hand into her hair.

'That's all right,' she mumbled, mesmerised by his intensity but even weaker now with wanton longing. 'I want you too.'

Heat flooded her as he kneed her legs apart. He had said

he felt wild, and what he did to her *was* wild. Nothing could have prepared her for the storm of powerful need he released. He took her hard and fast, and then so slowly and so agonisingly sweetly that she was plunged into a mindless glory of acute pleasure, afterwards savouring every precious moment of satiated contentment in his arms, certain that they had turned a corner to forge deeper bonds.

She slept for a while then. She wakened, feeling ridiculously shy, to focus on Raul, where he lay fully dressed again in a careless sprawl, an unusually peaceful aspect to his stillness. Assuming he was asleep, she sat up. His lashes were as lush as black silk fans, his sensual mouth relaxed in repose, dark stubble already outlining his stubborn jawline. She could not resist running a loving finger down gently over one proud cheekbone.

He opened his eyes and she froze, like a thief caught in the act.

Whipping up a hand, he closed his fingers round her wrist and planted a kiss to the damp centre of her palm. 'You make me feel good,' he confided softly.

And the rush of love that surged through her in response left her dizzy.

Raul sat up, still retaining a light hold on her hand, and dealt her a wry look. 'How do you feel about having another baby in about nine months?'

'I…I b-beg your pardon?'

'I didn't take any precautions…' Raul raised two expressive hands, clearly primed for a furious outburst. 'I just didn't think…I was very excited.'

Hugging the dress he must have tossed over her while she slept, Polly reflected that he had gone from never having taken that risk to repeating it over and over again with a devastating lack of inhibition. But then she was his wife—once a chosen baby machine, she conceded rather sourly. No doubt he imagined it would be no big deal for her to find herself pregnant again so soon. But right at that moment Polly cringed at the prospect of her freshly slender and now apparently sexually attractive shape vanishing again. Raul wouldn't find her remotely attractive any more and he might stray, she thought fearfully.

'I'm sorry...' Raul breathed tightly as the silence stretched and stretched.

'It's all right for you...you're not going to get all fat and clumsy, are you?'

Instantly Raul closed an arm round her. 'You were not fat and clumsy...you were gorgeous.'

'You like babies. You're not likely to tell me the truth—and I've never been gorgeous in my life!' Polly added for good measure.

'Why did I find you so tempting while you were in the clinic, then?'

Polly stilled. 'Did you?'

'I thought you were incredibly sexy...like a lush, ripe peach.'

She supposed peaches were at least round. But she looked at him, saw his sincerity and swallowed hard on another tart retort. 'My body hasn't settled down yet,' she shared, striving not to be prim about discussing such a thing with him. 'So I don't know how much of a risk there is.'

As Polly shimmied back into her dress, Raul glanced at his watch and swore succinctly in Spanish. '*Caramba*...look at the time—and we have guests coming to dinner!'

As she stood up, Raul zipped her dress for her. She was conscious of her body's decided tenderness, the result of their frantic lovemaking. He was oversexed, as well as careless, but she still loved him to death. Otherwise she probably would have killed him at that moment for simply dropping on her this late in the day the fact that they were entertaining guests.

'Who's coming?' she asked, balancing to slide into her second shoe.

'Melina D'Agnolo and—' A firm hand snaked out swiftly to steady her as she staggered on one leg and nearly went headlong down the slope. *'Dios mío, mi esposa*…take care!' Raul urged.

'You were saying?' Her head bent to conceal her shock, Polly breathed in very shakily.

'Melina, our closest neighbour,' Raul shared, with what Polly considered to be megawatt cool. 'She grew up on the ranch she's currently renting from the estate. She's bringing the Drydons—mutual friends. Patrick will join us. He used to work for Rob Drydon.'

'I'll enjoy meeting them.' Polly sneaked a glance at Raul to see if he looked even slightly self-conscious. He didn't.

Raul swept up the hamper and even joked about the fact that they had eaten nothing. They strolled back to the car. Raul helped her into the passenger seat.

'I'm a brute,' he murmured, scanning the bluish shadows of tiredness under her eyes. 'But it was fantastic, *es verdad*?'

Melina was a neighbour. The *llanos* looked empty for miles and miles, but they harboured the poisonous Melina somewhere close by. It was ghastly news. Worse, Raul expected her to entertain his ex-mistress. He was cooler than an ice cube. But then he wasn't aware that she knew about that former relationship. *Former*, she emphasised to herself with determination.

Raul was a sophisticated male and she was being naive. His intimate relationship with Melina D'Agnolo might be over, but that didn't mean he would cut her out of his life altogether. She had to taken an adult view of this social encounter.

CHAPTER TEN

'I AM so very pleased for you both,' Melina murmured, with a look of deep sincerity in her green eyes as she reached for Polly's hand in an open and friendly manner.

Dear heaven, she could act me off the stage, Polly registered in dismay, not having been prepared for quite so impressive a pretence. Stunning, in a black lace dress which clung to her superb figure like a second skin, Melina curved a light hand over Raul's sleeve and recounted a witty little story which made him laugh.

Polly had been feeling really good in her scarlet off-the-shoulder dress—until just before she came downstairs. Now her head was aching. She hoped Melina's pleasantries were more than surface-deep.

Rob Drydon and his wife, Susie, were from Texas, and eagerly talking horses with Patrick Gorman. As they transferred to the dining room Melina was in full flow of conversation with Raul, and Polly was left to trail behind them. Patrick caught up with her.

'The *condesa* will walk all over you if you let her,' he whispered in her ear.

Polly's eyes widened. She glanced up at him.

Patrick gave her a rueful look. 'The scene she threw on your arrival was too good a story for the staff to keep quiet. I heard the grooms talking about it,' he confided. 'And as Raul needs the least protection of any male I know, why is he the only person around here who *doesn't* know about the warm welcome you received?'

Polly tensed. 'There wasn't any need to involve him.'

'If you'd involved Raul, she wouldn't be here now, spoiling your evening,' Patrick dropped gently.

As Patrick tucked Polly into her chair at the foot of the table she encountered Raul's level scrutiny, and found herself flushing without knowing why. Picking up her wine glass, she drank.

'Raul told me to pick out a decent mount for you,' Patrick shared chattily.

Polly's wine went down the wrong way. She spluttered, cleared her throat, and gave her companion a pleading look. 'Can you keep a secret, Patrick?'

He nodded.

Leaning her head guiltily close to his, Polly whispered, 'I'm afraid I wasn't entirely honest about my riding ability.'

Patrick frowned. 'In what way?'

'I've never been on a horse in my life.'

After a startled pause, Patrick burst out laughing.

'Don't be selfish,' Raul drawled silkily. 'Share the joke with the rest of us.'

Clashing with shimmering dark eyes, Polly flushed. 'It wasn't really funny enough.'

'The English sense of humour isn't the same as ours,' Melina remarked sweetly. 'I've always found it rather juvenile.'

Patrick grinned. 'I have to confess I'm not into your wildly dramatic soap operas. Each to his own.'

Under cover of the ensuing conversation, Patrick murmured, 'See you tomorrow morning at six while Raul's out riding. I'll teach you enough to pass yourself, and then you can tell him you're just not very good and he can take over.'

'You're a saviour,' Polly muttered with real gratitude, and turned to address Rob Drydon.

After dinner, they settled down with drinks in the drawing room. Melina crossed the room with another one of her super-friendly smiles, saying in her clear, ringing voice, 'I want you to tell me all about yourself, Polly.'

Sinking deep into the sofa, to show the maximum possible amount of her incredibly long and shapely legs, Melina asked, 'So how's married life treating you?'

'Wonderfully well.' Polly emptied her glass in one gulp and prayed for deliverance, uneasily conscious that Raul was watching them both from the other side of the room. She wished she was feeling more herself.

'I don't think Raul likes to see you drinking so much. He rarely touches alcohol...the occasional glass of champagne on important occasions.' Registering Polly's surprise, Melina elevated a brow. 'So you didn't know? How couldn't you know something that basic about your own husband?'

Polly clutched her empty glass like a drunkard amongst teetotallers, bitterly, painfully resenting the fact that Melina could tell her anything she didn't know about Raul. It reminded her all over again that until very recently there had been nothing normal about her relationship with Raul.

'That's none of your business,' she told Melina flatly, determined not to play the blonde's spiteful double game. Now, when it was too late, she saw how foolish she had been not to tell Raul about her initial clash with Melina. If she tried to tell him now, he probably wouldn't believe her, not with Melina putting on the show of the century with her smiling friendliness.

'Raul *is* my business, and he always will be,' Melina said smugly. 'Did you make a huge scene when he came to see me that very same night?'

Polly froze and then slowly, jerkily turned her head, which was beginning to pound unpleasantly. 'What are you saying?'

'That even I wasn't expecting him quite *that* soon.' Glinting green eyes absorbed Polly's growing pallor with satisfaction. 'I didn't need ESP to realise that you'd obviously had a colossal row. It was your first night in your new home and yet Raul ended up with me.'

'You're lying...I don't believe you.' That night had been the equivalent of their wedding night. Raul couldn't have—

he simply couldn't have gone to Melina beforehand! But he *had* gone out riding. In sick desperation, she strained to recall what he had told her. Hadn't he admitted calling in with a neighbour? Numbly, Polly let the maid refill her glass. Melina was a neighbour. Technically Raul hadn't lied to her...

'He came to me to talk. Raul needs a woman, not a little girl.'

Polly took a defiant slug of her drink. 'He needs you like he needs a hole in the head!' she said, and then frowned in confusion as Melina suddenly leant past her to start talking in low-pitched Spanish.

'I hope you're feeling better the next time I see you, Polly,' Melina then murmured graciously as she rose to her feet.

An icy voice like a lethal weapon breathed in Polly's shrinking ear, 'I'll see our guests out, *mi esposa*. Don't you dare get up. If you stand up, you might fall over, and if you fall over, I'll put you under a very cold shower!'

Devastated to realise that Raul must have overheard her last response to Melina, and doubtless believed that she had been inexcusably rude for no good reason, Polly sat transfixed while everyone took their leave, loads of sympathetic looks and concerned murmurs coming her way once Raul mentioned that she was feeling dizzy.

Patrick hung back to say with a frown, 'Do you think you'll make it down to the stables in the morning?'

Polly nodded with determination.

Recalling how wonderfully close she and Raul had been earlier in the day, Polly began to droop. *Had* Raul been with Melina that night? Only a fool would believe anything Melina said, she decided. But a split second later she was thinking the worst again, imagining how easy, how tempting it would have been for Raul in the mood he had been in to seek consolation with his mistress, a beautiful, self-assured woman whom he had known for so many years...

Two minutes later, Raul strode back in and scooped
Polly off the sofa.

'I'm so miserable!' Polly suddenly sobbed in despair.

Taken aback, Raul tightened his arms around her and
murmured what sounded like soothing things in Spanish.

'And I haven't had too much to drink…I just feel *awful*!'
she wept, clutching at the lapel of his dinner jacket and
then freeing him again, because she didn't want to touch
him, didn't want to be close to him in any way if he was
capable of such deception.

Raul carried her upstairs, laid her gently down on his
bed and slipped off her shoes.

'I'm in agony with a headache!' Polly suddenly hurled.

'You're tipsy,' Raul murmured with total conviction as
he unzipped her dress.

'My head's so sore,' Polly mumbled, drowning in self-
pity.

Raul extracted her from her dress and deftly massaged
her taut shoulders. 'You're so tense,' he scolded. 'Relax,
I'll get some painkillers.'

Hadn't he heard what she had said to Melina after all?
Had she jumped to conclusions? Surely he would have said
something by now?

'Why were you angry with me?' she whispered.

'You were flirting like mad with Patrick.'

'I like him,' Polly muttered, distracted by that unexpected response.

'I *know*,' Raul growled, in an undertone that set up a
chain reaction down her sensitive spine as he undid her bra
and deftly disposed of it. 'I didn't realise you were feeling
ill. I was surprised you were drinking so much.'

'I knew I had a bad head when I came downstairs,' Polly
sighed, wriggling her way out of her tights at his behest. 'I
felt rotten.'

'You should've told me,' Raul purred. 'Melina said you
were talking about our annual fiesta here…were you?'

Polly tensed. 'Don't remember...my head was splitting. You seem to know her very well.'

'Inside out,' Raul agreed silkily.

'When did you invite Melina to dinner?'

'The same evening I visited my grandfather. Fidelio is the foreman of the ranch Melina rents,' Raul revealed.

'Oh... *Oh*...' Polly gasped slightly, slowly putting that together for herself.

Raul had called in with Fidelio that night to tell him he had a great-grandson. And that was why Raul had seen Melina. How silly she had been! And why hadn't it occurred to her before now that at some point Raul would have *had* to see Melina face to face to inform her of his marriage? As she came to terms with that rational explanation, a giant tide of relief started rolling over her.

'I'm awfully tired,' she confessed.

Raul tugged her up against him and gently slotted her into the silky pyjama jacket he had fetched. He carefully rolled up the sleeves. 'I have a villa on the coast. I think we should spend a few days there...'

'Sounds good,' Polly mumbled, and closed her eyes.

She slept like a log but she had the most terrifying dream. She was living in the house at the foot of the garden and Melina was queening it at the ranch. History repeating itself in reverse. She woke with a start, perspiring and shivering, just in time to see Raul reach the door in his riding gear.

'What time is it?'

'Only five-thirty...go back to sleep.'

Abruptly recalling the arrangement she had made with Patrick Gorman, Polly leapt out of bed the instant Raul closed the door behind him.

After a quick shower, she pulled on jeans and a T-shirt, frantic because she knew she was running late. She rushed down the corridor to see Luis, which was always the first thing she did in the morning. In the doorway of the nursery, she stopped dead in surprise and some dismay.

Raul was lounging back in a chair with Luis lying asleep on top of him. Garbed in a little yellow sleepsuit and sprawled trustingly across his father's muscular chest, their son looked impossibly small in comparison.

'I thought you'd already left...' Her voice drained away again, because all of a sudden she felt the weight of her silly deception. It hit her the instant she registered what going behind Raul's back actually entailed.

Brilliant dark eyes veiled, Raul gave her a glinting smile that had the odd effect of increasing her discomfiture. 'If you feed him, Luis is very appealing at this hour.'

'You fed him yourself?' Polly was astonished.

'Since I woke him up by coming in, it didn't seem fair not to. He went through that bottle like he hadn't eaten in days!' Raul confided, smoothing light fingers down over his son's back as Luis snuffled and shifted his little froglike legs, content as only a baby with a full tummy can be. 'His nursemaid changed him for me. He looks so fragile stripped, I didn't want to run the risk of doing it myself.'

Polly reached down and stole Luis into her own arms, and lovingly rubbed her cheek against her son's soft, sweet-smelling skin before she reluctantly tucked him back into his cot.

'I gather the jeans mean you've finally decided to come out riding with me,' Raul drawled from the door. 'You won't find those jeans very comfortable...but then I assume you already know that.'

Still leaning over the cot with her back turned to him, Polly's jaw dropped.

'You're lucky I stopped off in here. You'd have missed me otherwise,' Raul added casually.

Outside the silent house, Polly clambered into the four-wheel drive with a trapped look in her eyes.

'It's been ages and ages since I've been on a horse, Raul,' she said, rather abruptly.

'It's a skill you never forget,' Raul asserted bracingly.

'A couple of hours in the saddle and you'll wonder how you ever lived without it.'

A couple of *hours*? Polly was aghast. Raul shot the vehicle to a halt at the side of the stables.

Patrick Gorman strolled out of the big tack room and then froze when he saw Raul.

'I'm not accustomed to seeing you abroad at this hour, Patrick. Polly's coming out with me this morning.'

'I'll be in the office if you want me.' Without even risking a glance in Polly's direction, Patrick strode off.

Polly stood like a graven image while a pair of grooms led out two mounts. El Lobo, Raul's big black stallion, and a doe-eyed bay mare—who looked, somewhat reassuringly, barely awake.

Raul planted a hard hat on her head and did up the strap. Then he extended a peculiarly shaped garment that reminded her of an oversized body warmer.

'Protection…since you mentioned being out of practice. If you take a toss, I don't want you hurt.' He fed her into the ugly bulky protector and deftly pushed home the clasps. It weighed her down like armour.

Sweeping her up, Raul settled her into the saddle, where she hunched in sudden complete terror.

'I can't ride… Raul, do you hear me? I can't ride!' Polly cried.

'I know…' Raul murmured, so softly she had to strain to hear him as he shortened the stirrups and slotted her feet into them. 'I'd have to be a complete idiot not to know.'

'You *kn-know*?' Polly gasped in disbelief as he swung up on El Lobo with fluid ease.

'*Dios mío*…how could I not guess? Your body language around the horses yesterday was not that of an experienced horsewoman. And I could hardly miss the fact that you hadn't a clue what I was talking about,' Raul delineated very drily.

Polly turned a dull red. 'I thought you'd find it a complete bore if I admitted I was a greenhorn.'

His stunning dark golden eyes gleamed with grim amusement. 'Are you really so naive about men? Is there any male who doesn't relish imparting his superior knowledge of a subject to a woman?'

'I told Patrick I couldn't ride last night...he offered to take me through the basics this morning,' she volunteered in an embarrassed rush. 'It was stupid of me.'

In response, Raul shot her a chilling glance as piercing as an arrow of ice. His lean, strong face was hard. '*Infierno!* I suspected something of the sort last night. Let me tell you now that I do not expect my wife to make furtive assignations with my employees!'

'It *wasn't* an assign—'

'And from now on you will ensure that you are never in Patrick Gorman's company without the presence of a third party.'

Thoroughly taken aback, Polly exclaimed, 'Don't be ridiculous!'

His brilliant eyes flashed. 'As your husband, I have the right to demand a certain standard of behaviour from you.'

Polly was outraged and mortified. 'But you're being totally unreasonable. "The presence of a third party"!' she repeated in a fuming undertone of incredulity.

'If you disobey me, I'll dismiss him.'

Raul held her shaken eyes with fierce intensity, and then simply switched channels by telling her that she was sitting on the mare's back like a seasick sack of potatoes. The riding lesson which followed stretched Polly's self-discipline to the limits. She had to rise above that abrasive exchange and concentrate on his instructions, and Raul had high expectations.

Finally, Raul led her out onto the *llanos* at a walking pace. 'You're doing very well for a greenhorn, *mi esposa*,' he drawled, surprising her.

Polly focused on his darkly handsome features. As her tummy lurched with reaction, she despised herself. Not an hour ago Raul had been talking like a Middle Eastern po-

tentate who thought no woman could be trusted alone with
a man.

A frown line forming between his brows, Raul reined in
his mount a few minutes later. A rider was approaching
them—an elderly *llanero* with a bristling silver moustache,
clad in an old-fashioned poncho and a wide-brimmed hat.

Raul addressed him in Spanish.

'My grandfather, Fidelio Navarro,' he told Polly flatly.

With a sober look of acknowledgement, his posture in
the saddle rigid, the older man responded in softly spoken
Spanish. He was as unyielding as Raul. Polly glanced between them in frustration. Raul and his grandfather greeted
each other like strangers, each as scrupulously formal and
rigid with unbending pride as the other.

Polly leant out of the saddle to extend her hand, a warm
and determined smile on her face. After some hesitation,
Fidelio Navarro moved his mount closer and briefly clasped
her hand. 'It would please me very much if you came to
see our son, Luis,' Polly said quietly.

'He doesn't speak English,' Raul breathed icily.

Not daring to look at him, conscious that he was angrily
disconcerted by her intervention, Polly tilted her chin.
'Then please translate my invitation. And could you also
tell him that as I have neither parents nor grandparents living, it would mean a great deal to me if Luis was given
the chance to know his great-grandfather?'

Silence followed, a silence screaming with tension and
Raul's outright incredulity.

Then Raul spoke at some length. His grandfather met
Polly's hopeful gaze and sombrely replied.

'He thanks you for your warmth and generosity,' Raul
interpreted woodenly. 'He will think the idea over.'

But there had been more than that in Fidelio's sun-
creased dark eyes: a slight defrosting of his discomfiture,
an easing of the rigidity round his unsmiling mouth. As
they parted to ride off in different directions, she heard Raul
release his breath in a stark hiss.

'*Caramba!* How can you justify such interference in what is nothing to do with you?' Raul gritted in a tone of raw disbelief that actually shook with the strength of his emotion. 'Do you think I have not already invited him to my home without success?'

'Well, if you glower at him like that when you ask, I'm not surprised. Maybe he thought you were only asking out of politeness, privately recognising the relationship without really wanting to get any closer...' Daringly, Polly proffered her own suspicions. 'I think you and Fidelio are both so scared of losing face that you're afraid to talk frankly to each other.'

'I am afraid of nothing, and how you can *dare*—'

'I did it for Luis,' Polly lied, because she had spoken up first and foremost for Raul's benefit—Raul, who definitely wanted closer ties with his grandfather. 'Neither of us have any other family to offer him.'

'What do *I* know about family?' Raul growled, spurring on El Lobo in the direction of the ranch.

'What do I know either?' Polly thought of her own less than perfect childhood, with her controlling, judgemental father. 'But we *are* a family now, and we can learn like everybody else!'

'A family?' Raul repeated in frowning acknowledgement, and with perceptible disconcertion. 'I suppose we are.'

Only sparing the time to inform her that they were leaving for his villa on the Caribbean coast that afternoon, Raul took his leave. Polly went for a bath to ease her tired muscles. It was all swings and roundabouts with Raul, she thought heavily. One moment he was alienating her with his tyrannical and utterly unreasonable threat to dismiss Patrick Gorman simply because *she* had unthinkingly stepped over the formal boundary lines Raul expected her to maintain. And the next?

The next, Raul was filling her with an almost overwhelming desire to close her arms round him in comfort and reassurance. For Raul, she recognised, the years between birth and adulthood had been dogged by traumatic experiences.

What had it been like for him? The son of Eduardo Zaforteza's mistress, his mother isolated by a relationship that had been flaunted rather than more acceptably concealed. Behind her lover's back, Pilar must have been shunned and despised, and how had that affected Raul? Until his father had adopted him, nothing had been certain or safe in Raul's life.

Raul must have developed his own defences at an early age. After his mother's death, he'd lived as a bitter bone of contention in a destructive, acrimonious marriage. He had once remarked that in disputes between couples the child was often the weapon, that she had to know that as well as *he* did, only at the time she hadn't picked up on what he was telling her about his own background. In the same way, she remembered his unexpected outrage when she had made a crack about what he might consider a 'decent mother'. She had never dreamt what a sensitive subject that might be, and now winced at the recollection.

Finally she was beginning to understand the man she loved, but her dismay increased in proportion to that new understanding. At some stage in that damaged childhood and adolescence Raul had begun protecting himself, by keeping emotional ties that might threaten his equanimity on a superficial level. It showed in his relationships with women, even in his hopelessly defensive attitude to his estranged grandfather. He didn't risk himself, he held back, and yet he didn't hold back with Luis, Polly conceded painfully. He loved their son with unashamed intensity, and was content, indeed happy to focus his emotions on their child.

And that meant that she herself was still chasing hopes that were unattainable. Raul would never love her. If their marriage was to survive, she had to get her priorities in order and stop expecting more from Raul than he was capable of giving her. And yet, according to Melina, a little voice gibed with cruel effect, he had *loved* her...

Sprawled with elegant indolence on the rattan seating, a look of amusement on his bronzed features, Raul studied Polly while she watched the dancers on the beach with unconcealed fascination. The *tambores*—African drums made out of hollow logs—supplied the frenzied beat for the male and female figures twisting and shaking with abandonment.

'I thought you would enjoy this,' Raul murmured with lazy satisfaction. 'That's why I organised it.'

Meeting his stunning dark golden eyes, Polly burned. She had to drag her attention back to the dancers. The intensely sensual movements of the gyrating couples were becoming ever wilder.

Raul curved a long arm round her and she felt her whole body quicken with instant awareness. Over the past twelve days Raul had taught her to value every hour that they spent together, and every morning she got up, apprehensively waiting for him to announce that they were leaving the villa. After all, this coming weekend the fiesta would be held at the ranch. But right now Polly wanted time to stand still, because here nothing else seemed to touch them.

Raul made a lot of phone calls and used a computer to stay in touch with the world of business, but he was with her almost all the time, more relaxed and less restless and driven than she had ever known him to be. He never seemed bored. In fact he was rather like he had been in Vermont, she registered, with slight surprise at that acknowledgement. Talking to her, interested in her, amusing, entertaining, even tender, all the tension gone, the sole difference being that sexual intimacy now deepened their relationship.

As the dance appeared to be reaching a climax, Polly was astonished when another woman stepped in. With frantically twitching hips she shoved the original female dancer away from the male and triumphantly took her place.

'A comment on the fickleness of the male sex,' Raul drawled, amused at her bemused frown over such an unromantic development. 'You're so innocent, *querida.*'

Not so innocent, Polly reflected tensely, enervated by that unexpected change of partners that came too close for comfort to her own deepest fears.

How long was she going to live with the secret terror that Raul might some day return to his discreet liaison with Melina D'Agnolo? Melina had already made it abundantly clear that she was prepared to wait for him, and no doubt she was equally ready to do whatever it might take to get him back. When would fidelity become a challenge to a male who didn't love her? At what stage would her novelty value in the marital bed become boring and predictable? Disturbed by the insecure thoughts with which she was tormenting herself, Polly shut them down.

After thanking the dancers, they went back indoors to the marbled splendour of the spacious villa. Set beside a secluded palm-fringed beach of golden sand, complete with crystal-clear water to bathe in, the villa rejoiced in the surroundings of a tropical paradise.

They tiptoed in to see Luis, out for the count in his cot. Raul curved his arms round her from behind. 'He really *is* special,' he said huskily.

'Naturally…he's yours,' Polly teased. 'And because he's your son, he is the most super-intelligent and advanced baby on this planet!'

'You think so too, *querida*,' he reminded her in a sensual growl as he slowly spun her round to crush her soft, willing mouth hungrily under his own. Her body sang with feverish hot excitement.

He carried her through to their bedroom and settled her on the bed, standing over her, intent golden eyes roaming over her slender length with the bold and unashamed desire that never failed to ease her secret fears. How could Raul want her so much and have room to even think of any other woman? How could he make love to her day after day and night after night with a seemingly insatiable appetite for her body and find anything lacking in her?

In heaven, Polly closed her eyes as he peeled off her clothes, piece by tantalising piece, pausing to kiss and caress every newly revealed curve and line of her until there wasn't a single part of her quivering, wantonly aroused being that didn't ache for him to possess her.

'I'm going to teach you to dance like that with me,' Raul murmured.

Polly's eyes opened very wide on his devastatingly handsome face. He actually looked serious.

'But only in private. I don't want anyone else seeing the way you look at me, the way you move against me...' he admitted hoarsely.

He was so intense about sex. In fact, for someone who had informed her that sex was merely another physical appetite, Raul seemed to be set on proving that every time he touched her it was another variation on an endlessly fascinating theme that pretty much absorbed him more with every passing day. He couldn't keep his hands off her. He had gone from being a male who was not remotely tactile out of bed to a male who usually had her anchored in some way to him no matter where they were.

She framed his cheekbones with possessive hands and let the tip of her tongue dart provocatively between his lips. With a groan of hunger, Raul practically flattened her to the bed and kissed her with a fierce sexual need that melted her skin over her bones. And all cool was abandoned at that point.

A long while later, she lay limp with satiation while Raul abstractedly wound a strand of her hair round a long brown forefinger. 'Tell me about the first time you fell in love,' he invited without warning.

Polly glanced at him in surprise. Raul didn't ask things like that. And it was an awkward question. One crush and one short-lived infatuation were all she had to talk about, barring himself.

He shrugged a bare bronzed shoulder. 'Curiosity.'

'He was called—'

'I don't want to know his name,' Raul intervened instantly, jawline hardening.

Somewhat disconcerted by that interruption, Polly breathed, 'Yes…er, well, he was another student—'

'I don't need to know that either…what I want to know is how you *felt*,' Raul stressed.

'How I…felt,' Polly echoed. 'Silly and dizzy, and then gutted about covers it. The minute I got to know what he was really like, I couldn't understand what I'd seen in him.'

'You fell out of love again that fast…what did he *do*?' Raul enquired darkly, raising himself up to stare down at her.

'He hustled me into a bedroom one lunchtime and told me it was my lucky day.'

She now had Raul's interest. 'You're kidding?'

'When I said no, he got abusive. He thought I'd be a push-over.'

'Major misjudgement,' Raul framed, a slight shake in his dark, deep voice. 'How old was this guy?'

'Nineteen.'

'All teenage boys think about is scoring.'

'You weren't much older when you and Melina…I mean—' Biting back the remainder of that impulsive remark, Polly coloured at the sudden narrowing of the shrewd dark eyes above hers. 'Well, she mentioned you'd once been an item.'

'Did she really?' His black spiky lashes screened his gaze, his wide, sensual mouth hardening on that information.

Polly lowered her eyes, more disturbed by that silence than she would have been by any explanation. Why was it that the unknown was always so much more threatening?

'We'll fly home on Friday morning,' Raul informed her.

'But the fiesta…' Polly groaned, torn between relief and anxiety. 'There must be loads of arrangements to make, and I haven't even made a start—'

'After all these years of practice, the staff could stage it on their own.' Rolling over onto his back, Raul reached for her again. His gleaming scrutiny raked over her pink face with unsettling efficiency. 'Have I ever told you how extraordinarily expressive those gorgeous blue eyes are, *mi esposa*?' he asked huskily. 'Do you know they close every time I kiss you?'

Polly studied him with the focused intensity of a woman in love, a kind of agony coiling tight as a spring inside her. If he betrayed her, she would die. If their marriage ended, her future would end with it. She could not bear to think of life without him. She wanted to cling like a vine, but clinging would be as much out of order as probing personal questions which might well have answers she'd be better off not hearing.

And suddenly he *was* kissing her again, evoking a wild hunger that clawed at her slim body, awakening all over again that frantic, feverish, elemental need that overwhelmed every restraint and blanked out every thought.

Polly woke up alone on the morning of their departure. There was nothing unusual about that. It was a challenge to keep Raul in bed after dawn. Early rising and a two-hour break at midday were the norm in Venezuela. Trying not to feel sad that they were leaving the villa, she went for a shower.

As she leafed through a wardrobe that had grown mightily in size since leaving the ranch, she hugged precious memories of their stay to herself. Strolling hand in hand along the Paseo Colón boulevard in Puerta la Cruz, enjoying the cool breezes coming in off the ocean; speeding in a motor launch through the eerie mangroves in the Mochina National Park; eating crispy *churros* with hot chocolate for breakfast *and* supper on Margarita Island; driving up to

Caracas to shop in the CCCT and Paseo las Mercedes malls, discovering that there *was* such a thing as a male who loved shopping and indeed that there were no greater worshippers of the consumer society or the art of being beautiful than the Venezuelans.

She was happy—yes, she had to admit it, she was very, very happy. Feeling good in a beautifully tailored leaf-green short skirt and top, she glanced into Luis's room and smiled at the sight of the empty cot. Luis was probably sitting in his infant seat watching his father work and enjoying a somewhat one-sided conversation in between times.

She could already hear Raul talking as she reached the door of the room he had been using as an office.

'...am I bored?' Raul was saying with husky amusement. 'On my honeymoon, Melina?' And then, ruefully, 'I'm *thinking* in English these days!'

Polly froze in her tracks. Her heart was thumping so hard it felt as if it was banging in her ears, and she had to strain to hear. The silence went on and on. She peered round the door lintel and glimpsed Raul, poised with his back to the door, wide shoulders bunching with tension below the superb cut of his lightweight cream jacket, bronzed fingers beating out a rapid soundless tattoo on the edge of the desk.

'Of course I appreciate your loyalty, Melina,' Raul continued in a roughened sexy undertone. 'I'm looking forward to seeing you tonight too. No, I don't think it should be too difficult. I'm not on a leash yet.'

CHAPTER ELEVEN

'YOU still look rough. You should lie down,' Raul decreed as he walked Polly up the steps into the ranch.

'What about the fiesta...all the people coming?' Polly mumbled sickly, edging away from him as soon as she decently could.

'It's been happening for over a hundred years without you, *mi esposa*,' Raul responded in a teasing tone as he bent to lift her gently up into his arms and stride towards the magnificent staircase. 'Just go to bed and stay there until you feel better. That's the only important thing.'

Shock had unsettled her stomach. She had been sick during the flight, convincing Raul that she had caught some bug. He could not have been more caring and concerned had she developed a life-threatening illness. And she couldn't bear it, couldn't bear him near her, yet couldn't bear him out of her sight either for fear of what he might be doing or even thinking.

Listening to Raul on the phone to Melina D'Agnolo had shattered her. Now, as he carried her past the superb flower arrangements which had appeared everywhere, and the frantically busy staff excited about the party which kicked off the weekend festivities, Polly felt like the weakest of the weak. No way was she going to be lying in bed this evening like a party pooper while Melina held the floor!

Raul set her upright in their bedroom. Confront him, screamed through her mind in letters of taunting fire. She walked over to the windows, torn by conflicting desires. She wanted to see them together first. She wanted to confront them. If she tried to confront Raul now, what did she base her accusations on? His appreciation of Melina's loyalty? Or that simple sentence 'I'm looking forward to see-ing you tonight'?

It wasn't enough. It wasn't evidence of anything he couldn't explain away. But the very fact he had been on the phone talking to Melina like that…it ripped Polly apart. She had genuinely trusted him, sincerely come to believe that it was only her own insecurity which was tormenting her…

'Do you think a married man needs a mistress?' she asked abruptly.

Silence stretched.

Polly spun round. Raul looked slightly bemused, a frown line etched between his expressive brows. Then a splinter-ing smile slashed his beautiful mouth. 'Not if he spends as much time in bed with his wife as I do!'

'It was a serious question, Raul.'

'Only not a very sensible one. With my background, the answer would be absolutely not. A divorce would be a bet-ter option,' Raul drawled reflectively.

Having invited that opinion, Polly's stomach curdled. She turned back to the windows on unsteady legs.

'Is there something you want to discuss with me?' Raul enquired in smooth invitation.

'Nothing.' Not without proof. She wasn't about to risk tearing their marriage apart without proper proof.

'I have this feeling that something is playing on your mind…it's not the first time I've had it.'

Taken aback by that assurance, Polly linked her unsteady hands tightly together and stared out of the window, seeing nothing. She might as well have been staring into space. Raul strolled to her side and followed the apparent path of her gaze.

Patrick Gorman was giving instructions to a group of workmen who were stringing up extra lighting in the gar-dens below.

'If I was the jealous type,' Raul breathed with sudden

startling rawness, 'I'd go down there and kill him because you're looking at him!'

Polly focused on Patrick for the first time in complete bewilderment, like someone who had missed a crucial sentence that made sense of inexplicable behaviour. 'I wasn't looking at him...why would I want to look at him, for heaven's sake?'

Raul punched the button that closed the curtains with what struck her as quite unnecessary force. Polly surveyed him. A devastatingly handsome male in a seething rage. She blinked. He strode out of the room without a backward glance.

He's jealous of Patrick. Polly slowly shook her head at that strikingly obvious revelation. Why hadn't she made that connection before? Right from the minute he had seen her chattering happily to the young Englishman Raul had been warning her off him. Yet how could he possibly be jealous of another man when he was planning to continue his affair with Melina?

But then wasn't that men the world over? she reflected with newly learnt cynicism. Some men only valued a woman when another man admired her, or when they thought that they themselves were no longer desired. And then a man could be possessive without loving. Which category did Raul fall into? Or was it simply that, as his wife, he now regarded her in the light of a possession?

She sank down on the edge of the bed, dry-eyed but pale as milk. Was Melina simply a habit with Raul? When he had told her that he appreciated her loyalty what had he meant? Had he been thanking her for patiently waiting for him? Did he honestly think he had a hope in hell of continuing such an affair without being found out?

The door opened again. Raul hovered for a split second, as if somewhat unsure of his welcome, and then extended his hand to her, one of his sudden flashing smiles driving all reserve from his lean bronzed features. 'We have a visitor, *gatita*,' he announced. 'My grandfather is here.'

Fidelio Navarro was stationed in the hall, curling his hat round and round between strained hands. Polly hurried down the stairs to greet him, breaking the ice by going straight up to him and leaning forward to kiss him on both cheeks, as one did with family members. He smiled and relaxed perceptibly while Raul translated her welcome with the air of a male grateful for the distraction.

Upstairs, Polly lifted Luis out of his cot and laid him in Fidelio's sturdy arms. The old man heaved a giant sigh and slowly shook his silvered head, openly overcome by the sight of his great-grandson.

'He says...Luis has my mother's eyes,' Raul translated gruffly.

Fidelio's eyes swam, his mouth tightening, his emotions too near the surface for him to say anything more. Polly accepted Luis back and looked at Raul hovering, her own gaze expectant. 'You go and have a celebration drink and talk now,' she instructed, knowing she had to spell it all out, afraid that, left to his own devices, Raul might duck the issue and take grateful refuge in polite conversation. 'You'll talk about your mother...and how much you loved her, and how good things are going to be now in this family.'

'Sí...' Raul dug his clenched fists tautly into his trouser pockets and bent his imperious dark head, swallowing hard.

Fidelio and Raul walked out of the room together about a foot apart.

Polly drew in a slow, deep breath and said a prayer that with a little give and take on both sides the barriers would finally come down between the two men. The older man needed to be completely sure of his welcome in this house. Without that confidence, he wouldn't visit again.

Two hours later, from the vantage point of an upper window, she watched Fidelio wrap his arms round Raul and hug him fiercely before he climbed back onto his horse outside the house. A tide of relief rolled over her. Clearly

Raul hadn't backed off and stood on his dignity. She was satisfied then.

'I wouldn't call them gifts,' Raul delivered some hours later, looking deadly serious in the reflection Polly could see of him in the mirror as she dazedly fingered the fabulous diamond necklace and earrings he had just presented her with. 'They belonged to my mother, so now they're yours.'

Polly stared down at the fabulous river of diamonds and the teardrop earrings with a lump in her throat. 'They're out of this world.'

Lifting the necklace, Raul clasped it round her throat. 'No one but me ever saw her wear them. My father never took her out in public.'

Polly gulped. 'Oh, heavens…that's so sad!'

'No, *mi esposa*.' Raul watched her put on the earrings and then stand up. 'We're a different generation, and the Zaforteza family has enjoyed a rebirth. I'm very grateful that the warmth I foolishly condemned you for has helped to heal the wounds of the past and persuade Fidelio to become a part of our lives.'

Wrinkling her nose to hold back tears in receipt of that surprisingly humble accolade, Polly turned to study her reflection in the cheval mirror. She looked elegant, with her hair swept up in a French roll, loose tendrils curling round her face. And then there was the dress, the designer sleeveless evening gown in green with the wonderful sweeping neckline and elaborate gilded embroidery, not to mention the spike-heeled shoes and all the diamonds catching fire under the lights. But none of that meant anything when set beside the burning sincerity she had glimpsed in Raul's stunning golden eyes. That filled her to bursting point with love.

Without the slightest warning, Raul reached for her hand and practically crushed the life from her fingers with the

unwitting fierceness of his grip. He exhaled in a stark hiss.
'I think I love you...'

Polly's eyes opened very wide, and then flooded with
pain. She hauled her fingers free in a gesture of repudiation.
'No, you don't. You're just feeling grateful and more emotional than usual,' she told him unevenly. 'Don't call that
love.'

'I said it wrong, but I haven't had a lot of practice at
this!' Raul gritted rawly. 'I shouldn't have said, I *think*—'

'You shouldn't have said anything. I'm sorry if I've
made you feel that nothing short of true love will satisfy
me,' Polly responded tautly, the stress and strain of the day
mounting up to betray her into saying exactly what she was
thinking. 'Actually, fidelity would do...so there, I've finally
lowered my expectations to a more realistic level!'

His fabulous bone structure prominent with tension beneath his bronzed skin, Raul dealt her a thunderous look of
disbelief that shook her. He parted his lips to respond at
the same moment that an urgent knock sounded on the
door.

'Our guests have begun to arrive,' he relayed seconds
later.

Before he could leave the room, Polly rushed over to
him, all cool abandoned in the growing awareness that she
had reacted in the worst possible way, her blue eyes deeply
troubled and full of guilt. 'Raul, I didn't mean...you took
me by—'

'Relax...you've cured me of my delusional state,' he derided, silencing her, convincing her that he could only have
spoken those words out of an impulsive need to reward her
in some way for helping to bring him and his grandfather
to a closer understanding.

It was not a good moment to go downstairs and discover
that Melina D'Agnolo had arrived with the first wave
of guests. Melina—spectacular in a glittering scarlet dress,
blonde hair gleaming and a brilliant smile on her ripe
pink mouth.

'What a lovely dress,' she said sweetly, and passed on.

Loads of baggage was being carried upstairs. Not everyone was staying the whole weekend, and not everyone was sleeping in the house. The equestrian centre had a spacious block of comfortable accommodation, used when Raul staged polo matches and occasional conferences, and many of their guests would be staying there. In the busy buzz of people, several different languages filling the air, Polly suffered a stark instant of panic, and then she drew in a deep, steadying breath and took her place at Raul's side.

Since being nice had never been a challenge for Polly— ironically with anyone but Raul—she soon found that natural friendliness was all that was required, and the approval in Raul's eyes soon dissolved her anxiety about socialising. Mid-way through the evening a fabulous fireworks display brought everyone out into the gardens. Polly was walking back indoors, hanging back to wait for Raul, who was chatting to a group of men, when Melina approached her.

'You watch him like an anxious mother, don't you?' It was an open sneer.

Polly coloured, suddenly painfully conscious that, whether she liked it or not, she *had* been sticking to Raul rather like superglue.

'Draped in diamonds worth millions,' Melina scorned with glittering green eyes. 'I hope they comfort you for sleeping alone at night.'

As Polly paled, the beautiful blonde flung her a triumphant look and strolled past her.

A pair of lean hands settled unexpectedly on her taut shoulders from behind. '*Dios mío*, how wonderfully friendly Melina's being!' Raul drawled above her slightly downbent head.

Polly jerked as if he had slapped her. 'Actually…'

'Actually?' Raul encouraged silkily.

'She was admiring my diamonds,' Polly completed dully.

'She's very fond of jewels…but not of her own sex.'

And who would know that best but him? That statement

only served to remind Polly that Raul had intimate knowledge of Melina's character. It made her feel more isolated
than ever.

The musicians began to play the haunting country music
of the *llanos* and one of them began to sing. 'What is he
singing about?' she whispered.

'A broken heart…it may well be mine,' Raul breathed
with stark impatience, releasing her to stride back indoors.

Did he care about Melina? *Really* care? Might he only
have realised that after their marriage? Stranger things had
happened, and she could not say that Raul was a male noticeably in touch with his own feelings except where Luis
was concerned. So why had he told *her* that he thought he
loved her?

As a reward? Those words were so easy to say. Out of
guilt? Knowing that he was about to betray her, had he
tossed that declaration at her like a consolation prize? Or
to take the edge off any suspicions she might develop about
his fidelity? And yet, strangely, that was the second time
Raul had invited her to talk to him about what she had on
her mind. Raul knew something was wrong. He had freely
admitted that Melina didn't like her own sex, almost as if
he didn't trust the beautiful blonde…

Any more than *you* trust *him*? That accidental comparison shocked Polly. For trust had been there until she'd
overheard that phone call. And before that call, whenever
she'd thought of telling Raul all the horrible things which
Melina had slung at her, she had remembered that nasty
little scene on the jet, and then the way he had walked out
on her that same day after calling her obsessively jealous.
Furthermore, she had no evidence of anything that Melina
had said. Was she now trying to work herself up to running
and telling tales like an immature little girl? Or was she
seriously waiting for Raul to make some sort of move on
Melina, who already seemed so unbearably smug tonight?
Like a temporarily forsaken mistress aware that her star was
now in the ascendant again?

Patrick wandered over to speak to her. 'I thought I'd avoid you while Raul was around,' he shared in an undertone, glancing rather anxiously around himself, like a man watching out for trouble.

'Why's that?'

'Raul is a Latin American male to his fingertips. I used to think he wasn't, except when he was being a killer on the polo field. Then he married you, and all of a sudden that cool front is cracking. I honestly don't think he can stand another man within twenty feet of you.'

'Really?' Polly lifted her head, a fledgling smile curving her lips because she was ready at that moment to snatch at any straw.

'So, if you don't mind, I won't ask you to dance.'

'No problem. I want to dance with Raul.' Polly drifted off, her mind made up. Time to stop avoiding the issue and allowing Melina to make her miserable and call all the shots. It was time to fight back and do the sensible thing, which was to talk to Raul.

So, in the mood she was in, it wasn't pleasant to find Raul, standing in a corner with a brooding look of darkness on his starkly handsome features, and Melina, chattering in that covert, intimate way she always embraced around him, her exquisite face soft with a cloying smile.

But Polly walked right over. 'Would you like to dance, Raul?' she asked in a rather high-pitched voice, and with a sudden spooky horror that he might say no and humiliate her.

Melina raised a brow and averted her eyes, a self-satisfied little smile playing about her lips. Raul strode forward, eyes blazing hot gold as they whipped over his wife's flushed and unhappy expression.

He closed an arm around her, and instead of taking her onto the floor to dance, he guided her out into the softly lit greater privacy of the gardens.

'I didn't really want to dance,' Polly admitted unevenly, wondering why on earth he should look so scorchingly angry. 'I needed to talk to you in private. And if you're annoyed now, you're probably going to be even more annoyed when I've finished talking...so possibly we should take a raincheck on this until later...'

Polly got two steps away, and then was unceremoniously pulled back by the lean hand that closed round hers.

'No raincheck. You were saying?'

Polly breathed in deep to steady herself. She could not say that harsh tone was the most inviting she had ever heard. 'I heard you talking to Melina on the phone at the villa—'

'Did you indeed?' Raul threw that query like a gauntlet.

It wasn't quite the response she had expected.

Polly became even more flustered. 'I want you to know that up until that point I trusted you...and you may wonder why I should say that, but, you see, Melina told me she was your mistress the first day I came here, and she said that you'd go back to her...and that night you *did* go over there, and even though you *said* it was to see Fidelio—'

'One point at a time,' Raul intervened levelly. 'Melina called me at the villa to inform me that, after wrestling with her non-existent conscience, she had decided that it was her duty to tell me that you were meeting up with Patrick Gorman in secret.'

In shock at that news, Polly felt her mouth simply drop open.

Raul dealt her a grim look of amusement. 'I thought that would take the wind out of your sails.'

It did. Polly was poleaxed to realise that Melina had been working on both her and Raul.

'Divide and conquer. Not very original or clever, at least not clever enough to fool me,' Raul delineated grittily, shooting Polly a forbidding glance of reproach. 'I didn't believe a word of it, but I strung her along to see how far she was prepared to go in her determination to cause trouble between us. It also confirmed my suspicion that she had been working on you as well.'

He hailed a passing maid with a snap of his fingers and spoke to her in Spanish.

'I want to know everything that Melina told you,' he said next, his lean, strong face hard and unyielding.

'Maybe you should pull up a chair. She said a lot,' Polly muttered uncertainly, suddenly not knowing whether she was on her head or her heels, and getting the horrendous feeling that every time she parted her lips she was digging another foot of her own grave. There was no doubt that the more Raul heard, the angrier he became.

'Her poison couldn't have fallen on more fertile ground,' Raul remarked grimly when she had finished speaking. 'That first night she joined us for dinner I watched her with you, and I was immediately suspicious of her behaviour. She was too friendly towards you and too flirtatious with me…you should have come straight to me with the truth. When you said nothing, I thought I might've misjudged her.'

Polly grimaced, suddenly feeling such a total idiot. 'I didn't want you to think I was jealous again.'

Firmly closing a determined hand over hers, Raul took her back indoors through the entrance that led into his suite of offices.

'How much proof do you need to trust me?' Raul challenged. 'We are about to face Melina together!'

At that disconcerting announcement, Polly gulped.

'I sent the maid to tell Melina that I wanted to see her in private.'

Raul thrust open the door before them. Melina was inside, lounging back against Raul's desk. She straightened with a bright smile that froze round the edges, her brow furrowing, when she saw Polly.

'After all the lies you've told, I'm amazed that you can look either of us in the face,' Raul drawled in icy condemnation.

Taken aback by that direct opening, Melina's eyes rounded. 'What are you—?'

'I've been more than fair to you,' Raul cut in. 'When you came to me last year, distraught about your financial problems, I was sympathetic.'

Two high spots of red now burned in Melina's cheeks. 'I wanted more than sympathy, Raul!'

'I paid you to act as my hostess when I entertained here. You were excellent in the role, but it was strictly a business arrangement.'

Melina's face twisted with fury. 'If it hadn't been for her and that wretched child we would've ended up with a lot more than a business arrangement—'

'There was never any question of that,' Raul dismissed with stark impatience. '*Dios mío*...I learned my lesson with you at nineteen, but I was willing to help you as a friend. The lies you've fed Polly...and attempted to feed me...merely prove that you haven't changed at all, Melina.'

'I don't know what you *see* in her!' Melina raged at him incredulously. '*I* should have been your wife!'

'You wouldn't know love if it smacked you in the face,' Raul responded with contempt. 'Greed and ambition are no more attractive to me now than they were years ago.'

Melina reddened, sent him a look of loathing, and then seemed to collect herself. Tossing her head high, she parted her lips, but Raul got in first. 'I expect you to vacate your present accommodation by the end of the month. I won't be renewing the lease and you are no longer welcome here. A car will take you home.'

Without another word, Raul swept Polly back out of the room. Her legs felt hollow and butterflies were dancing in her tummy. She could not credit what a fool she had been to listen to the other woman's insidious lies. 'She's *never* been your mistress...'

'We had a brief affair when I was nineteen,' Raul admitted grimly. 'Although I didn't know it, I was far from being her only lover at the time. She's several years older than me. I *was* infatuated with her, but I wasn't a complete fool. Melina couldn't hide her greed. No matter what I gave her, she wanted more. When she realised I had no plans to marry her, she married a wealthy industrialist in his sixties—'

'And he died?'

'No, she's been married twice. Her first husband divorced her; the second died, leaving her in debt.'

'And that's when she came to you for help?'

Raul nodded, his jawline squaring. 'I should've known better than to take pity on her, *gatita*. She was always a bitch.'

'She resented me…she was just furious that you'd married me…'

'*Dios mío*, I didn't even realise that she was hoping I might become involved with her again. I'm not attracted to her now, but she can be amusing company.'

'I've been an idiot,' Polly mumbled ruefully.

'I should've made you tell me the truth. Your silence protected her.'

They returned to the party. Polly was light-headed with relief but thoroughly humbled by the awareness that she had been very naive in her dealings with Melina, and that it had taken Raul to sort it all out. OK, she had finally surrendered to the need to tell him the truth, but it had taken her too long to reach that point.

She wanted so much to be alone with Raul then, but it was impossible with so many people around. It was near dawn before the last of their guests dispersed. By then Polly felt stressed out emotionally, riven with guilt that she had so misjudged Raul and appalled that he knew of the suspicions she had cherished. And, worst of all, how could she have reacted as she had when he'd talked about loving her? Hadn't he already shown in lots of ways that he cared about her, desired her, enjoyed her company? So maybe that still didn't quite amount to her estimation of love, but it was probably as close as she was likely to get to being loved!

Raul thrust the bedroom door shut behind him, his screened gaze zeroing in on her aimless stance in the mid-

dle of the carpet. 'I wish every one of our guests would
evaporate,' he admitted with real fervour.

'But—'

'No buts, *mi esposa*, privacy is at a premium this weekend, but thankfully we're leaving for London on Sunday
evening. I have a surprise for you. Monday *is* your birthday,' Raul reminded her.

'London...a *surprise*?' Polly's cup of guilt positively
overflowed. 'I'm really sorry I listened to Melina.'

'You didn't know what you were up against.' Reaching
for her, Raul eased her slowly into the circle of his arms.
'And now it's time for you to keep quiet and listen to me.'

Polly gazed up into clear dark golden eyes and her susceptible heart quickened.

'I fell in love with you in Vermont,' Raul delivered almost aggressively, strain hardening his sensual mouth. 'But
I didn't realise that until recently. I basked in your response
to me then. You asked nothing from me, but your love
made you feel as much mine as the baby you carried.'

Polly was transfixed. 'Did it?'

'I felt very possessive of you even then. I'm not prone
to analysing my emotions...I didn't have to,' Raul admitted
bluntly. 'When you went missing, you went missing with
my baby inside you, so I never had to question the strength
of my need to find you both. I was always able to use Luis
as a justification. And when I found it a challenge to keep
our relationship impersonal, I told myself it was solely because you were the mother of my child.'

'You were pretty good at convincing yourself,' Polly
whispered unevenly, almost afraid to believe in what he
was trying to explain to her.

'I even had a good excuse to marry you—'

'I forced you into it.'

'I could've said no, and I didn't. You made it easy for
me to avoid facing up to the fact that I wanted you on any
terms...and then you vanished and I was climbing the walls
with frustration again,' Raul confessed, and shifted a shoul-

der in a jerky shrug that signified unpleasant recollection. 'I was angrier than I've ever been in my life, and yet so scared that I wouldn't be able to find you a second time…'

She rested her brow against his broad chest, disturbed that she had caused him that much pain without even suspecting the fact. 'Oh, Raul…I thought it was only Luis you'd be worrying about and missing.'

'I didn't know what was happening inside my own head,' he confided grittily. 'I even assumed that once I'd satisfied my overpowering desire to make love to you I would go back to feeling like myself again. But it didn't work like that.'

'It doesn't,' Polly agreed shakily, eyes stinging with happiness because believing that Raul loved her was becoming easier with every word he spoke.

'When I came back in from that late-night ride and you weren't where I expected you to be I really lost it, and that's when I realised how much power you had over me…that was a very threatening discovery for me,' Raul conceded with driven honesty. 'And then it got worse…'

'Worse?' Falling in love wasn't always fun, but Raul was making it sound like being plunged into hell.

'With women, it was always easy come, easy go with me, and then you smiled at Patrick Gorman just the way you once smiled at me in Vermont, and I wanted to knock his teeth down his throat! It was so irrational, so childish, querida,' he grated, with a highly revealing combination of regret and embarrassment.

'I didn't really notice…I was too busy worrying about Melina and my own insecurities.' Polly winced at how blind she had been.

'It slowly dawned on me that this was what love felt like…all these crazy feelings, and rage and moments of weakness and fear, and just needing you there all the time…' His sculpted cheekbones were sharpened by a rise of dark colour. 'Infierno…I can't believe I just said all that!'

'But it's like that for me too, and, believe me, loving you was not fun when we met up in London again, so I tried to tell myself I hated you,' Polly complained feelingly, but she wrapped her arms round him so tightly when she said it he wasn't in any danger of feeling rejected on the basis of his past sins.

'I wanted to haul you into my arms and I couldn't let myself…and now I can,' Raul appreciated, with a blazing smile of satisfaction and relief. He crushed her to him and proceeded to kiss her until her head swam. They ended up on the bed, discarding clothes with more haste than finesse, sealing their words of love with a passionate joining that released every last scrap of tension between them.

'Yes, you *do* like being loved,' Polly teased him as she smoothed possessive fingers through his damply tousled hair and met the tender look of satisfaction in his brilliant dark eyes.

'You should've guessed how I felt at the villa, *gatita*. I don't think I've ever felt that happy before…except now,' he conceded reflectively.

'Why are we going to London?'

'Surprise…'

'But I'm curious…' Polly ran a not entirely innocent hand down over a lean, hair-roughened thigh.

Raul gave her a wolfish grin even as he hauled her closer. 'You could torture me and I wouldn't tell you!'

'Am I going to be pleased?'

'You're worse than a child,' Raul groaned with vibrant amusement, and glanced at his watch. 'Are you aware that we have to rise to be hosts again in two hours?'

Polly was aghast.

'And if I fall asleep on El Lobo's back during the polo match, guess who I'm likely to blame?'

'It's only a game,' she said comfortingly.

Lowering his head, Raul studied her with frankly adoring but slightly pained eyes. 'I must be in love. Once I'd have slaughtered any woman for saying that…'

*   *   *

'Why are you bringing me here?' Polly exclaimed three days later as the limousine wafted them up the long driveway to Gilbourne, her late godmother's beautiful Georgian house in Surrey.

'Happy birthday. I bought Gilbourne months ago. A whim. Don't ask me why... I came here looking for you and I remembered how much you'd talked about this place in Vermont. The estate agent was showing the most obnoxious couple round the grounds, and they were giving forth about how they would rip out the rose garden where you used to sit with your godmother.'

It took Polly the entirety of that speech to catch her breath. 'You bought it for *me*?'

'When we come to England we can stay here,' Raul pointed out.

Polly was staring out at the other limousine already parked in front of the house, and then her eyes widened even more at the sight of the helicopter on the front lawn.

'Who's here?'

'Your friends, Maxie and Darcy—'

'Maxie and Darcy?' Polly gasped, barely over the first shock of discovering that she was now the owner of the gorgeous mansion she had always adored visiting as a child.

'I did try to bring them over for the fiesta, but Maxie's pregnant, and couldn't face the prospect of a long flight, so I decided to arrange the reunion here.'

Polly was touched, but she had also paled with dismay. 'Raul...the last time I was in the same room with Maxie and Darcy it was like holding off World War Three. We all used to be great friends, and then three years ago it all went wrong. Darcy was getting married and Maxie was her bridesmaid, and Darcy's bridegroom fell head over heels for Maxie. Relations have been strained ever since.'

'But not so strained that they weren't both prepared to come here to see you,' Raul countered reassuringly.

And, minutes after walking into the gracious drawing

room where all three women had last met for the reading
of Nancy Leeward's will, Polly was engulfed by a very
warm welcome from her friends. Both Maxie and Darcy
were chattering nineteen to the dozen—to her, to *each
other*, and throwing stray comments in the direction of the
men in the background.

'I recognise Angelos from his photo,' Polly whispered.
'But who's the other one?'

'My husband, Luca,' Darcy announced with lashings of
pride. 'Gianluca Raffacani. He's Zia's father.'

Since Polly had entirely the wrong idea about who had
fathered Darcy's little daughter, those twin announcements
left her fairly bereft of speech.

'They're all listening, scared they're missing something.
Look, what do you say we dump the men for half an hour?'
Maxie suggested in a covert whisper.

So off they went on a supposed tour of the house. And
Polly heard about how Darcy had called Maxie and had
lunch with her a couple of weeks earlier.

'We made up,' Darcy completed.

Polly beamed. 'That's brilliant. So, congratulations on
your marriage…and I hear you're pregnant, Maxie?'

'Never been so sick in my life,' Maxie moaned, her
beautiful face a tinge paler than was the norm. 'But it
should pass off in a couple of weeks. It'll be worth it if I
land a cute little sprog like Luis.'

They stood looking down on the rose garden where they
had often sat with their godmother, and finally settled in a
row on the window seat.

'Do you think Nancy's pleased with us now?' Darcy said
hopefully.

Maxie grinned. 'She did me a favour…I got Angelos.'

'Luca's changed my life,' Darcy confided.

Both women looked at Polly, and she went pink. 'Raul's
fabulous.'

'Oh, *no!*' Maxie groaned with a comical expression of

dismay. 'I just know the men think we're up here talking about them, and here we are actually doing it!'

Hours later, Polly climbed into the elegant, beautifully draped four-poster bed in the main bedroom, marvelling that Raul had simply bought the furniture with the house and engaged new staff. He hadn't worked it out yet, but she knew what had been going through his mind all those months ago. He had walked around Gilbourne, imagining her here, and he had bought the house as a result.

'So what *were* the three of you giggling like drains over?' Raul persisted as he slid into bed beside her, all bronzed and gorgeous and sexy against the pale linen.

Pulses quickening, Polly gave him a secretive smile. 'That would be telling.'

'You were talking about us.' Raul lay back against the banked up pillows, his trust in that belief complete. '*We* talked business.'

'Get away—you were in the billiard room by the time we came back, but you hadn't closed the door, so we tip-toed up to see how the three of you were getting on without us around,' Polly confessed with a growing smile. 'And Angelos was talking about what a great mother Maxie was going to be, Luca was talking about Darcy's amazing knowledge of antiques. And *you* were talking about my inborn talent for horse-riding!'

Raul rolled over and trapped her beneath him, stunning golden eyes laughing down into hers. 'I may have exaggerated a little, but then it was male bragging session, and I couldn't say what I really wanted to say…'

'And what was that?' Polly enquired, scarcely able to breathe for excitement with him that close.

'I just adore you, *gatita*…'

'Me too.' Polly sighed ecstatically as he kissed her, closed her eyes the way she always did, and gave herself up without a care in the world to loving pleasure.

Special Offers
Lynne Graham Collection

An intense and passionate collection of international
bestselling author Lynne Graham's trademark
powerful, hot-blooded heroes

Collect all 4 volumes!

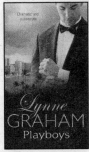

On sale 3rd February

On sale 2nd March

On sale 6th April

On sale 4th May

 Save 20% on Special Releases Collections

Find out more at
www.millsandboon.co.uk/specialreleases

Visit us Online

0312/52/MB365

Book of the Month

We love this book because...

Hollywood starlet Lily Wild is caught in a scandal that has every paparazzi flashbulb exploding! Her only escape is world-class lawyer Tristan Garrett—a man convinced of her guilt! Michelle Conder's feisty, sexy debut is strikingly contemporary and utterly unmissable!

On sale 6th April

Visit us Online

Find out more at
www.millsandboon.co.uk/BOTM

0312/BOTM

Special Offers

Every month we put together collections and longer reads written by your favourite authors.

Here are some of next month's highlights— and don't miss our fabulous discount online!

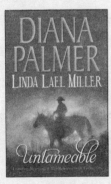

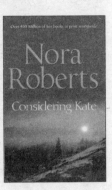

On sale 16th March   **On sale 16th March**   **On sale 6th April**

Save 20%
on all Special Releases

Find out more at
www.millsandboon.co.uk/specialreleases

Visit us Online

0312/ST/MB364

The World of Mills & Boon®

There's a Mills & Boon® series that's perfect for you. We publish ten series and with new titles every month, you never have to wait long for your favourite to come along.

Blaze.
Scorching hot, sexy reads

By Request
Relive the romance with the best of the best

Cherish™
Romance to melt the heart every time

Desire
Passionate and dramatic love stories

Browse our books before you buy online at
www.millsandboon.co.uk

M&B/WORLD

Mills & Boon® Online

Discover more romance at
www.millsandboon.co.uk

- **FREE** online reads
- **Books** up to one month before shops
- **Browse our books** before you buy

...and much more!

For exclusive competitions and instant updates:

 Like us on **facebook.com/romancehq**

 Follow us on **twitter.com/millsandboonuk**

 Join us on **community.millsandboon.co.uk**

Visit us Online | Sign up for our FREE eNewsletter at
www.millsandboon.co.uk

WEB/M&B/RTL4

What will you treat yourself to next?

 Ignite your imagination, step into the past...

INTRIGUE... Breathtaking romantic suspense

Medical Romance™ Captivating medical drama—with heart

MODERN™ International affairs, seduction and passion

n o c t u r n e™ Deliciously wicked paranormal romance

RIVA™ Live life to the full – give in to temptation

You can also buy Mills & Boon eBooks at
www.millsandboon.co.uk

Visit us Online

M&B/WORLD